A297 READING CLASSICAL LATIN

The Open
University

Study Guide

This publication forms part of an Open University course A297 Reading Classical Latin. Details of this and other Open University courses can be obtained from the Course Reservations Centre, P.O. Box 724, The Open University, Milton Keynes MK7 6ZS, United Kingdom; tel. +44 (0)1908 653231, email ces-gen@open.ac.uk

Alternatively, you may visit the Open University website at http://www.open.ac.uk where you can learn more about the wide range of courses and packs offered at all levels by the Open University.

To purchase this publication or other components of Open University courses, contact Open University Worldwide Ltd, The Berrill Building, Walton Hall, Milton Keynes MK7 6AA, United Kingdom: tel. +44 (0)1908 858785; fax +44 (0)1908 858787; e-mail ouwenq@open.ac.uk; website http://www.ouw.co.uk

The Open University Walton Hall, Milton Keynes MK7 6AA

First published 1999. Copyright © 1999 The Open University

Edited, designed and typeset by The Open University.

Printed and bound in the United Kingdom by Bell and Bain Ltd., Glasgow

ISBN 0 7492 87799

1.1

22004B/a297sgi1.1

CONTENTS

The Course Team

Acknowledgements

Special thanks are due to Dr Joan Booth of Swansea University. As External Assessor of A297, Dr Booth has read, commented in detail, and encouraged the Course Team writers at every stage. Her scholarship and specialist knowledge have been invaluable.

The Course Team would also like to acknowledge the Committee of the Joint Association of Classical Teachers for allowing the Introduction section of this Study Guide to draw on a number of examples and definitions from the introductory section of their *Study Guide to Reading Latin* (published by Cambridge University Press).

The Committee of the Joint Association of Classical Teachers

Ken Dowden	The University of Birmingham
Lorna Kellett	Blyth Jex School, Norwich
Sally Knights	Filton College, Bristol
Alison Lewis	Teesside H.S., Stockton-on-Tees
Sarah Parnaby	Northwood College, Middlesex
Phillip Parr	The Haberdashers' Aske's School, Elstree
Helen Price	Westonbirt School, Tetbury
David Tristram	Weavers School, Wellingborough
Hilary Walters	Loughborough Grammar School

Cover illustration: 'Cave canem', mosaic. Museo Nazionale, Naples. Photograph: Alinari.

Introduction

written for the Course Team by Paula James

YOU ARE ASKED TO READ THIS INTRODUCTION BEFORE YOU START ON THE *READING LATIN* SET TEXTS.

Welcome to A297, Reading Classical Latin. This Study Guide is a key component of your course materials in the coming year. It contains detailed guidance on the best way to work through the course materials and pinpoints and explains challenging concepts. Don't neglect it!

The scope of the course

A297 is based on the Latin text books, *Reading Latin: Text* and *Reading Latin: Grammar, Vocabulary and Exercises*. For this course you are expected to study Sections 1–4 of the text books. By the end of the course you should have acquired a good understanding of Latin grammar, a considerable amount of vocabulary, and should be able to translate fairly long and complicated sentences in Latin. Latin is a rich and complex language with sophisticated forms. A number of these forms must remain beyond the scope of this course. You will have learned a considerable amount by the end of the course and should have a good grasp of working Latin at university second level but you should not expect to emerge from the course able to translate all Latin texts from the original.

By the end of the course you should have sufficient grounding in Latin to think about taking your study of Latin to a higher level. There is a whole section of the course books that is not covered by the course and this section leads you into continuous Latin of a more complex nature.

Finding your way around the course materials

Provided as part of your course materials, you have two volumes produced by the Joint Association of Classical Teachers (published by Cambridge University Press) especially for people beginning to learn Latin at university level and/or as mature students. These are:

Reading Latin: Text (referred to as *RLT* in this Study Guide)

Reading Latin: Grammar, Vocabulary and Exercises (referred to as *GVE*).

You will be working through the first four sections of *RLT* and the associated *GVE* sections in this course.

This Study Guide contains commentaries to help you as you work your way through the course text books section by section, and, in Appendix 1, provides answers to the exercises that are set from *GVE*. Apart from this Study Guide, you also have a supplementary Translations Booklet and an audio-cassette tape, which, like this Study Guide, have both been prepared specially for Open Univeristy students.

The Translations Booklet provides you with an English translation of the passages that you will meet in *RLT*, but please take note from the outset that it is there for you to consult only *after* you have made valiant attempts to make sense of the passages yourself. The same is true of the answers to exercises in Appendix 1 at the back of this Study Guide.

The audio-cassette is divided into four bands. Band 1 contains a general introduction to Latin pronunciation, a short discussion on the way the Latin language works and a brief background of the genre of early Latin comedy. Band 2 introduces the playwright Plautus and discusses issues of performance. Band 3 introduces you to vital features of the language (with a little bit of humour thrown in!). It also provides a 'recital' of word endings in Latin, a tried and tested method of memorizing basic structures of the language. Band 4 is for the very end of the course and discusses the skill, structure and composition of Latin poetry.

The Study Calendar indicates when you should listen to each of the bands. Further information about the audio-cassette tape will be found in the booklet of Audio-cassette Notes.

Using the course materials

This Study Guide is designed to support you in your work with the JACT *Reading Latin* volumes in several ways. The Study Guide and Study Calendar will direct your work through *RLT*, section by section, along with the associated sections of *GVE*.

The usual pattern of study will be that you will translate the text in *RLT* as directed by the Study Guide, keeping to hand and working through the related section of *GVE*, where the grammar is explained and additional vocabulary is given. The exact order in which you tackle these elements will emerge according to your own preference. Since you will be working through a great deal of the text on your own, you may find it best to work through the grammar (and possibly also the exercises) *before* trying the translation of the running text as the course progresses. The explanatory grammar is likely to be a good place to begin each section as it will support you in grasping the sense of the running text as it becomes progressively more demanding.

When you tackle the translation passages in *RLT*, you may prefer to work out the sense of the passage in your head or to start out by writing your translation down. Use whichever method is best for you, unless you are specifically asked to write out a translation. The Translations Booklet provides translations of the *RLT* texts but you should take care to use this resource to check your work only *after* you have attempted the translation yourself, and not as a constant hand-holding facility when you are actually working through the passages. Please note that you *must* work through and make sense of *all* of the set translation passages in *RLT*.

GVE provides a great many practice exercises and you will not have time to do them all, so this Study Guide suggests which of the exercises are the most useful to work through for reinforcing and clarifying your understanding. You should consider these as set activities, representing the bare minimum of exercises that you must do in each section.

If you have time, you will also find the Reading Exercises very useful for consolidating your work in each section, but these are not considered as compulsory in this course. These exercises basically rehash the content and structures of the parallel running text in *RLT* and so provide useful further practice. You are advised to read the running text in *RLT* thoroughly and, if you are managing to go through the text twice, as suggested, then you may feel that the Reading Exercises in *GVE* are a dispensable luxury and may prefer not to spend extra time on them. However, they might prove very useful for exam revision.

The answers for all the set exercises are supplied in Appendix A at the end of this Study Guide, but again, please use these answers as a self-marking mechanism *after* you have completed the exercises. Additionally, the answers are also given for the optional Reading exercises and for selected other exercises that might be useful for revision.

This Study Guide provides a running commentary, in step with the course books, dealing with selected areas of the language work, and should be referred to alongside your study of both the *RLT* translation and the *GVE* exercises. The Study Guide commentary may not expand upon *all* the learning pressure points, but its additional explanations of certain aspects of the language should give you an extra perspective and a better understanding of the concepts.

Finally, you will, of course, need to memorize the grammar constructions and new vocabulary introduced in each section of the course, and regularly find time to revise grammar and vocabulary from your earlier study. The vocabulary that you should learn is listed section by section in the Assignment Booklet.

As you work through the course, you will soon get a 'feel' for the language and for the culture and people which speak through it. This process is what makes Latin such a rich and fascinating ancient language to learn.

Figure 1 Small fresco panel from House of Marcus Lucretius Fronto, Pompeii, showing a villa maritima. Photograph: Fototeca Unione, American Academy in Rome.

Pacing your work

The Study Calendar should never be far from your side. This timetable gives a detailed breakdown of the work you should aim to complete each week. For example, you are now in Study Week 1 of the course and the Study Calendar indicates that you should read this Introduction and listen to Band 1 of the audio-cassette this week. In Study Weeks 2 and 3, you should work through Section 1A of *RLT* and attempt the recommended exercises in *GVE*. Two weeks have been allowed for Section 1A as you will be finding your way around some new terms and definitions, getting used to the structure of Latin sentences and so on.

You should move on to Section 1B in the fourth week of study, and should be ready to complete and submit the first assignment by the date marked on the Study Calendar. The week before the assignment is due has been left clear to allow you time to consolidate what you have covered so far, as well as to produce the assignment itself. You should continue at the steady pace laid out in the Study Calendar, and should have completed the all the sections indicated before you tackle the second assignment.

With language study a particular kind of pacing is advisable. A phrase you will meet more than once is 'little and often'. This is not *one* possible approach to learning Latin; it is really the *only* way to succeed when you are studying an ancient language. You really need to set aside a realistic amount of time each week, and ideally a period each day, since progress is best made if constantly reinforced. (Keep in mind that the expected study each week for a 30-point course is 7–8 hours.) The learning curve in language work is steady and progressive. You should be constantly building on previous stages. **It is not possible to miss out sections and recommended exercises in the hope of returning to them later. If you do this, you will lose your way in the language and the course.** Having said this, the Course Team is aware of and sympathetic to the fact that the reality of adult life is being beset with distractions and that other claims on your time can work against a regular rhythm of study. If for any reason you do fall behind, try to catch up in the next week, so that you are at the appropriate point in the work to cope with your next assignment.

The good news is that much of the preparatory and consolidation work you will need to do in order to progress can fit really well into busy lifestyles. The 'little and often' approach can be much more user-friendly than the prolonged and protracted learning session. For example, the vocabulary and grammatical sets for memorizing can be carried about on cards or in small exercise books and revised while you are on trains, tubes and buses, at spare moments through the day.

To sum up then, throughout this guide, I have suggested strategies for study, for ways of working and learning, and for retaining what you learn. The intention is not to be prescriptive especially in regard to your framework of study; you may have already developed very effective work patterns and ones that suit you and your particular circumstances as a distance learner. But the advice should help you to plan and pace your work.

Assessment strategy

Your four tutor-marked assignments (TMAs) will not be essays but a straightforward testing of your understanding of the language. The general pattern for each TMA is for Part 1 to require one-word answers identifying the correct Latin for an English phrase or word, and for Part 2 to consist of a piece of Latin prose for translation into idiomatic (natural-sounding) English. TMAs must be submitted to your tutor by the dates indicated in the TMA booklet (also shown on the Study Calendar) and will be marked and graded by your tutor. Your tutor's comments on your TMAs form part of the teaching strategy for the course and you should take note of the advice given in this feedback.

Tuition

One of the most enjoyable and enriching aspects of learning a language with the Open University is the experience of face-to-face tuition. If you are able to attend tutorials you will find them immensely valuable. However, do remember that whenever explanations need revisiting or teasing out, your tutor expects to hear from you and s/he is likely to give you convenient times to ring for a helpful discussion of any aspect of the course. Please contact your tutor as early in the course as possible and consult him or her about your study strategy.

As with other OU courses, your tutor will not only provide tutorial support, but will also grade and comment on your TMAs.

This Study Guide will act as an additional tutorial voice to support you through your work. You should return to the Study Guide at the beginning of each study section. Working through the *RLT* sections and consulting the Study Guide as you go, you should find that a fair few of your questions have been anticipated and that you have a friendly voice to listen to in moments of stress!

Further reading

There are a number of books about Roman history and civilization on the market. Any reading you can do in your spare time about Roman life will help to put the language you are learning into its historical and cultural context. The closer your acquaintance with the civilization of the Romans, the easier it will be to make sense of what they write about themselves and their society. However, no such further reading is prescribed or expected as an examinable part of this course.

Conventions used in this Study Guide

1 *RLT* = *Reading Latin: Text*

   GVE = *Reading Latin: Grammar, Vocabulary and Exercises*

   N.B. Page numbers come at the bottom of the page in *GVE*.

2 *V* and *U* are written in Latin with the same letter: capital *V*, lower case *u* – so we write *QVIS* in capitals but *quis* in lower case. (See p.xiv of *GVE*.)

3 Marking long vowels. You will notice that some vowels in *RLT* and *GVE* are marked with a macron (a bar above the letter), such as: ā ē ī ō ū. These markings indicate the pronunciation of so-called 'long vowels'. The pronunciations are given on p.xiv of *GVE*. The macrons not only help you pronounce the word correctly but can thus also help with meanings, since, as in English, words that are spelt the same but pronounced differently can have different meanings (for example, in English, the word 'lead'). You do not

need to put in the macron when you are writing Latin. So you can write *auarus* rather than *auārus*.

4 You will notice a marking: ⌢ linking some words together. As explained on p.ix of *RLT*, these markings are provided as a translation aid and indicate groups of words that should be taken together; but again, you need not worry about including them in your own writing.

5 Literal translation. Sentences can be translated into English in various ways; the aim should be to keep to the original Latin phrasing without making the English sound too tortured and unnatural. English which keeps very close to the Latin but which does not really sound like familiar or idiomatic English is called a 'literal' translation. It is useful in so far as it demonstrates how the Latin language works. However, you should avoid forcing English into unnatural phrases when you do your own translations. You should aim to produce good natural-sounding English translations. With practice, you will soon become confident that the sense and meaning of the Latin are still being preserved.

ABBREVIATIONS

To simplify presentation this Study Guide uses the following abbreviations for common grammatical terms. (We will come on to their meanings in the next section.)

Abbreviation:	Stands for:
masc. *or* m.	masculine
fem. *or* f.	feminine
neut. *or* n.	neuter
sing. *or* s.	singular
pl.	plural
nom.	nominative
acc.	accusative
gen.	genitive
dat.	dative
abl.	ablative

The approach to Latin

written for the Course Team by Paula James and Chris Emlyn-Jones

Latin in the European context

The particular prominence of Latin in our everyday life can be explained by two significant historical developments. First is the importance of the language in the monastic tradition of European Christianity (and until quite recently, in the liturgy of the Roman Catholic church) and, along with the Greek, in the terminology of intellectual traditions of philosophy, science and law in medieval, renaissance and (until the nineteenth century at least) modern culture. For example, 'essence' derives from the Latin *esse*, meaning 'to be'; similarly words such as 'substance', 'momentum', 'inertia', 'evidence', 'utilitarianism' and phrases such as *a priori* come directly from Latin.

The second development is easily demonstrated by the similarities between modern west European languages and can be traced back to the direct descent of these languages from Latin. We would expect the Roman influence to be pervasive in Italian but it is also prominent in French, Spanish, Portuguese, Romanian and a host of other languages conventionally called 'Romance' languages. Of course, the Roman empire spanned the continent of Europe and beyond for hundreds of years, and language is not the only aspect of its wide cultural interaction.

The Romance languages have developed from dialect forms of Latin as it was spoken across the Roman empire and in areas where the Latin language was adopted as the main form of verbal and written communication. There are plenty of examples of words of this type; for instance, Latin *carus* (dear) has become *caro* in Italian, Spanish and Portuguese, and *cher* in French. The Latin *campus* (field) can be detected in the Italian, Spanish and Portuguese *campo* and in the French *champ*.

English belongs to the Romance linguistic family to a certain extent. For example, Latin *schola* (which in turn derives from the Greek word *schole*) has become English 'school', in company with Italian *scuola*, Spanish *escuela*, Portuguese *escola* and French *école*. However, Britain never developed Latin as a main spoken language in the way that France and Spain did. Rather, it developed a Germanic language, English, alongside the Celtic Welsh, Irish and Scots Gaelic. The resemblances between English and the Romance languages derive from a multitude of borrowings and adaptations from the period of the Roman occupation of Britain right up to the nineteenth century CE.

If Latin's place in the history of languages interests you, there is more detailed information in *GVE* pp.548–56 (Appendix: 'The Latin language').

What do we mean by 'grammar'?

Grammar is the system we use to facilitate our understanding of how a language works. Because it is a system it has certain organizing principles and a set of technical terms. At its most basic level the grammatical system analyses how a sentence is put together and how words relate to each other. Understanding the grammar of Latin is essential for an understanding of the meaning and spirit of the words on the page.

If you are innocent of grammatical concepts then you can start by making some exciting discoveries about your own language. If your mother tongue is one of the Romance (Indo-European) languages, then you will have a head start on understanding how Latin works. If your first language has a different origin and history from this Indo-European family but you have become competent in English, then you have already acquired the enviable skill of learning a very differently structured language and Latin should hold no fears for you.

The next section of this Study Guide gives basic definitions and examples of grammar, first in relation to English and then to Latin. If you have never learned a language (modern, ancient or your own) in an analytical way, looking at structures and parts of speech, you should find the following introduction particularly useful. There is a also glossary of grammatical terms in *GVE* (pp.xvii–xxiii) which will be useful as a reference guide throughout your study.

Parts of speech and sentence structure

In order to understand and discuss grammar, you need to be familiar with the basic terminology. The explanations below give a slightly more expansive and helpful introduction to some essentials than the list of terms in the *GVE* glossary. You might not absorb all the information at once, but don't get anxious if this is the case. You will become familiar with the terminology as you begin to meet it and use it regularly.

A more detailed account of the functions of the parts of speech is given in the section on Latin Grammar on p.21 below, but the following notes are intended as a basic outline of how they work.

Every word can be classified as one of the following:

noun
pronoun
verb
adjective
adverb
preposition
conjunction
interjection.

These are known as the 'parts of speech' and each part of speech serves a particular function in a sentence. You will find them all (except interjection) defined in the *GVE* glossary. Briefly, their functions are as follows:

noun (*or* pronoun)	a name of a person, place, thing or abstraction, e.g. child, London, table, courage
verb	a word expressing action or state, e.g. run, jump, think
adjective	a word that describes ('qualifies') a noun or pronoun, e.g. red, clever, pretty
adverb	a word that describes ('modifies') a verb, e.g. quickly, enthusiastically
preposition	a word coming before a noun or pronoun to indicate the relationship of that word to other words, e.g into, from, by, over
conjunction	words that link parts of a sentence, e.g. when, and, but
interjection	an exclamation, e.g. Oh! Alas! Hurrah!

Nouns and verbs are the most important ingredients in sentences. The most straightforward type of sentence has somebody (noun) doing (verb) something.

Brutus	smiled.
NOUN	VERB

Nouns can also refer to abstract things:

Cleanliness	is	next	to	godliness.
NOUN	VERB	ADJECTIVE	PREPOSITION	NOUN

Pronouns stand in place of a noun. Words such as 'you', 'he', 'she', 'it', 'we' and 'they' are pronouns.

Adjectives are words that tell you something more about nouns: they are said to *qualify* the noun: 'This is a *steep* hill'; 'This hill is *steep*'. In both these cases, 'steep' is an adjective.

Adverbs tell us something more about how an action was performed: 'He spoke *impudently*'. Adverbs are said to *modify* a verb (a different term, notice, from the one used about adjectives, which *qualify* a noun or pronoun). Many adverbs in English end in '-ly', for example 'greedily', 'mostly'; but some do not, such as 'often', 'quite', 'much' (as in 'much more'), and 'fast' (as in 'How fast does your chariot go?').

Prepositions connect to a noun or a pronoun to indicate the relationship between words in a sentence. Words such as 'at', 'from', 'to', 'by', 'with' and 'of' are all prepositions. 'She's too good *for* him!' 'The cat sat *on* the mat.' In both Latin and English, prepositions in a sentence invariably link up with nouns ('on *the mat*') and for this reason they have a special relationship with that noun.

Conjunctions provide links between phrases and sentences, for instance 'and', 'but', 'when', 'although', 'if', 'however', 'nevertheless'.

Interjections are stand-alone words as far as the structure of a sentence is concerned. They are exclamations that express emotion; for example, 'Alas!' and 'Hurrah!'.

Finally, there are two more important words to mention at this point. In English and many other languages, the words 'the' and 'a' (or 'an') are used to identify nouns. These are really a sort of adjective, but are called the *definite article* ('the') and the *indefinite article* ('a'). The important thing to remember about them in relation to Latin is that Latin doesn't have either of them.

In the following sentence, all the parts of speech are used. Try to identify them yourself before looking at the answer overleaf.

Well,		grammar	and		grammatical	terms

are	simple	for		us	when

we	see	them		in	action.

Figure 2 Pigeons, mosaic Museo Capitolini, Rome.
Photograph: Alinari-Anderson.

Well,	grammar	and	grammatical	terms
INTERJECTION	NOUN	CONJUNCTION	ADJECTIVE	NOUN

are	simple	for	us	when
VERB	ADJECTIVES	PREPOSITION	PRONOUN	CONJUNCTION

we	see	them	in	action.
PRONOUN	VERB	PRONOUN	PREPOSITION	NOUN

Starting with the sentence

Analysing a sentence is basic spade-work when you are learning Latin. Strictly speaking, a sentence should express a complete thought and contain a verb. A verb expresses an action or a state of being; for example, 'run', 'think', 'say', 'be' (this definition can be found in *GVE* p.xxiii). One word may serve as a sentence if that one word is a verb, for instance the command 'Go!', a short sharp order but a sentence, nevertheless.

Latin does not have to confine itself to the command form in order to produce a one-word sentence. We can translate the Latin word *timeo* as 'I am afraid'. Latin verbs contain within their endings the vital information of who is performing the action. *Timemus* is translated as 'We are afraid'. Note that the *-eo* of *timeo* has become the *-emus* of *timemus* but the root or stem *tim-* indicates that we are still dealing with the same verb.

In English formal prose, punctuation divides sentence from sentence by capital letters at the beginning and full stops at the end. However, if you have ever written or read a leaflet, you will know that punctuation can be an unreliable guide in the search for a grammatically complete sentence.

'*More wage cuts? Not on your life!*' These are phrases not sentences because they do not contain a verb. However, they do express two thoughts quite clearly and could be interpreted as a political and economic statement or imply an ideological agenda. Nevertheless we have to be quite technical and formal about the sentence in order to get to grips with the structure of Latin.

Let us take a well-known English sentence and identify the two essential components, the subject and verb. *The cat sat on the mat* is a perfectly acceptable sentence. What we have here is *the cat*, centre stage, noun and subject. In the case of the cat, we could have used a pronoun and said *it sat on the mat* and we would still have had a legitimate sentence. *Sat* is a verb and indicates what the cat was doing. Remember that verbs express actions and conditions. Remember, too, that, in theory, you cannot express a complete sentence without a verb. *The cat* on its own would not have got us very far, but *the cat sat* tells a story, although it is a short one.

This is not the end of the sentence – we are given even more information about where the cat sat, i.e. *on the mat*. This may not give you a terribly thrilling or enlightening mental picture but it does introduce you to the joys of a prepositional phrase. The preposition in the prepositional phrase is the word *on*. Other examples of prepositions are words such as 'in', 'at', 'from', 'to', 'by' and 'with'. There are Latin words equivalent to many of the English prepositions: *in* for example, means the same in both Latin and English. In both languages prepositions in a sentence invariably link up with nouns (*on the mat* in our sample sentence) and for this reason they have a special relationship with that noun.

In Latin this relationship is clearly expressed not just by the indivisibility of the phrase – prepositions cannot generally be left hanging on their own without a noun or pronoun – but by changing the ending of the noun to reinforce its relationship with the preposition. In Latin, prepositions 'govern' the nouns they are linked to and can determine the ending of the noun, so that the noun itself signifies and reinforces its own role in the phrase.

This does not happen in English but in Latin the noun *mat* would need to be in a particular case, i.e. have a distinct ending associated with the preposition *on*. This is an example of the inflected nature of the Latin language and a good place to start in investigating the implications of inflection, generally.

Latin grammar

An important feature of Latin is that it is an inflected language; that is, it changes the endings of nouns, pronouns, adjectives and verbs according to the context in which they are used. In traditional grammar, the system of inflection (the changing forms) of nouns, pronouns and adjectives is called *declension* (nouns and adjectives 'decline') and the system of inflection of verbs is called *conjugation* (verbs 'conjugate').

There are many patterns of word endings (known as *paradigms*) to learn, and it is a good idea to compile your own lists of them in a notebook, as you come across them.

Nouns

In English the relationship of words within a sentence is largely determined by position. In Latin, nouns have different endings depending on their role in a sentence. The different forms are called *cases* and each has a different word to describe it. The list of cases is as follows.

1 Nominative
  The nominative is the case for the subject, i.e. for the person or thing doing something. '*Brutus* killed Caesar.' '*Rain* was falling'. In English, the subject almost always comes before the verb (although we sometimes meet an inverted construction such as 'said she' or 'alleged the President').

2 Vocative
  This is the case for the names of people who are being addressed directly. '*Fido*, come here!' 'And now, *ladies* and *gentlemen*...'

3 Accusative
  The accusative does more than one job.
  (i) It expresses the direct object of a verb. The direct object is a noun or pronoun which in English usually follows the verb and is not introduced by a preposition. The direct object is on the receiving end of the action. 'Brutus killed *Caesar*.' Brutus is the subject, doing the killing. Caesar is the direct object, receiving the action of the fatal attack.

       Watch out for nouns following the verb to 'to be'. As a noun that follows the verb 'to be' refers to the same thing or person as the subject of the verb, giving us additional or alternative information about that subject, both nouns must be put in the nominative case. For example, 'Augustus is the emperor'. In this sentence it is quite clear that Augustus and the emperor are one and the same person. The grammatical term for this second noun, emperor, is called the *complement* quite simply because it complements our information about Augustus and completes the sense of the verb. The complement denotes a noun following a verb but not in any way on the receiving end of an action.

(ii) Prepositions meaning 'motion towards' and quite a number of others take the accusative – i.e. the noun they govern (are inseparable from) always goes into the accusative case (**to** the gate, *ad portam*).

It is interesting to think about this kind of case system in relation to modern English. Most words in English only really have a nominative and a genitive case:

	singular	**plural**
nominative	king	kings
genitive	king's	kings'

Even these few inflected forms in English are now falling into disuse and misuse, as fewer and fewer people know where to put the apostrophe ('). There are some accusatives left amongst the pronouns: 'him', 'her', 'me', 'them'; the obsolete 'thee' (nominative: 'thou'); and 'whom', which we do still encounter in modern English, as in the title of Ernest Hemingway's novel, *For Whom the Bell Tolls*.

There is a popular tendency, which is often met with a wry smile from language scholars, to misuse or misapply the nominative form of the pronoun 'I' in English. Mistakenly thought to sound genteel, it is grammatically quite wrong to say 'between you and I' as the preposition 'between' requires the accusative 'me'. Similarly the sentence: 'He has made lunch for you and I'. What should it be?

4 Genitive

The genitive case denotes possession, equivalent to -'s, -s' or *of* in English (the king's, kings', *of* the king).

5 Dative

The dative has various detailed uses; a very common one is the dative of the indirect object and in English accompanied by the prepositions 'to' and 'for'. 'I give a book *to him*'; 'I am doing this *for you*'.

Note the difference between the direct objects, 'book' and 'this', and the indirect objects, 'to him' and 'for you'. Although 'him' and 'you' are on the receiving end, they are not directly acted upon in the same way as the direct objects.

6 Ablative
   Like the accusative, the ablative does more than one job.
   (i) It expresses 'by' or 'with' a thing:
        'He hit me *with* a club'; 'We will be coming *by* chariot'.
   (ii) Prepositions amounting to 'from' and some others too, take the
        ablative: *'from* the gate'; *'out of* the town'.

There is also a locative case, which you will hear mentioned on the
audio-cassette and will meet in *GVE* Section 4C. It will not figure
largely in your life with Latin, however.

As in English, you can tell from the ending of a noun whether it is
singular or plural ('king' or 'kings'). This is known as its *number*.

In Latin, nouns also have a *gender*. They belong to masculine,
feminine or neuter groupings (*neuter* is the Latin for *neither* and
indicates that the noun is *neither* masculine nor feminine but in a third
category.) You would expect nouns such as 'father', 'mother', 'son' and
'daughter' to belong to masculine or feminine gender groups but in
Latin you must also learn a gender designation for inanimate things
and for abstract nouns.

Verbs

In English, in order to express a verb fully we need not only the
verb itself but also information as to who is carrying out the action,
i.e. a noun (or pronoun). This noun or pronoun (that is, the person
who is carrying out the action) is called the 'subject' of the verb. In
Latin, all this can be conveyed by a single word because the
changeable ending of the verb carries information about the person
performing the verb. Latin verbs thus have two elements:

1 a stem, the front part of the word which does not generally change;
2 the ending, the end part of the word which does change according
   to context.

For example, to say 'I love' in Latin we need just one word, *amo*.
The *-o* ending indicates that 'I' am performing the action or having
the feeling. If we wanted to say 'I would have loved', again Latin
can express all this by changing the ending again: *amavissem*. *Amo* is
still detectable but the new ending has altered the time of the action
and also brought in room for doubt about the actual loving, a state
English needed two more words to convey, i.e. 'would have'.
Groups of words such as 'He-him-his', 'she-her-hers', 'I-me' and
'call-calls' demonstrate that English, too, sometimes changes forms
of words depending on their function, but keep in mind that it does
so much less frequently than Latin does.

Verbs in Latin have endings to indicate the following:

Voice

active: Brutus *is killing* Caesar; it *is raining*.

passive (*GVE* p.243):   Caesar *is being killed* by Brutus.

Tense

present: Brutus *is killing/kills* Caesar.

future: Brutus *will kill* Caesar.

imperfect: Brutus *was killing* Caesar.

perfect: Brutus *killed/has killed* Caesar.

pluperfect: Brutus *had killed* Caesar.

future perfect: Brutus *will have killed* Caesar.

Mood

indicative: Brutus *is killing/kills* Caesar.

subjunctive: (survives in English – it's there in our 'would have loved' example on p.24, but is more pervasive and serves more functions in Latin. You don't meet the subjunctive mood until the fourth section of *RLT*)

imperative: Brutus, *kill* Caesar.

infinitive: *To kill* Caesar/*to have killed* Caesar. *To be going to kill* Caesar

participle: *Killing* Caesar, he felt sick; *having killed* Caesar, he felt better.

Whatever the mood or the tense of the verb, verb endings will also show what person is performing the action.

person	singular	plural
1st	I	we
2nd	(thou), you	you
3rd	he, she, it	they

Another aspect of verbs is the *gerund*. An English example would be *'seeing* is *believing'* (although Latin would use the infinitive for this phrase, *uidere est credere* – 'to see is to believe'). In Latin there is also the *gerundive*, which has no real equivalent in English, but we have adopted some vocabulary words in English that are actually Latin gerundives, because they can be convenient and succinct; for example, the word 'agenda' is Latin for 'things that must be done'.

Adjectives

Adjectives in Latin have endings to match the specification of their nouns: they must be in the same case as their nouns and in the same number. But also, like nouns, they must show what gender the noun is – whether it is masculine, feminine, or neuter – and this can be a fairly arbitrary business in Latin.

Yes, men are masculine and women feminine, but the word for 'gate' (*porta*) is feminine, as is 'house' (*domus*) and mind (*mens*) and all sorts of words ending in -*tas*: *tempestas* (storm), *ciuitas* (state). *Ictus* (a blow) is masculine, *amor* (love) is masculine (but *cupido*, desire, is feminine!). *Bellum* (war) is neuter, as are *tempus* (time) and *cornu* (horn).

Participles and gerundives (see under Verbs, above) are treated as honorary adjectives and need to show case, number, gender.

Learning Latin words

Let us draw for a moment on the experience of encountering a foreign language. Picking up spoken language is obviously not an option with Latin, so the following discussion focuses on the written word. Translating from one language to another can be an exciting and stimulating activity. It involves a certain amount of interpretation and sometimes you have a choice of more than one equivalent for a particular word. In fact, translating is a cultural exchange which can enrich your understanding of your own language as well as of the one you are learning.

The bonus of translating from a heavily inflected language like Latin is the careful scrutiny each word demands in order to find out its exact function in relation to the words around it. It encourages you to be comprehensive in your approach, to take account of several different factors before you can be sure you have understood the word correctly.

The *meaning* of the Latin word *filius* is 'son' in English and that is how you will learn it in your word lists (vocabularies). In English the word 'filial' is recognizably from the Latin root. If you have not met the English word 'filial' before, look it up in a dictionary. Also related to *filius* are, not surprisingly, the Italian word for son, *figlio*, the French *fils*, the Romanian *fiu*, the Portuguese *filho* and, less obviously, at first sight, the Spanish *hijo*.

When you come across the Latin word *filia* you might assume a relationship with the Latin word *filius* and you would be right. *Filia*

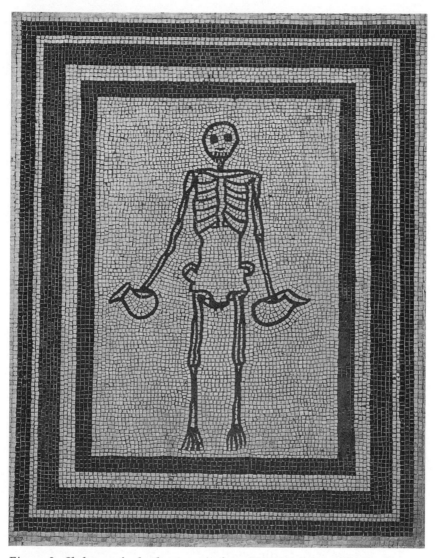

Figure 3   Skeleton of a butler, mosaic from Pompeii, Museo Nazionale, Naples. Reproduced from Roman Painting, *text by Amedeo Maiuri, 1953, Editions d'Art, Albert Skira, with permission of the publishers.*

means daughter and is a cognate of the word *filius*. In other words they look alike and come originally from the same word family. You will encounter a couple of cognates in your first section of text and grammar, *seruus* and *serua*, meaning male and female slave. (English 'servile' and 'servant' – the first *u* in the Latin words is pronounced as a *w* sound but it corresponds to our letter *v*. There is an explanation of this in Band 1 of the audio-cassette.)

By looking closely at these examples we have found out about Latin cognate or related words. You have now encountered several examples of European derivatives of Latin words. You might have noticed another distinguishing feature of the examples we just discussed, that the words denoting males ended in *-us* and those denoting females ended in *-a*; well done, if you did get this last point. All these things give clues to a word's function and meaning. There will be times when apparent similarities are misleading, so-called 'false friends', but there will be plenty of occasions when you can work out a Latin word internally, by reference to another Latin word, or by recognizing it from an English or European derivative.

Section One

1 Read the brief introduction to Plautus on *RLT* p.1.
2 Listen to Audio-cassette Band 2.
3 Read on in this Study Guide for help with approaching Section One of *RLT*.

Section 1: Plautus' *Aulularia*
Section 1A

Section 1 of *RLT* is based on a play by Plautus, *Aulularia* ('The pot of gold').

As you come to translate the Latin, you may stumble occasionally over meaning. Remember that the verb is the anchor of the sentence so make sure you have identified it as soon as possible.

It's probably best not to dwell on a sentence or phrase you find difficult but to return to it after you have read through the notes and done the exercises in *GVE*. If that does not clarify the awkward passage, then, *and only then*, check out the translation provided in the Translations Booklet. Make sure that you understand how the English version has been arrived at.

There is plenty of guidance in *GVE* for this first section. You may find the detailed dissection of sentences and structures *GVE* provides almost too much information but actually this attention to detail is very important for your study. Also the painstaking approach should clarify areas already raised in this Study Guide and in *GVE*'s own introduction and grammar glossary.

You are now ready to make sense of the Latin on *RLT* pp.2–6. Do not try to do too much at once! The golden rule bears repeating; remember, when learning any language it is best to work on the principle of 'little and often' (especially 'often'). Keeping this Study Guide and the relevant part of *GVE* to hand (pp.1–4 initally), work through the text in *RLT*, referring to the commentary below as you go along, as appropriate.

RLT pp.2–3 Introduction

RLT p.2 introduces the cast list. The purpose of the text on this page is to familiarize you with the verb 'to be', *esse* in Latin.

GVE tells you that in Latin there is no need to attach a separate word for each person. In Latin *sum* is the equivalent of two English words, *I am*. *Es* means *you are* and so on. However, the cast list does add in Latin personal pronouns, *ego*, *tu*. When they do appear they are extras for emphasis. Each character needs distinguishing; for instance: *ego sum Euclio* – *I am Euclio*.

Note carefully what *GVE* says about word order: subject, complement and verb. The complement is defined for you on p.xviii of *GVE* and is discussed further in the introduction to this Study Guide. With the verb 'to be', *esse*, and also with verbs such as *seem*, and *appear*, we can be given two pieces of information about a character's identity. So we find out in the sentence *Euclio senex est* that Euclio is an old man. Old man *complements* or completes the information we have already about his name. I am driving this point home because the complement must not be confused with the object of a verb! Euclio and the old man are the same person.

Once the characters of the play have been described, they go into action (Scene I). You have moved from the verb conveying a condition to the verb as an action word. Most of the verbs you meet in Section 1A belong to the first conjugation (the family of verbs with an 'a' stem). A few have an 'e' stem and these are second conjugation verbs.

The only verbs not conforming to the above patterns are *aperit*, a stage direction, line 24, p.4 and *cognovi*, line 36, p.5. They are both translated in the vocabulary list and you will meet their conjugation patterns in due course.

By the way, you may have noticed a bit of a mix-and-match in the stage directions. Occasionally they appear in English but most of them are in Latin and you should have a go at translating the Latin into English.

You are confined to the present tense of the verb in 1A. It suits the dramatic medium very well and lets you into verb forms gently. Make sure that you do translate the present tense in Latin by the present tense in English. It can be easy to slip into past or future tenses if you are not vigilant. *GVE* prints the first and second conjugations, present tense on pp.4–5.

Exercises

Attempt the following exercises from *GVE*.

p.4   Morphology: 1–2
p.4   Reading: (a)–(h)
p.4   English–Latin: (a)–(f)

Vocabulary

Learn Learning vocabulary for Introduction (Assignment Booklet).

RLT pp.3–6

Translate the text, using the vocabulary (*GVE* pp.5–7) and grammar
notes (*GVE* pp.7–13) to help you.

Additional grammar notes

The *Reading exercise*, 3(a) and (b), on p.16 of *GVE*, encourages you to
identify subject, object and prepositional phrasing. If you would prefer to
cut your teeth on some structurally simpler English poetry, try identifying
parts of speech (nouns, adjectives, verbs and so on, as well as subjects and
objects), in the nonsense poem extract below. For instance, in the first line
we could speculate that 'toves' might be some kind of creature and
therefore they would come into the category of nouns. 'Slithy' can then be
identified as an adjective describing the 'toves', and so on.

Jabberwocky
'Twas brillig and the slithy toves
Did gyre and gimble in the wabe;
All mimsy were the borogroves
And the mome raths outgabe.

"Beware the Jabberwock, my son!
The jaws that bite, the claws that catch
Beware the Jubjub bird, and shun
The frumious Bandersnatch!"

He took his vorpal sword in hand.
Long time the manxome foe he sought –
Then rested he by the Tumtum tree
And stood awhile in thought.

Lewis Carroll

Exercises

Attempt the following exercises from *GVE*.

p.9   Exercises 1–3
p.13   Exercises: 1–3 (N.B. all nouns are either nominative or
           accusative)
p.14   Exercise: Write the Latin for... (in the middle of the page)
pp.16–17 Reading exercise: 4
p.17   English–Latin (N.B. Don't be tempted to translate the 'it
           is' in brackets. This is simply the English way of
           emphasizing what the slaves are carrying. Latin achieves
           the same effect with the word order.)

If you have time, also attempt:

pp.15–16 Reading exercise: 1, 3(a) and 3(b) (see also the activity
           suggested below)

Vocabulary

Learn the vocabulary for 1A as listed in the Assignment Booklet.

The verbs *uoco* and *clamo*, which both appear in the Learning
Vocabulary at this point, both have a meaning connected to 'calling',
but you will see from the context in the *RLT* passage that *uoco* implies
summoning someone whereas *clamo* is a general shout or exclamation.
The verb *uoco* can take a direct object and for this reason is what we
call a 'transitive' verb, e.g. *Euclio seruum uocat* – 'Euclio summons the
slave' whereas *clamo* in this passage is intransitive and does not take a
direct object: *Euclio clamat* – 'Euclio calls out'.

Finally, for Section 1A...

- Ensure that you know all the grammar for the Introduction and
  Section 1A, especially the endings of the nouns and verbs. Recite
  them in their due order until you have memorized them.
- Read again *RLT* pp.2–3.

Section 1B

RLT pp.6–8

Translate the text, using the vocabulary (*GVE* pp.18–19) and Grammar notes (*GVE* pp.20–25) to help you.

Additional grammar notes

Amare and *habere* are infinitives, the part of the verb we express by putting 'to' in front; for example, 'to love', 'to have'. (In other European languages such as French, German, Italian and Spanish, the infinitive of a verb is just one word, as in Latin; for instance, the French *aimer*, meaning 'to love' and the Spanish *tener*, 'to have'.)

The infinitive has no direct attachment to any person but it is enormously useful to know the infinitive form of verbs in Latin for this can give a firm clue about their conjugation patterns (whether they are 'a' stem, 'e' stem or 'i' stem verbs, for instance). *GVE* does not introduce you to the nature and function of the Latin infinitive until Section 1F but you will find it helpful to find out the infinitive of each verb as you meet it from this point on.

Exercises

Attempt the following exercises from *GVE*.

p.22   Exercises: 1–3*
p.24   Exercises: 1–3
pp.25–6   Exercises: 1–5**
p.29   Reading exercise/Test exercise

If you have time for further practice, also attempt:

p.28   Reading exercises: 2–3

* Exercise 3 does not continue to emphasize the direct objects even when they appear first in the sentence.

** *GVE* p.26 question 2 is on agreement of adjectives. Note that agreement of adjectives does not mean that the endings of nouns and adjectives will necessarily always look the same or be matched in sound, for example, *multi fures* – many thieves (nominative masculine plural).

Vocabulary

Learn the vocabulary for 1B as listed in the Assignment Booklet.

When learning nouns and verbs it is helpful to keep lists, putting them in columns according to their declension or conjugation; for nouns, for example:

First declension	Second declension	Third declension
cura, curae fem. *corona, coronae* fem.	*deus, dei* masc. *coquus, coqui* masc. *aurum, auri* neut.	*fur, furis* masc. *senex, senis* masc.

and similarly for verbs:

First conjugation	Second conjugation
amare	*habere*

Add the other conjugations as they occur.

Finally, for Section 1B...

- Ensure that you know all the grammar for Section 1B, especially the endings of third declension nouns. Although *aedes* is used in its plural form for 'house' in the Reading Text, it is rather a bothersome noun to use as a model because of its eccentricity. In its singular form it means 'temple'. I advise concentrating on the other third declension nouns for your models.
- Ensure that you know all of the vocabulary so far.
- Read again *RLT* pp.6–8.

Section 1C

RLT pp.8–10

Translate the text, using the Vocabulary (*GVE* pp.35–6) and Grammar notes (*GVE* pp.37–40) to help you.

Additional grammar notes

In case you had any difficulties with the explanation on p.39, note 3 (the objective genitives), here is further clarification.

If you were putting 'My love is like a red, red rose' into Latin, you would start with *amor meus* because the love is a feeling which belongs to you. You need *meus* which behaves like an adjective but also demonstrates possession and is related to the pronoun, *me*.

If you were translating the sentence, 'Love of/for me is quite understandable', you would start with *amor mei* (using the genitive case of the personal pronoun). It might help to split the sentence into 'They (person or persons unknown) love me. This is quite understandable.' This is where the *object* element of the *objective genitive* manifests itself, in that *me* is clearly the direct object of 'love' when the sentiment is expressed using a verb.

Exercises

Attempt the following exercises from *GVE*.

p.37   Exercises: 1–3
p.38   Exercises: 1–2
p.39   Exercises: 1 (*meus* only) and 2
p.40   Exercises: 1–3
p.41   Exercise: top of page
pp.42   Reading exercise/Test exercise
pp.42–3 English–Latin

Vocabulary

Learn the vocabulary for 1C as listed in the Assignment Booklet.

Finally, for Section 1C...

- Ensure that you know all of the grammar for Section 1C.
- Ensure that you know all of the vocabulary so far.
- Read again Section 1C, *RLT* pp.8–10.

Section 1D

RLT pp.10–12

Translate the text, using the vocabulary (*GVE* pp.45–6) and grammar notes (*GVE* pp.47–51) to help you.

Additional grammar notes

Quis? Qui? When you are learning the interrogative pronouns and adjectives, *quis? qui?*, it would be a good idea to write them out afresh, separating out the interrogative and the adjectival *quis, qui*. Their doubled-up layout on p.50 of *GVE* is not a happy saving of space.

Third declension nouns. Remember that it is only in the nominative form that third declension nouns (and the same goes for the third declension adjectives) seem to be so varied in form. Once past the nominative, they basically behave in the same way.

Exercises

p.48   Exercises: 1–3
p.50   Exercises: 1 (*miser* and *pulcher* only) and 2
p.51   Exercises 1
pp.54–5   English–Latin

If you have time, also attempt:

pp.52–3   Exercises: 1–6
p.53   Reading
p.54   Reading exercise/Test exercise

Vocabulary

Learn the vocabulary for 1D as listed in the Assignment Booklet.

Finally, for Section 1D...

- Ensure that you know all of the grammar for Section 1D, especially the noun and verb endings.
- Ensure that you know all of the vocabulary so far.
- Read again *RLT* pp.10–12.

Section 1E

RLT pp.12–14

Translate the text, using the vocabulary (*GVE* p.57) and grammar notes (*GVE* pp.58–61) to help you.

Additional grammar notes

Questions with -*ne*. Remember this is an economical way to express a question and should not be confused with negative *ne* when you encounter it.

Exercises

p.60   Exercises: 1–2
p.61   Exercises: 1
pp.61–2   Exercises: (a)–(j)
p.62   Exercises 1–3
p.63   Reading exercises: 1
p.64   Reading exercise/Test exercise
p.64   English–Latin

If you have time, also attempt:

p.61   Exercises: 2

In this exercise, decide first the case, gender and number of the given form of *pulcher*; check alternatives (see *GVE* pp.48–9). Also check carefully the declension and gender of each noun before deciding what case it is.

Vocabulary

Learn the vocabulary for 1E as listed in the Assignment Booklet.

Finally, for Section 1E...

- Ensure that you know all of the Grammar for Section 1E especially the forms of *uolo* and *fero* and the endings of all imperatives.
- Ensure that you know all of the vocabulary so far.
- Read again *RLT* pp.12–14.

Section 1F

RLT pp.14–17

Translation

Translate the text, using the vocabulary (*GVE* p.67) and grammar notes
(*GVE* pp.68–72) to help you.

Additional grammar notes

In general, third declension adjectives have the same endings as third
declension nouns – except that the ablative singular usually ends in -*i*
and not -*e*. Learn these adjectives in the following pattern and you
should have few problems in dealing with them.

First and second declension adjectives

bon*us*	bon*a*	bon*um*	=	good
mise*r*	miser*a*	miser*um*	=	wretched
pulch*er*	pulch*ra*	pulchr*um*	=	beautiful

Third declension adjectives

inge*ns*	inge*ntis*	=	huge
auda*x*	auda*cis*	=	bold
omn*is*	omn*is* (but note that *omnis* in the nominative goes *omnis, omnis, omne*)	=	all

Notable features of third declension adjectives

For all those adjectives which have only one form in the nominative
(*audax, ingens* etc.) you need to learn the genitive singular because this
is the only way you can see the stem (*audacis, ingentis*). You also need
to learn the top horizontal line of nominative singulars for third
declension adjectives which have two forms in the nominative, one for
the masculine and feminine and another for the neuter (e.g. *omnis,
omnis, omne*), because that is the key to their stem.

Additional grammar notes

Like the third declension nouns, third declension adjectives are not as variable and capricious in their patterns as they might appear at first sight. You have seen how those on the pattern of *omnis* reveal their stem in the nominative form and so their inflection pattern can be worked out from then on. Adjectives such as *ingens* and *audax* do not reveal their stem in the nominative form. We need to find out their genitive singular (as we do with nouns) in order to know how they decline. The same formula applies with slight variations with adjectives such as *diues*, *uetus* and *pauper*.

Exercises

p.69   Exercise: centre of page
pp.71–2   Exercises: 1–3
p.73   Exercises: 1–3*
pp.74–5   Reading exercise/Test exercise

If you have time, also attempt:

p.75   *English–Latin*

* N.B. Adjectives can be used on their own without a noun (see *GVE* p.23, note 7)

Vocabulary

Learn the vocabulary for 1F as listed in the Assignment Booklet.

Finally for Section 1F...

- Ensure that you know all the grammar for Section 1F, especially infinitives and third declension adjectives.
- Ensure that you know all of the vocabulary so far.
- Read again *RLT* pp.14–17.

Section 1G

RLT pp.17–20

Translate the text, using the vocabulary (*GVE* pp.77–8) and grammar notes (*GVE* pp.78–80) to help you.

Exercises

pp.79–80 Exercises: 2–4
pp.80–81 Exercises: 2–5
pp.81–2 Reading Exercises: 1–2
p.83   English–Latin

If you have time, also attempt:

p.82   Reading exercise/Test exercise

Vocabulary

Learn the vocabulary for 1G, as listed in the Assignment Booklet.

Finally for Section 1G...

- Ensure that you know all the grammar for Section 1G, especially the various uses of the dative.
- Ensure that you know all the vocabulary so far.
- Read again *RLT* pp.17–20.

You have now finished Section One of *RLT* and should have acquired a basic understanding of how the language works. If you feel uncertain of any points, go over the relevant sections again. You will probably find that what you found difficult at the first attempt is now much easier.

If you have not already done so, go through the *Deliciae Latinae* which come at the end of each sub-section. These pages will not only help you with your vocabulary but will also enable you to appreciate the Latin language in its cultural setting and to see how modern languages have developed from Latin.

This is a good place to listen to the recital of paradigms (audio-cassette Band 3) which covers nouns, pronouns, adjectives and verbs you have learned so far. Ignore paradigms you have not met, for the present.

Section Two

The Study Guide commentary on Section One gave clear instructions on how to use and work through *GVE*. From this point on, the Study Guide will be more discursive, discussing points of interest and clarifying new concepts as they appear. The learning agenda in 2A is a varied one, which makes it interesting but demanding. Don't rush at this section – the Study Calendar allows two weeks' study for it.

It would be a tall order to work through all the exercises, so focus on the ones set in each section. You may wish to come back to some of the other exercises for exam revision, or use them towards the end of the course for further practice if you identify a weak area in your understanding.

For Sections Two–Four, follow the same pattern of study as you did for Section One. Take each part of a section at a time, go through the text and work out the meaning with the help of the notes in *GVE*. Learn the vocabulary as given in the section-by-section lists in the Assignment Booklet, and do the set exercises, checking the answers as you go. Appendix 1 in this Study Guide provides answers for all of the set exercises and also for the optional Reading exercises and some selected others which may be useful for further practice. You are advised also to go through the *Deliciae Latinae* for each section; this will help you with vocabulary, as well as putting the language and culture into context.

Section 2A

p.88 The future indicative active

In Section 2A you meet the future tense, and the more you practise this tense, the better. By the way, verbs that end in *-bo* in the present tense, such as *scribo*, 'I write', may fool you momentarily if the future tense is a recent acquaintance. You should be able to work out for yourself why this is so.

pp.89–90 Irregular verbs

The irregular verbs, accessibly set out on *GVE* pp.89–90, will become familiar in time. Return to *GVE* p.59 at this point and revise *uolo* before plunging in here, and then set out all four verbs together in your personal notebook on verbs. There are not many abnormally behaving verbs in Latin and their very distinctiveness can be an aid to memorizing them. Exercises 1 and 2 (p.90) are a useful test of *possum*, *nolo*, *malo*.

p.91 Adjectives

The key to success when learning adjectives, as *GVE* occasionally reminds you, is to be fully aware of the declension you are dealing with. Just as you need to find out the grammatical status of a noun in order to sort out its pattern of inflection, so you also need to know where the adjectives belong. For instance, the noun *puer* ('boy') is a second declension noun whereas *pater* ('father') follows the third declension pattern. On the same principle, the adjective *celer* ('speedy') is third declension and so cannot be declined on the second declension pattern of the adjective *miser* ('wretched').

Remember that even a pocket Latin dictionary will give both the nominative and the genitive singular of the noun and, where necessary, of the related adjective, and this second piece of information will indicate the appropriate declension.

p.93 Fourth declension nouns

The advice above about double-checking declensions needs to be universally applied to your learning experience. The model noun *manus* ('hand') is neither second declension masculine like *seruus* nor third declension neuter like *tempus*. Instead it seems to exist in a paradigm of its own. Actually, if you look closely (and of course you are going to learn it off by heart!) you'll see that it is not so individual or free-standing but combines second and third declension endings. This realization might demystify the pattern.

You may find the Latin sentence below an interesting one: it demonstrates the challenge of the inflected language for those of us who are simply not used to such a rich weave of word endings. It perhaps points up, too, the hurdles we face if we try to 'translate as we go' without the benefit of the Roman mindset. *GVE* is perfectly right to suggest that this is the least artificial and contorted way to deal with a Latin sentence but in the early days the 'dissect and re-order' approach may be the most practical method of arriving at a translation which makes sense.

> *militi dant dona puellae.*

The word order of this sentence combined with cursory reference to the dictionary or instant recall of the vocabulary might lead you to translate this sentence as: 'The soldiers give gifts to the girl'. Unfortunately, this will not work. If you remind yourself that the word for 'soldier', *miles*, is a third declension noun, then you will speedily see that *militi* can only be dative singular not nominative plural (although an '-*i*' ending is a nominative or subject ending for second declension nouns). What would the nominative plural of *miles* be? (Answer in footnote below[1].)

You must look elsewhere for the subject of the verb *dant* which is a third person plural ending in the present tense. *Dona* (gifts) could be the subject as this form could be a neuter plural nominative (*donum* is a second declension neuter noun) but then neither *militi*, as discussed, nor *puellae* will do as the direct object (the thing being given). Sense should tell you that the gifts are the things being given, but if we want to exclude the word *puellae* (girls) on grammatical grounds, then the direct object or accusative form would have to be *puellas*, not *puellae* (*puella* is a first declension feminine noun).

There is only one way this sentence can make sense grammatically and that is the following translation:

> The girls [nominative plural] give gifts [accusative plural] to the soldier [dative singular].

It was no use relying on the word order for sense here, as for some reason 'soldier' (*militi*) had a privileged first position. (This word

---

[1] Answer: *milites*

order could suggest a translation with an emphasis on the soldier: 'It is the soldier the girls give gifts to'.)

This analysis of the syntax, the way the sentence is structured, demonstrates how vital it is to know how different declensions behave, especially when word order can be flexible, in the interests of emphasis, or where poetry is concerned, to maximize variety of sound and metre.

Endnote

GVE is a little cavalier with its statements on p.93. *Manus* with a short '*u*' can only be nominative singular, this is true; but if you come across it in any future text which does not mark long vowels with macrons, you'll be spoilt for choice as far as identifying the case is concerned. Only context will reveal whether unmarked *manus* is nominative singular, nominative plural, accusative plural or genitive singular.

Just a few words on gender – look out for the misprint on p.153 of *GVE*, where *manus* is wrongly labelled as masculine. Also, saying that most fourth declension nouns are masculine may be misleading. The Latin words for different species of trees are usually feminine and many of these words have fourth declension '-*us*' endings (e.g. *quercus*, *quercus*, the oak tree, a noun which, like *domus*, sports both second and fourth declension endings). Some trees are second declension feminine nouns (e.g. *ulmus*, the elm tree).

Exercises

p.89   Exercises: 1–5
p.90   Exercises: 1–2
p.93   Exercises: 1–2
p.94   Exercises: 1–2
pp.96–7 Reading exercise/Test exercise
p.97   English–Latin

Vocabulary

Don't forget to make sure that you know all the vocabulary to date.

Section 2B

pp.102–4 Deponent verbs

The deponent endings introduce you to the look and shape of the
passive voice. Any active verb which takes a direct object (the technical
term is *transitive* verb) can have a passive voice. For instance, 'I call'
can be turned into 'I am called'; *uoco* becomes *uocor.* You may
remember the distinction made between *uoco* and *clamo* on p.32. *Clamo*
cannot be used in quite the same way but *clamo* could take a direct
object of a person (call upon) or of a thing, e.g. *magnum clamorem clamo!*
('I shout out a loud shout!')

   You will meet the passive voice and a more thorough explanation
about its uses and meaning at a later stage, but it is good to be aware of
what's on the horizon, especially when it sets this new form in a broader
context. The deponent verb has an active sense but a passive appearance,
and meeting it here acquaints you with endings that you will need to
know when you meet the passive of active verbs. Cherish the deponents,
because learning their forms now will save you time in the future.

pp.105–6 Fifth declension nouns, third declension nouns and special adjectives

The fifth and third declensions and two irregular adjectives complete
your learning tasks in 2B. As usual there is no effective substitute for
rote learning (and don't forget that reciting the declensions out loud
and listening again to the examples on Band 3 of the audio-cassette are
recommended reinforcements).

p.107 Reading exercise

Do note that Latin is a more rigorous time-keeper than English when it
comes to the tense of the verb. The word 'tense' derives from the Latin
for 'time', *tempus,* and a vital function of the verb is telling the time:
when, exactly, is the action taking place? The precision timing of Latin
comes to the fore in the Reading exercise on p.107, sentences (a)–(c),
where a more natural-sounding English translation will not use the
future tense as often as Latin does (even when the action is clearly
taking place in the future). This is one of the very few occasions when
you are allowed – indeed encouraged – to translate a Latin tense by a
different, not a corresponding, tense in English.

Exercises

Vocabulary

Ensure that you know all the vocabulary to date.

Figure 4 Italian marble relief of coppersmith's workshop, probably a shop sign, from Pompeii Museo Nazionale, Naples. Photograph: Alinari.

Section 2C

pp.113–4 *Hic haec hoc*

You continue your discovery of pronouns with *hic haec hoc*. This is featured on the audio-cassette readings so listen to the relevant section of Band 3 as part of your study of this section. *Hic haec hoc* should, in all its forms, become second nature to you, along with *ille illa illud* (and eventually *is ea id*, which you will meet in Section 3A).

Exercises

p.115   Exercises: 2, 3, 4, 5
p.115   Optional revision: 1, 2
p.116   Exercises: 1, 2, 3
p.117   Reading exercise/Test exercise
pp.117–8   English–Latin

Vocabulary

Ensure that you know all the vocabulary to date.

Figure 5 Still life with eggs and game, from the house of Julia Felix, Pompeii Museo Nazionale, Naples. Reproduced from Roman Painting, *text by Amedeo Maiuri, 1953 Editions d'Art, Albert Skira, with permission of the publishers.*

Section 2D

pp.122–4 The perfect tense (completed actions in the past)

Here you meet another set of endings attached to this new tense but with the familiar faces of the model verbs. The perfect endings are not too difficult to learn but the preceding stem of each verb can and often does change. Don't be discouraged by verb stems that take unexpected turns. Take heart from the fact that there are plenty of challenges in English past tenses too, which the learner of English has to accept and get used to. These might involve a simple vowel change or even an unrecognizable transformation in either or both the perfect tense and the past participle. For instance, *do did done*; *go went gone*; *see saw seen*; *drink drank drunk*; *lie lay lain*.

There is a helpful summary of irregular verbs so far on pp.124–6. Do get into the good habit of learning the principal parts of each new verb. These four parts will be an invaluable guide to the verb in all its manifestations (and dictionaries will either indicate that the verb straightforwardly follows a conjugation pattern or they will provide you with its particular variations by means of the principal parts). Exercise 3 on p.126 provides good practice in recognition.

pp.126–7 The ablative

This is the section in which you are alerted to a further use of the ablative. It's never too soon to start making your own table of uses for all the cases.

Exercises

p.126   Exercises: 1–5
p.127   Exercise: 1
p.128   Reading exercise/Test exercise
pp.128–9 English–Latin

Vocabulary

Ensure that you know all the vocabulary to date. Please note that in the Learning vocabulary on p.121 of *GVE*, *forum* is given the incorrect gender. It should be labelled as neuter, not masculine.

Section 2E

pp.134–5 Future deponent

Here you have the future of the deponent verb. *GVE* alerts you to an alternative to the second person singular. As this *-ere* ending occurs quite regularly in literary Latin, you may as well learn it at this early stage. When an alternative form given by *GVE* can be safely stored at the back of your mind, because it is unlikely to occur often, then the Study Guide will advise you of the fact.

Exercises

pp.135–6   Exercises: 2, 3, 6
p.136   Exercises: 1
pp.137–8   Reading and reading exercise/Test exercise: 1, 2

Vocabulary

Ensure that you know all the vocabulary to date.

Section Three

Section 3A

p.144 *is ea id*

The demonstrative pronoun *is ea id* comes in at this point to join your growing collection of these highly useful and versatile words in the Latin lexicon. For example, *is ea id* can feature prominently (although not in the nominative form) in the accusative-and-infinitive (indirect statement) construction which you will learn about in Section Four.

pp.145–8 Comparative and superlative adjectives

Even when these are irregular, they should not hold too many fears for you. In fact, the English derivatives are very helpful memory aids for these forms. You will see from *GVE* that the comparative and superlative forms of *bonus, malus* and *magnus* have obviously influenced English vocabulary. Latin derivatives have a wide European net – just one example, the Spanish *mejor* meaning 'better' is clearly related to the comparative of *bonus, melior*.

The Reading exercise on p.149 is a splendid reinforcer for the forms of the comparatives and superlatives and it also reminds you of the use of *quam* as described on p.146, note 4. Keep to the same case for both nouns when using *quam* in the comparison.

Exercises

p.145   Exercises: 3–6
pp.148–9   Exercises: 1–3
p.150   Reading exercise/Test exercise

Vocabulary

Ensure that you know all the vocabulary to date.

Section 3B

p.155

Please note that there is a mistake in *GVE* on the bottom line of p.155. It should read 2nd *conj.* verb.

p.158 The perfect participle deponent

This part of speech deserves to be introduced in a slightly less perfunctory manner than you will find in *GVE*. The beauty of the deponent verb's past (or perfect) participle is the fact that it has an active meaning. A non-deponent verb's perfect participle can only have a passive meaning. For instance, *amatus* from *amo* can be translated only as 'having *been* loved', never as '*having* loved'. *Vocatus* means 'having been called' not 'having called', and so on.

For this reason, when translating from Latin to English in future sections, be clear about what type of verb you are dealing with; deponent or non-deponent. In Section 3B you are practising the use of the deponent exclusively, so things at this stage are relatively simple.

You'll get a firm grasp of the participle if you remember that it is a hybrid, combining the function of both a verb and an adjective. The participle tells us something more about a noun; it adds to our information about that noun. So, the participle as adjective can qualify a person, a place, a thing, or even a feeling. For example, consider the following sentence:

> Sorrow, having besieged (attacked) the soul, grows daily.

In Latin using a deponent participle with its active force, this would translate as:

> *Tristitia animum aggressa* [from *aggredior* = I attack] *crescit in dies.*

Although the participle has to behave like an adjective and agree with the noun *tristitia* (hence *aggressa* in agreement with *tristia* is nominative feminine singular), it is actually telling us about an action performed by sorrow, and this is where the verb (*adgredior*) comes in. By the way, you may find *adgredior, adgressus* written as *aggredior, aggressus* in dictionaries and texts. It is certainly easier to pronounce if we dispense with the '*d*', and the written '*gg*' highlights its relationship with the English words *aggression, aggressive*.

Handy hints about participles generally

Just to consider further the meticulousness of Latin (as the educated writers and grammarians of the language practised it) and the more relaxed attitude to usage in English, read the following pithy paragraph from a Greek language course. You may find the humour rather *passé*, but the point is made memorably, nevertheless.

> We don't think much of participles in English. We have only two worthy of the name. There is the present participle – 'He paused with his hand on the door, *musing* a-while' or the past participle – 'There's that *cursed* knocker again!' We may consider the present participle to be active and the past to be passive. But we are abominably casual about the time of our participles. We may have to use our discretion in order to find out the time of an action referred to in a participle. Look at these:
>
> 1 He went out, crying bitterly.
>
> 2 Saying 'Bah!' she swept out.
>
> In the first sentence we may have a moist trail of evidence to prove that the exit and the tears were simultaneous. But nobody imagines in the second that the lady's departure was accompanied by a prolonged and continuous 'Bah!' like a benighted sheep with a faulty sound box. Yet there is nothing in the form of these two participles to suggest that their times, relative to that of the main verb, are different.
>
> (Kinchin Smith and Melluish, 1951, pp.90–91)

Exercises

Vocabulary

Ensure that you know all the vocabulary to date.

Reference

Kinchin Smith, F. and Melluish, T.W. (eds) (1951) *Kepos – Greek in Two Years*, English Universities Press.

Figure 6 Grand cameo of Sainte Chappell Bibliothèque Nationale de France, Cabinet des Medailles. Photograph: Giraudon.

Section 3C

Once you have conquered the concept of the participle and can appreciate
the beauty of its economy, the time sequence of the participle is not really
very complicated to work out. The economy of the participle is interesting
because English has to become rather wordy to express the future
participle in Latin. We have to resort to 'about to do', 'on the verge of
doing' or something equally cumbersome. 'Going to do' is often the best
way to render the future participle.

pp.168–71

The perfect participle passive, which completes the set, is often the
easiest to remember because it is frequently the basis of an English
derivative (think of the 'aggressive' example above). *GVE* does draw
your attention to this fact on p.177.

Cast your eye down the list of perfect participles on pp.169–70 of
GVE and you'll probably recognize several familiar words. Of course,
etymology works both ways, and you can work out the meaning of
certain items of English vocabulary from a knowledge of Latin. For
example, the verb 'to urinate' in Latin has the following principal
parts: *mingo mingere minxi mictus*. You can impress the medical
profession with your knowledge of the technical term for passing
water, *micturition*, if you are acquainted with this particular Latin verb.

Exercises

If you did the Reading exercise/Test exercise on pp.163–4 you will have
noticed that the translation in the Answers section of this Study Guide
offers a very literal rendering of the Latin participle constructions. You
might wish to try putting the piece in more natural-sounding and
idiomatic English now, avoiding so many 'having done' constructions.

Exercises

p.172   Exercises: 1–3
p.173   Exercises: 2
p.174–5   Exercises: 1, 2, 5
p.175   Reading exercise/Test exercise (N.B. In line 4, the second
          seruo should not be there.)

Vocabulary

Ensure that you know all the vocabulary to date.

Section 3D

p.180

Please note that *obsto* in the running vocabulary (*GVE* p.180) should be conjugation 1.

pp.181–3 The dative

You meet several more functions of the dative case in this section. The ethic dative is not something you are likely to encounter often in your early reading of Latin, if at all. It's useful to be aware of it, but more important, at this stage, that you learn to recognize the dative as the case ending for the indirect object, the possessive dative, and verbs which invariably take a dative case (as listed on *GVE* pp.182–3).

The predicative dative is a succinct expression which can encompass the notion of purpose as *GVE* suggests. But remind yourself of the meaning of 'predicative' on *GVE* p.xxi. It's important not to invest the term 'predicative' with notions of intentionality. It is much closer to the idea of the predicate in English grammar. The predicate is whatever follows the subject of an English sentence and completes our information about that subject. The Latin predicative dative is often best converted into understandable English by the use of words such as 'the object of', 'the source of', 'a means of'.

There are a number of easily learned set phrases involving the predicative dative. *GVE* has not revealed all of them on p.183, so additional phrases that you will find useful to learn are listed below.

admirationi esse   to be an object of amazement to, to amaze (plus the dative of the person amazed – until you get used to the predicative dative the doubling up of the datives can be a bit bemusing.)

auxilio esse   to be a means of assistance to, to help

bono esse   to be a source of benefit, to benefit

curae esse   to be a matter of concern, to cause anxiety

decori esse   to bring distinction, to adorn (remember *decus* neuter noun, nominative *decori* combined with *tutamen* on the rim of the one pound coin and translated as 'ornament and protection'.)

dedecori esse   to be a cause of shame, to disgrace

dolori esse   to be a cause of grief, to distress

exemplo esse   to be an example

exitio esse	to bring destruction, to ruin
honori esse	to be an honour
impedimento esse	to be a hindrance, to hinder
laudi esse	to be a credit
ludibrio esse	to be an object of ridicule, to be laughed at
odio esse	to be an object of hatred, to be hated
oneri esse	to be a burden, to weigh down
periculo esse	to be a source of danger, to endanger
praesidio esse	to be a means of protection, to protect
saluti esse	to be the salvation, to save
subsidio esse	to be of assistance to, to support, to help
usui esse	to be of use, to benefit
uoluptati esse	to be a source of pleasure to, to please

Exercises

pp.183–4 Revision exercises: 1, 3 (N.B. *All* 1st and 2nd declension dative plurals end in *-is* (except *deabus*, *filiabus*); and *all* 3rd, 4th and 5th declension dative plurals end in *-bus*.)

pp.184–5 Exercises (For question 2, look at *GVE* p.183 on the predicative dative.)

pp.185–6 Reading exercise/Test exercise

Vocabulary

Ensure that you know all the vocabulary to date.

Section Four

There is a lot to learn in Section Four, so do not skimp on the exercises in this final stage. Of course, recognizing the new endings continues to be a vital part of your study but later in this section you will need to concentrate particularly on the grammatical concepts involved in the subjunctive mood.

The final assignment for this course will cover the *whole* of Section Four, *including* the subjunctive, so you should be sure to work through all of the material.

Please note, however, that the examination will test your understanding and linguistic skills up to Section 4D only. You will *not* need to use the subjunctive in the exam.

Figure 7 Cicero.
Museo Vaticano, Rome.
Photograph: Alinari.

Section 4A

pp.194–6 The imperfect tense

The imperfect tense, expressing incompleted actions in the past, is another conjugation and another example of how precise (punctual) Latin is with its timings, making finer distinctions than English does. The imperfect tense has another set of straightforward endings. There are no variants here but just remember you are attaching the endings to the present stem of the verb, the first principal part, not to the perfect or to the participle.

pp.201–3 Indirect speech in Latin

The accusative-and-infinitive construction expresses something reported or perceived. It may seem a little odd at first but once you have understood the basic formula it is not difficult to recognize or to translate.

Consider the following sentence:

They say this.

It is clear that the word 'this' is the object of 'they say', answering the question, 'What do they say?'. Suppose that we were given more information, exactly what they said in answer to the question above. The answer might be:

They say that Caesar is a good man.

The phrase 'that Caesar is a good man' should still be regarded as the object of the verb. That's why you should expect to find the accusative case somewhere in the construction. We can imitate the Latin construction in this particular example, but need to modify the verb slightly for an idiomatic English sound:

They declare [say] Caesar to be a good man.

Now look at the Latin:

dicunt Caesarem esse uirum bonum.

Hold on to the fact that the subject of what was the original direct statement, 'Caesar is a good man', has to become the object because the whole subordinate clause is the object of the main verb (they say/ *dicunt*) in this new extended sentence.

A second important point concerns the verb and once again is a matter of time-telling. The infinitive form used has to correspond in time or tense to the tense of the original statement. The simple rule of thumb is that the *perfect infinitive* indicates action before the time of the main verb, the *present infinitive* indicates action at the same time as the main verb, and the *future infinitive* indicates action after the time of the main verb.

You may notice in the examples given on *GVE* p.202 that English needs to keep a past tense in the indirect statement when the tense of the main verb is in the past tense. However, Latin uses the present infinitive in the same situation. *Caesar dixit Romam se uenire* translates as 'Caesar said that he *was* coming to Rome'. Latin uses *uenire*, the present infinitive, 'to come', as if the translation were '*is* coming', because the present tense is the one Caesar would have used: original statement, 'I *am* coming to Rome'.

Exercises

The English–Latin exercise starting at the bottom of p.206 will be a test of your understanding but do note that in sentence (b) – 'Cicero said that the slaves entered the temple' – the more natural English would be: 'Cicero said that the slaves had entered the temple'. When translating this remember that the original words of Caesar's were: 'The slaves have entered the temple'. So what tense of the infinitive are you going to use?

Exercises

p.196   Exercises: 2, 4, 5
p.201   Exercises: 2, 4
pp.203–4 Exercises: 1–2*
p.205   Reading exercises: 2
p.206   Reading exercise/Test exercise
p.206   English–Latin

*N.B. The Latin is quoted incorrectly in this question and should read: *homo sum: humani nil a me alienum puto.*

Vocabulary

Ensure that you know all the vocabulary to date.

Section 4B

pp.213–5 The ablative

Section 4B provides plenty of practice on the various uses of the ablative case. Do take notice of *GVE*'s reminder about making comparisons, the first point in 100B (p.214), and the way a comparison works using the ablative instead of *quam*. You might find it slightly confusing that *GVE* illustrates the ablative expressing measure of difference in two sentences with comparative *quam* (point 5).

p.216 Pronouns and adjectives

Now is a good time to remind yourself of how pronouns and pronominal adjectives decline and how we might translate them, especially the ones you meet earlier, where quite delicate nuances of meaning distinguish them.

Exercises

p.216   Exercises: 1(b), (c)
p.218   Exercises: 2
p.219   Exercises: 3

Vocabulary

Ensure that you know all the vocabulary to date.

Section 4C

pp.227–8 The pluperfect

The pluperfect tense is a stage further back in the past than the perfect. *GVE* gives you its full designation as the 'pluperfect indicative active'. The first word, pluperfect, signifies the tense, and the last word, active, is self-evident. Indicative describes the mood of the verb, and as the definition of the word on *GVE* p.xx explains, it suggests definite, actual action.

The only moods of the verb you have met so far are the indicative and the imperative (command form). You are now ready to move on and think about the subjunctive mood, a mood which deals with the hypothetical and unfulfilled, rather than the real, the actual. You will meet the subjunctive in Section 4E but a summary at this point will complete your understanding of the verb conjugation's triple designation.

'Subjunctive' comes from the Latin *subiungo* and denotes something that is joined on; for instance, 'I am waiting here *in case you should come*'. The subordinate, or joined-on, clause is not referring to an actual arrival but only to the possibility of one. This is a natural place for the use of the subjunctive mood. You may have realized that English is capable of expressing the unfulfilled nature of the event by using 'should come', although 'in case you come' would probably be the regular way of ending the English sentence. Most *sub*ordinate clauses have their verbs in the *sub*junctive, but for the present you can relax, as you are about to meet those relative subordinate clauses which do not need verbs in the subjunctive mood.

p.229 The relative pronoun *qui quae quod*

The relative pronoun *qui* represents an exciting leap in the language as far as any student is concerned. Understanding how it works will enable you to translate and construct more complex sentences in Latin. *GVE* painstakingly explains how the relative clause works. Just remember that a relative pronoun has the same gender and number as the noun that it is replacing in the subordinate clause, but its case depends on the grammar of its own clause and is completely independent of the case of the original noun.

If it helps, try separating out the two pieces of information you are likely to be receiving in the sentence. Taking *GVE*'s example from 5(b)

on p.230, you could convert the sentence 'Diodorus, whom Verres
hated, was afraid' into 'Diodorus was afraid. Verres hated Diodorus'.
The Latin would be *Diodorus timebat. Verres Diodorum oderat.* Now
simply replace *Diodorum* with the matching relative pronoun –
laborious, perhaps, but it should get the right result if you are still in
doubt about the correct case of the relative.

p.232 The ablative absolute

The ablative absolute construction is introduced a little nonchalantly at
this point in *GVE*, considering that it is an exceedingly common Latin
construction. This construction is extremely useful for conveying
attendant circumstances and can denote temporal and causal
relationships between two events. Grammar books frequently discuss
the ablative absolute in the context of the participle and its use. The
ablative absolute can be used where English would use an active past
participle. Unless there is an appropriate deponent verb, this is not an
option in Latin.

Consider the following English sentence:

Having praised the slaves, the man cursed his friends.

The Latin for praise, *laudo*, has no active past participle – *laudatus*
attached to *vir* (man) would mean 'the man having been praised'. One
way around this, if we want to use a participial phrase, is to go for the
ablative absolute construction:

servis laudatis, vir amicos vituperavit.

This literally translates as:

With the slaves having been praised, the man cursed his
friends.

However it would be perfectly legitimate to translate the sentence back
into the original English that we started with above, or to say:
'Although the man praised the slaves, he cursed his friends' or 'After
the man had praised the slaves, he cursed his friends'.

Just remember that the 'absolute' part of the phrase 'ablative
absolute' is all about disconnecting (or 'absolving') the construction
from the rest of the sentence grammatically: *absoluo* means 'I
loosen'.

p.233 The locative

The locative case had a fleeting mention in the Monty Python sketch recorded on Band 3 of the audio-cassette, but although John Cleese and Graham Chapman arrived at the correct phrasing, *Romani, ite domum*, for 'Romans go home', *domum* is not a locative but the accusative of motion towards a place. *Domi*, the true locative form, is to be translated as 'at home'.

Exercises

Questions 4 and 5 of the exercises on p.229 cover a range of tenses, so if you complete them, you will have done some valuable revision of all the manifestations of the verb in its indicative mood.

p.229   Exercises: 3–5
p.231   Exercises: 1
p.235   Reading exercise/Test exercise

Vocabulary

Ensure that you know all the vocabulary to date.

Section 4D

pp.243–9 The passive

The good news in this section is that all the forms set out on pp.244–6 are familiar ones. You have learned them as endings for the deponent verbs. So, your main task here, as well as refreshing your memory about the conjugation patterns, is to grasp the concept of the passive.

In the sentence 'Tom hit the ball', you could think of the action of the verb going from left to right. The form of the verb is active and the subject acts upon the object. In the sentence 'The ball was hit by Tom' the action of the verb goes from right to left. It is the subject of the verb which receives or suffers the action of the verb. A verb which does not take a direct object cannot be used in a passive construction with an agent performing the action.

Don't worry about the rather fine distinction *GVE* makes in point 2 of the notes on p.249. Most of the time, the human agent needs to be translated with *ab* or *a* plus the ablative, and only inanimate agents dispense with the preposition.

Exercises

pp.247–8   Exercises: 1–2
p.250   Exercises: 2, 4, 5
p.251   Reading exercise/Test exercise

Vocabulary

Ensure that you know all the vocabulary to date.

Section 4E

pp.261–2 Present participles

Remind yourself of the definition of 'predicative' on *GVE* p.xxi. Note 3 on p.262 of *GVE* is the third occasion that a predicative use is mentioned. Do not imagine that there is necessarily any sense of purpose in the function of the present participle. Note, too, that the present participle is always active and is the meeting point for active and deponent verbs with regard to both appearance and role in a sentence; i.e. active verb and deponent verb present participles look and act exactly the same.

As the use of a present participle assumes that the action described in it takes place at the same time as the main verb, you should expect to find it even when the main verb is in the past tense, as the examples below demonstrate.

> *lupum in siluam intrantem conspicimus.*
> We catch sight of a wolf going into the wood.

> *lupum in siluam intrantem conspeximus.*
> We caught sight of a wolf going into the wood.

> *lupum agnum sequentem conspicimus.*
> We catch sight of a wolf following a lamb.

> *lupum agnum sequentem conspeximus.*
> We caught sight of a wolf following a lamb.

You might object that the last two sentences could technically be translated as 'the lamb following the wolf'. This is the sort of situation when common sense and *GVE*'s advice about translating as you go, at least on a first-sight reading, should produce the logical English version.

pp.263–5 Meeting the subjunctive

Unlike your previous experience where you started with the present tense, you are asked to familiarize yourself first with the past (pluperfect) endings of this mood of the verb. This is because it enables you to use the most appropriate tense of the subjunctive to construct some straightforward subordinate clauses where the subjunctive mood is required. The construction with *cum*, meaning 'since' or 'although', always takes the subjunctive.

Exercises

pp.262–3   Exercises: 1–3
pp.265–6   Exercises: 1–2

Vocabulary

Ensure that you know all the vocabulary to date.

Figure 8 Stone copy of the Clupeus Virtutis found in the Cryptoporticus at Arles Musée de l'Arles Antique. Photograph: Michel Lacanaud.

Section 4F

Generally, you should think of the subjunctive as the *tentative* mood. As you learn about the circumstances in which it should be used, this guideline should become clearer. The indirect command, for instance, introduced on pp.279–80, demonstrates the point in so far as an order does not necessarily result in an action. In example (a) at the bottom of p.279, although it is not likely that Caesar's orders were ignored we cannot assume that an action automatically followed, so we are still in the realm of the hypothetical. The translation GVE suggests has that revealing word 'should' in the English, which can help us to distinguish between the actual and the ideal. The list on GVE p.280 shows that all these verbs taking a subjunctive construction deal with strong wishes, psychological coercion, and command, but, even so, none can guarantee the outcome.

Exercises

p.279   Exercises: 1–2
p.281   Exercises: 1–2
p.282   Exercises: 1–2

Vocabulary

Ensure that you know all the vocabulary to date.

Section 4G

pp.291–2 Conditionals with subjunctive verbs

The *GVE* heading for this section may be misleading in that you will
sometimes find 'if' clause constructions which do not need a
subjunctive mood. These are known as 'open conditions' and they
deal with statements that are non-controversial in an ethical or legal
sense.

Below are examples of this sort of straightforward condition; the
key distinction between these statements and the ideal or unreal
conditions that require the subjunctive mood is that the action or
state described in the subordinate clause is assumed to occur and
therefore justifies the statement in the main clause.

Si hoc facis, peccas.
If you do this, you do wrong. [*pecco* = first conjugation]

si hoc fecisti, peccauisti.
If you did this, you did wrong.

si hoc facies, peccabis.
If you are going to do this, you will be doing wrong. [Both verbs in
future indicative]

(You might raise the objection in this last example that there is no way
of knowing if either action is to be carried out! It's not surprising,
perhaps, that some future endings can look rather like subjunctive
ones. You will just have to accept that the example using the
conditional in the future, still has an air of definiteness in it as far as
the result of the action is concerned.)

si hoc feceris, poenas dabis.
If you do [literally, if you will have done – future perfect
indicative] this, you will pay the penalty.

(Note how exact Latin is about the first action, the 'doing this', which
has to happen before the penalty is carried out, even though both
actions are taking place in the future; the future perfect, *feceris* is
therefore used to keep the sequence of events clear.)

With all these statements there is no room for doubt or negotiation.
The *GVE* examples of unreal conditions on p.291 emphasize the
difference quite forcefully. For instance, consider the first example
from that page.

If I were rich [add on 'which I'm not'] I would not be working now [add on 'but I am'].

These two manufactured asides (assumptions) demonstrate that the state described is not the reality of the situation. So, you can see that the subjunctive has to play its part.

Which tense?

The rules are summarized by *GVE* on the same page. As you learned the pluperfect subjunctive first, you may as well know about the use of pluperfect subjunctive in conditional clauses. It completes the pattern of unreal conditions for you and is probably the easiest to handle as it straightforwardly translates with the auxiliary 'had' in English.

si canis latravisset, furem cepissimus.
If the dog had barked, we would have caught the thief.

(The awkward but grammatically correct English for *furem cepissimus* would be: 'we had caught the thief'.)
So, remember:

- 'were to ... would' requires the present subjunctive in both clauses;
- 'were (now) ... would (now)' requires the imperfect subjunctive in both;
- 'had ... would have' requires the pluperfect subjunctive in both clauses.

pp.294–5 The subjunctive in reported speech

It may be helpful to bring out a little more explicitly why the subjunctive is needed in the examples *GVE* gives.

It is useful to add the word 'allegedly' when one is dealing with apparently factual statements in reported speech. In the first *GVE* example, remember that he said that everyone loved him because he was handsome. 'Everyone loved him' may well be true but the reason given is only his opinion or speculation.

Exercises

p.292   Exercises: 1–2
pp.297–8   English–Latin

Vocabulary

Ensure that you know all the vocabulary to date.

Postscript

The subjunctive makes an exciting finish to this course because with it, you are moving out of the realms of simple and largely factual narrative to more sophisticated thinking which requires more sophisticated forms of expression. This qualitative leap in your learning, if you complete it successfully, will mean you are much closer to an understanding and reading of the complex Latin sentence.

I was told quite firmly when studying for my classics degree that Latin should be quaffed like beer, not sipped like wine. If you are in the happy position of having plenty of leisure time in the future, the more Latin you can go on to read, the better!

What next?

You should spend the remaining time on the course revising and consolidating your work for the examination. Remember to study the Specimen Examination Paper and consult your tutor if you are in any doubt about what is required. You will also find that the vocabulary lists in the Assignment Booklet will help you to prepare for the examination.

After the course

Although you have covered a great deal of ground in this course, there will, however, still be some way to go before you can tackle continuous Latin in the original. If you would like to continue by working on the rest of *RLT* and *GVE*, you may be interested to know that answers and a translation of the running texts for Section 5 are available to help with informal further study. Please send a large self-addressed envelope marked *RLT Notes* to: The Course Manager, A297, Faculty of Arts, The Open University, Walton Hall, Milton Keynes, MK7 6AA.

Appendix 1:

Answers to Exercises in GVE

Section One

Introduction

p.4 Exercises

1.
you (s.) are	*es*
there are	*sunt*
he is	*est*
there is	*est*
you (pl.) are	*estis*
they are	*sunt*
it is	*est*
I am	*sum*
she is	*est*

2.
sum	I am	*sumus*	we are
sunt	they are	*est*	he is
estis	you (pl.) are	*es*	you (s.) are
est	he/she/it is *or* there is	*sunt*	they are *or* there are
sumus	we are	*sum*	I am
es	you (s.) are	*estis*	you (pl.) are

p.4 Reading

(a) It is the household.
(b) The slave girl is Staphyla.
(c) For the pot is full of gold.
(d) The cook is a slave.
(e) Phaedra is the daughter.
(f) In the house (there) are Euclio, Phaedra and the slave girl.
(g) The miser is an old man.
(h) Near the river there is a small field.

p.4 English–Latin

(a) There are, in the household Euclio, Phaedra (and) Staphyla.
est in familia serua.

(b) Euclio and Phaedra are in the house.
serua in aedibus est.

(c) I am Euclio.
es seruus/serua.

(d) Euclio's daughter is Phaedra.
serua Euclionis Staphyla est.

(e) Who are you? (s.)
Euclio sum.

(f) Who are you? (pl.)
Euclio et Phaedra sumus.

Section 1A

p.9 Exercises

1   *celamus*   *timeo*   *porto*   *habeo*
     celatis   *times*   *portas*   *habes*
     celat   *timet*   *portat*   *habet*
     celamus   *timemus*   *portamus*   *habemus*
     celatis   *timetis*   *portatis*   *habetis*
     celant   *timent*   *portant*   *habent*

2   *clamas*   you (s.) shout   *clamatis*
     habent   they have   *habet*
     intrat   he enters   *intrant*
     uoco   I call   *uocamus*
     sumus   we are   *sum*
     portamus   we carry   *porto*
     times   you (s.) fear   *timetis*
     habetis   you (pl.) have   *habes*
     est   he is   *sunt*
     timet   he fears   *timent*
     uocant   they call   *uocat*
     celatis   you (pl.) hide   *celas*
     timemus   we fear   *timeo*
     habeo   I have   *habemus*
     sunt   they are   *est*

3   you (pl.) have   *habetis*
     I do hide   *celo*
     we are carrying   *portamus*
     they call   *uocant*
     you (s.) are afraid of   *times*
     she is dwelling   *habitat*
     there are   *sunt*
     it has   *habet*
     there enters   *intrat*
     she is   *est*

p.13 Exercises

1 | *coquus* | *coqui* | *aula* | *aulae* |
   |---------|---------|--------|--------|
   | *coque* | *coqui* | *aula* | *aulae* |
   | *coquum* | *coquos* | *aulam* | *aulas* |
   | *coqui* | *coquorum* | *aulae* | *aularum* |
   | *coquo* | *coquis* | *aulae* | *aulis* |
   | *coquo* | *coquis* | *aula* | *aulis* |

2 | *seruarum* | gen. pl. |
   |-----------|----------|
   | *coquo* | dat/abl. sing. |
   | *coronam* | acc. sing |
   | *seruos* | acc. pl. |
   | *scaenae* | gen/dat. sing. *or* nom. pl. |
   | *filia* | abl. sing. (*filia* nom. sing.) |
   | *coquus* | nom. sing |
   | *serui* | gen. sing. *or* nom. pl. |
   | *coquum* | acc. sing. |
   | *filiae* | gen/dat. sing. *or* nom. pl. |
   | *scaenas* | acc. pl. |
   | *seruo* | dat/abl. sing. |
   | *coquorum* | gen. pl. |
   | *aula* | nom. sing. (*aula* abl. sing.) |
   | *seruis* | dat/abl. pl. |

3   **Translation**   **Plural/singular**
(a)   I am a slave.   *sumus serui.*
(b)   I carry a pot.   *aulas portamus.*
(c)   They have garlands.   *coronam habet.*
(d)   The slave girl fears the slave.   *seruae timent seruos.*
(e)   You call the slave girls.   *seruam uocas.*
(f)   The slave girls carry the pots.   *serua aulam portat.*
(g)   We hide the pots.   *celo aulam.*
(h)   The cooks hide the slave girls.   *seruam celat coquus.*
(i)   The household has a garland.   *familiae coronas habent.*
(j)   The slave calls the slave girl.   *uocant serui seruas.*

If you have made mistakes, first check the endings of the nouns to see whether they are nominative (subject) or accusative (object).

p.14 Exercise

onto the stage	*in scaenam* (acc. because movement towards)
in the pot	*in aula* (abl. because position)
onto the garlands	*in coronas*
into the pots	*in aulas*
in the household	*in familia*
towards the slave woman	*ad seruam*
in the slaves	*in seruis*
towards the daughter	*ad filiam*

pp.15–16 Reading exercise

1   (a)   The slave enters (onto) the stage. He (the slave) carries garlands.

     (b)   The cooks are in the house. They (the cooks) call the slave women.

     (c)   A slave woman is in Euclio's household. She (the slave woman) is Staphyla.

(d) Onto the stage enters Demaenetus. He (Demaenetus) has a pot full of gold.

(e) The cook and the slave woman are shouting. For they (the cook and the slave woman) fear the slave.

4 Demaenetus sees the cooks and flute-players. They are coming to his daughter's wedding. They enter the house of Demaenetus and prepare the wedding. Now the house of Demaenetus is full of cooks and flute-players. But Demaenetus is afraid. For he has a pot full of gold. For if the pot full of gold is in Demaenetus' house, Demaenetus is very afraid of thieves. Demaenetus hides the pot. Now the gold is safe. Now Demaenetus is safe. Now the pot is safe. For the Lar has the pot full of gold. Now the pot lies hidden near the Lar under the ground. Therefore Demaenetus now approaches the Lar and prays. 'O Lar, I, Demaenetus, call on you. O protector of my household, I bring to you my pot full of gold. My daughter's wedding is today. But I fear thieves. For my house is full of thieves. I beg and beseech you, protect Demaenetus' pot full of gold.'

p.17 English–Latin

(a) The cook carries Demaenetus' pot.
seruus coronas coquorum habet.

(b) You are shouting but I am carrying the pots.
serua timet. ego igitur coquum uoco.

(c) Why is the stage full of slaves?
cur aedes plenae sunt coquorum?

(d) I, the Lar, call you. Why do you fear me?
ego Phaedra intro. cur aulam celatis?

(e) If he has gold, Demaenetus is afraid.
si aulam celant, serui timent.

(f) It is garlands and pots the slaves are carrying.
coquum et seruam uocat Demaenetus.

Section 1B

p.22 Exercises

1 | *honor* | *honores* |
    |-----------|-------------|
    | *honorem* | *honores* |
    | *honoris* | *honorum* |
    | *honori* | *honoribus* |
    | *honore* | *honoribus* |

fur	*fures*
furem	*fures*
furis	*furum*
furi	*furibus*
fure	*furibus*

2 | *Euclionis* | gen. sing. |
    |-------------|-------------------------|
    | *furem* | acc. sing. |
    | *aedium* | gen. pl. |
    | *honores* | nom. *or* acc. pl. |
    | *Lar* | nom. sing. |
    | *senum* | gen. pl. |
    | *aedis* | acc. pl. (see *GVE* p.20) |
    | *honorem* | acc. sing. |
    | *fur* | nom. sing. |
    | *Laris* | gen. sing. |

3   (a)   Then the thief sees the old man's treasure.
          deinde thesauros senum fures uident.
    (b)   The Lar does not have honour.
          Lares honores non habent.
    (c)   Therefore the god does not look after the old man.
          igitur senes dei non curant.
    (d)   But why are you praying, old men?
          quare tamen supplicas, senex?
    (e)   At last the old man has the ointment.
          unguenta (2nd decl. neuter) *senes tandem possident/habent.*

(f) The old man now lives in the house.
in aedibus senes nunc habitant.

(g) A thief always likes a pot full of gold.
fures aulas auri plenas semper amant. (gold is usually singular)

(h) But a thief does not have respect.
honores tamen non habent fures.

(i) Why do you not enter (into) the house, old man?
quare in aedis non intratis, senes?

(j) The old man secretly loves the slave woman.
seruas clam amant senes.

p.24 Exercises

2 **Genitive plurals**

honorum	from *honor* 3rd decl. masc. = respect
furum	from *fur* 3rd decl. masc. = thief
unguentorum	from *unguentum* 2nd decl. neut. = ointment
senum	from *senex* 3rd decl. masc. = old man

3 **Plural nouns**

ingenia	from *ingenium* 2nd decl. neut. = talents
unguentis	from *unguentum* 2nd decl. neut. = ointments
somnia	from *somnium* 2nd decl. neut. = dreams
pericula	from *periculum* 2nd decl. neut. = dangers

pp.25–6 Exercises

1 *multas curas*
multum aurum
multi or *multos fures* (nom. *or* acc. pl.)
multum senem
multi honoris
multam aedem
multorum seruorum
multorum senum
multas aedis (acc. pl.)
multae coronae (gen./dat. sing. *or* nom. pl.)

2 *multus* (masc. nom. sing.)   *senex, seruus*
   multi   (masc/neut. gen. sing. *or* masc. nom. pl.)   *Laris, senes, serui*
   multis (masc./fem./neut. dat./abl. pl.)   *honoribus, senibus*
   multas (fem. acc. pl.)   *aedis, familias*
   multae (fem. gen./dat. sing. *or* nom. pl.)   *seruae, aedi*
   multa   (fem. nom. sing. *or* neut. nom./acc. pl.)   *unguenta, cura*

3 many slave girls   *multae seruae*
   of much respect   *multi honoris*
   of many garlands   *multarum coronarum*
   much gold   *multum aurum*
   many an old man   *multum senem*
   of many thieves   *multorum furum*
   many old men   *multos senes*

If you have made any mistakes in the last three exercises, check the gender and declension of the noun.

4 (a) Many thieves are in the house.
   (b) Many old men have many cares.
   (c) Many slave girls are full of cares.
   (d) Euclio has much gold (and) many pots full of gold.
   (e) The old man has many slaves.

5 (a) No power is long-lived.
   (b) Life is neither a good nor a bad thing.
   (c) Nobility is the only unparalleled goodness.
   (d) Life is long if it is full.
   (e) Fortune is blind.

p.28 Reading exercises

2 (a) *clamant* is plural; *serui, senex, seruae* are all subjects.
        The slaves, the old man and the slave girls are all shouting.
   (b) *dat* is singular; *multum honorem* is the object, *Phaedra* is the
        subject.
        Therefore Phaedra gives much respect.
   (c) *possidet* is singular; *Lar* is the subject, *aedis* is the object.
        Now the Lar possesses the house.

(d)   *amant* is plural; *di* is the subject, *multum honorem* is the object.

The gods like much respect.

(e)   *dat* is singular; *aurum* is the subject (N.B. neuter noun), *multas curas* is the object.

Gold gives many worries.

(f)   *habitant* is plural; *serui* is the subject.

Slaves also live in the house.

(g)   *est* is singular; *aurum* is the subject.

Much gold is in the pot.

(h)   *timent* is plural; *fures* is subject *or* object, *senes* is subject *or* object, *multi* must be subject.

Either: However, many thieves fear old men.

Or (better sense): However, many old men fear thieves.

(i)   *intrant* is plural; *senex* and *seruus* are both subject.

Why are the old man and the slave entering (onto) the stage?

(j)   *explicat* is singular; *Lar* is the subject, *curas* is the object.

At last the Lar explains the old man's worries.

p.29 Reading exercise/Test exercise

The Lar enters (onto) the stage. He is the god of Euclio's household. The Lar protects Demaenetus' treasure under the earth. Much treasure is in a pot. But Euclio does not know about the treasure because he does not look after the Lar. For he gives (him) no ointment, no garlands (and) no respect. But the Lar likes Phaedra, the daughter of the greedy old man. For Euclio's daughter gives (him) much ointment, many garlands (and) much respect. Therefore the Lar gives Demaenetus' pot to Euclio, because Euclio's daughter is good. But Euclio places the pot under the earth again, because he is greedy (a miser). For Euclio fears thieves very much! He has many worries! The treasure bothers the greedy and worried old man. For the house(s) of the rich men are full of thieves.

Section 1C

Exercises p.37

1   *time, timete*
     roga, rogate
     tace, tacete
     cogita, cogitate
     mone, monete
     cura, curate
     posside, possidete

2   give a garland!
     carry water!
     stay in the house!
     be quiet!
     guard the treasure!
     warn (your) daughter!

3   *uidete!*
     roga Euclionem!
     tacete!
     celate aulam!

p.39 Exercises

1	*i*	go (sing.)	*ite*
	eunt	they go	*it*
	itis	you (pl.) go	*is*
	eo	I go	*imus*
	it	he/she/it goes	*eunt*
	imus	we go	*eo*
	exitis	you (pl.) go out	*exis*
	abimus	we go away	*abeo*
	abitis	you (pl.) go away	*abis*
	redeunt	they return	*redit*
	reditis	you (pl.) return	*redis*
	ite	go (pl.)	*i*
	redeo	I return	*redimus*
	exeunt	they go out	*exit*

2   *abimus*
     redeunt
     abi
     aditis
     exit
     eo
     redite
     is

p.39 Exercises

1   *meo, tuo igne*   abl. sing.
     meas, tuas aedis   acc. pl.
     mei, tui honoris,   gen. sing.
     mea, tua familia   abl. sing.
     meorum, tuorum oculorum   gen. pl.
     meo, tuo domino   dat./abl. sing.
     meae, tuae aquae   gen./dat. sing., nom. pl.
     meum, tuum, Euclionem   acc. sing.
     meus, tuus senex   nom. sing.

2   *misero Euclioni*   dat. sing.
     misera Phaedra   abl. sing.
     miser deus   nom. sing.
     miseram filiam   acc. sing.
     miseris aedibus   dat/abl. pl.
     miseri domini   gen. sing. *or* nom. pl.
     miserarum seruarum   gen. pl.
     miseris coquis   dat./abl. pl.
     miserorum senum   gen. pl.

p.40 Exercises

1 (a) Neither slave girls nor slaves stay in my master's house.
       manet in dominorum meorum aedibus neque serua neque seruus.
       N.B. **aedes**, when it means 'house', is plural.

   (b) The wicked old man's wicked slave girl is annoying my master.
       malorum senum malae seruae dominos meos uexant.

   (c) Your neighbour sees my neighbour.
       tui uicini uicinos meos uident.

   (d) The poor old man's slave never stays in the house.
       senum miserorum serui in aedibus numquam manent.

   (e) The poor slave girls never approach or pray to my Lar.
       serua misera ad Lares meos numquam adit neque supplicat.

   (f) The wicked master immediately thrashes his slave girls,
       poor wretches.
       domini mali seruam statim uerberant miseram.

2 (a) *malus* – nom. masc. sing. = *senex*
       multum – acc. masc. sing. = *honorem*
       The wicked old man does therefore not have much respect.

   (b) *mea* – abl. fem. sing. = *aula*
       tuus – nom. masc. sing. = *ignis*
       Your fire is in my pot.

   (c) *meis* – dat./abl. fem. pl. = *aedibus*
       multi – nom. masc. pl. = *patres*
       In my house however live many fathers.

   (d) *malos* – acc. masc. pl. = *senes*
       meus – nom. masc. sing. = *Lar*
       For my Lar does not like wicked old men.

   (e) *meus* – nom. masc. sing. = *pater*
       tuum – acc. masc. sing. = *ignem*
       Does my father keep your fire safe?

3 (a) Money alone reigns.
   (b) The truth never dies.
   (c) A greedy man is always in need.
   (d) Death does not frighten a wise man off.
   (e) Death in a rout is disgraceful, but death in a victory is glorious.

p.41 Exercise

ex aqua
in oculum
ab igne
ad dominos
ab aedibus
in scaenam

p.41 Reading exercises

1 (a) *timet*   The poor old man is afraid of his neighbour.
   (b) *celat*   For my master is hiding your fire.
   (c) *amas*   I do not like my slave and you do not like yours.
   (d) *uerberant* Then the wicked slaves beat me.
   (e) *uocat*   My neighbour calls the wicked slaves.
   (f) *portat*   The wicked slave girl, my dear master, is carrying the pot.
   (g) *moneo*   I also warn the poor thief.
   (h) *do*   You are giving fire, I, water.
   (i) *uexat*   Your slave girl always troubles my eyes.
   (j) *possidet*   Why does poor Euclio never possess gold, ointment and garlands?

p.42 Reading exercise/Test exercise

EUCLIO (*SHOUTING*): Get out! Get out of the house, slave girl.

The slave girl comes on to the stage.

SLAVE GIRL: What is it, my dear master? Why are you calling me out of the house? (*Euclio thrashes the slave girl.*) O poor me. How my master annoys me, for now he is thrashing me. But why are you thrashing me, master?

EUCLIO: O dear me. Be quiet. How wicked you are! How you annoy poor old me! Stay there, Staphyla, stay put. Don't move. I'm warning you.

Euclio goes into the house.

SLAVE GIRL: O dear me. How unhappy my master is.

Euclio comes out of the house on to the stage.

EUCLIO: It's safe. But why are you standing there? Why are
                         you not going into the house? Go away! Go into
                         the house! Close the door! (*The slave girl goes into
                         the house.*) Now I'm going off to the praetor,
                         because I'm a poor old man. How unwillingly I
                         go! But if I stay here, my neighbours* say 'Aha!
                         The wretched old man has a lot of money'.

* You may feel you want to say 'will say' here, but you have not yet
met the future tense.

pp.42–3 English–Latin

(a)   Staphyla, go away and carry water!
      seruae, exite et ignem rogate!

(b)   However, as for you, my master, why do you have wicked
      worries?
      tu autem, mi Euclio, quare seruam miseram amas?

(c)   How a lot of gold worries wretched old men!
      ut malus senex seruos uerberat miseros!

(d)   O dear me! How my eyes trouble me!
      o me miserum! ut miser senex sum!

(e)   Wicked are the masters unhappy slaves have.
      miserum senem misera filia amat.

(f)   The eyes of the wicked slaves do not see the worries of the
      unhappy master.
      malae seruae oculi filiae miserae curam non uident.

Section 1D

p.48 Exercises

1   *dicit*
    ducunt
    audimus
    dicimus
    auditis
    dic!
    audite!
    ducite!
    dicis
    audit
    audiunt

2 | | | |
    |---|---|---|
    | *curo* | 1 | I look after |
    | *celat* | 1 | he/she hides |
    | *habetis* | 2 | you (pl.) have |
    | *ducunt* | 3 | they lead |
    | *rogas* | 1 | you ask |
    | *possidemus* | 2 | we possess |
    | *audio* | 4 | I hear |

3 | | |
    |---|---|
    | you say | *dicis* |
    | they hear | *audit* |
    | we make prayers to | *supplico* |
    | you (s.) hear | *auditis* |
    | I say | *dicimus* |
    | we lead | *duco* |
    | we hear | *audio* |
    | they shout | *clamat* |
    | you are silent | *tacetis* |

p.50 Exercises

1 | *nomen* | *magnum, miserum, pulchrum* |
    | *nominis* | *magni, miseri, pulchri* |
    | *nomine* | *magno, misero, pulchro* |
    | *nomina* | *magna, misera, pulchra* |
    | *nominum* | *magnorum, miserorum, pulchrorum* |

2 | *uxorum* | *pulchrarum miserarum* |
    | *sororibus* | *pulchris miseris* |
    | *uiro* | *pulchro misero* |
    | *uxoris* | *pulchrae miserae* |
    | *feminae* | *pulchrae miserae* |
    | *fratri* | *pulchro misero* |
    | *aedis* | *pulchras miseras* |
    | *Larem* | *pulchrum miserum* |
    | *serua* | *pulchra misera* |
    | *aedes* | *pulchrae miserae* |
    | *feminis* | *pulchris miseris* |
    | *domini* | *pulchri miseri* |
    | *seruos* | *pulchros miseros* |

p.51 Exercises

1   (a) *cuius*
    (b) *quas*
    (c) *quid*
    (d) *quod*
    (e) *quem*
    (f) *cuius*
    (g) *quam*
    (h) *qui*

pp.52–3 Exercises

1   (a)   *multam* – acc. fem. sing. = *pecuniam*
          Excellent wives do not possess a lot of money.

     (b)   *multi* – nom. masc. pl. = *filii*
          Many sons love my sisters.

     (c)   *optimi* – nom. masc. pl. = *senes*
          Excellent old men do not annoy wretched slaves.

     (d)   *pulchras* – acc. fem. pl. = *sorores*
          Wicked brothers beat their beautiful sisters.

     (e)   *multi* – nom. masc. pl. = *senes*
          Many old men take beautiful women home (*or* marry them).

2   into the house
     in the pot
     towards the Lar
     from the fires
     into the water
     out of the pots
     in the house
     in the water
     from the master
     out of the eyes

3   *in aedibus*
     ad puellam
     ad fratres
     ab uxore
     in scaenam
     in aedibus   (this is a misprint, a repetition of the first phrase of this question)

     ex aqua
     ab ignibus

4   too many garlands
        enough slaves
        too much water
        enough names
        too many sisters
        enough fire

5   (a)   What man do I hear?
        (b)   Whose name are you now saying?
        (c)   There is always enough gold in Euclio's house.
        (d)   Euclio's unhappy daughter has too many cares.
        (e)   As for you, however, which woman are you taking home
              (marrying)?

6   (a)   Who is a good man?
        (b)   Who is not terrified of poverty?
        (c)   Who hides his love well?
        (d)   What is a happy life? Freedom from worry and continual
              peace.
        (e)   What is death? Either the end or a transition.
        (f)   Unrestrained anger produces madness.
        (g)   Fate controls our life, not wisdom.

p.53 Reading

1   (a)   *facit*   At last the man is making me his son.
        (b)   *habet*   Euclio considers his neighbour rich.
        (c)   *faciunt*   *You could choose any person of the verb because
                           the subject is not specified, e.g.* They make
                           Euclio poor.
        (d)   *facit*   Megadorus makes Euclio's daughter his wife.
        (e)   *habeo*   I however consider rich men unfortunate.
        (f)   *facit*   The master makes wicked slaves unhappy.

p.54 Reading exercise/Test exercise

Eunomia, his sister, calls Megadorus, a rich man and Euclio's
neighbour, out of the house. For Eunomia is worried, because
Megadorus does not have a wife. Megadorus however does not want a
wife. For wives make rich men poor. Megadorus has enough gold and

does not like pretty women. For when a woman is pretty, so she
annoys her husband. When a man is rich, so his wife makes him a poor
man. However Megadorus considers Eunomia an excellent sister.
When therefore his sister makes demands, her brother acts
accordingly. For he considers Phaedra, Euclio's daughter, an excellent
girl. However as Euclio is a poor man, so Phaedra has now dowry.
Megadorus however does not want a dowry. For if wives are rich and
have a large dowry, great is the expense after the wedding, and the
husbands give too much money.

p.54–5 English–Latin

(a)   As I am an excellent sister, so you are an excellent brother.
      ut Phaedra optima filia est, ita Euclio pater optimus.

(b)   My master considers his brother an excellent man.
      pulchras feminas uxores malas habeo.

(c)   What is the name of your wife?
      quis frater uicini est mei?

(d)   A poor man marries a poor wife.
      optimi uiri pulchras uxores in matrimonium ducunt.

(e)   The women are standing in the house.
      puellae in aquam eunt.

(f)   I have enough gold and enough money.
      nimis diues pecuniae habet, nimis curae.

Section 1E

p.60 Exercises

1   *facis*
    audite!
    ferunt
    fer/duc
    uult
    facimus
    fert
    ite!
    uis
    posce!
    facio
    cape dotem

2

facimus	we make	1st pers. pl.	*facio*
fert	he brings	3rd pers. sing.	*ferunt*
uult	he wishes	3rd pers. sing.	*uolunt*
ferunt	they bring	3rd pers. pl.	*fert*
dic	say!	sing. imperative	*dicite*
ferte	bring!	pl. imperative	*fer*
uolumus	we wish	1st pers. pl.	*uolo*
est	he is	3rd pers. sing.	*sunt*
eunt	they go	3rd pers. pl.	*it*
facis	you make	2nd pers. sing.	*facitis*
ducite	lead!	pl. imperative	*duc*
ite	go!	pl. imperative	*i*
capite	capture!	pl. imperative	*cape*

p.61 Exercises

1

onus	nom./acc. sing.	*multum*
oneris	gen. sing.	*multi*
onere	abl. sing.	*multo*
onera	nom./acc. pl.	*multa*
oneribus	dat./abl. pl.	*multis*

2   *pulchro* (masc./neut., dat./abl. sing.)   *scelere* (neut. abl. sing.)

pulchra (fem. nom. sing. *or* neut. nom./acc. pl.)

femina (fem. nom. sing.)

facinora (neut. nom./acc. pl.)

scelera (neut. nom./acc. pl.)

pulchrum (neut. nom./acc. sing. *or* masc. acc. sing.)

opus (neut. nom./acc. sing.)

seruum (masc. acc. sing.)

Larem (masc. acc. sing.)

scelus (neut. nom./acc. sing.)

pulchrorum (neut./masc. gen. pl.)

nominum (neut. gen. pl.)

deorum (masc. gen. pl.)

scelerum (neut. gen. pl.)

pp.61–2 Exercise

(a)   *est bona puella.* — She's a good girl.

estne bona puella? — Is she a good girl?

(b)   *imus ad aedis Euclionis.* — We are going to Euclio's house.

imusne ad aedis Euclionis? — Are we going to Euclio's house?

(c)   *fert bene onus serua.* — The slave-woman carries the load well.

fertne bene onus serua? — Does the slave-woman carry the load well?

(d)   *optimum consilium habent.* — They have the best plan.

optimumne consilium habent? — Do they have the best plan?

(e)   *Euclio filiam statim promittit.* — Euclio promises his daughter at once.

Euclione filiam statim promittit? — Does Euclio promise his daughter at once?

(f)   *Megadorus satis pecuniae habet.* — Megadorus has enough money.

Megadorusne satis pecuniae habet? — Does Megadorus have enough money?

(g) *soror fratrem bene audit.* — The sister listens to her brother well.

sororne fratrem bene audit? — Does the sister listen to her brother well?

(h) *scaenam uidetis.* — You see the stage.

scaenamne uidetis? — Do you see the stage?

(i) *Euclio honorem numquam dat.* — Euclio never gives respect.

Euclione honorem numquam dat? — Does Euclio never give respect?

(j) *uxores nimis auri semper habent.* — Wives always have too much gold.

uxoresne nimis auri semper habent? — Do wives always have too much gold?

p.62 Exercises

1 into the house
out of the dowry
in mind
towards the men
from the water
out of the fires
at home
out of danger
into death
towards the waters
into danger

2 (a) Where is Megadorus? What plan does he have?
(b) Does the rich man want a beautiful wife? What's the problem?
(c) I therefore consider you to be good men.
(d) The slaves commit too much villainy and too many wicked deeds in the house.
(e) What burden are you carrying? Where are you going to?

3   (a)   Hasten slowly. (i.e. more haste, less speed!)

      (b)   Virtue alone makes life happy.

      (c)   The wise man does nothing unwillingly.

      (d)   An author praises his work.

      (e)   There is no moderation in the mob.

      (f)   Pleasure is neither a good nor an evil.

p.63 Reading exercises

1   (a)   Masc.; refers to Megadorus.

          Megadorus marries Euclio's daughter without a dowry. He is therefore an excellent man.

      (b)   Neut.; refers to the fact given in the first sentence.

          At home today, Megadorus neither prepares the marriage-rites nor summons cooks. That is bad.

      (c)   Fem.; refers to Eunomia.

          Eunomia is the sister of Megadorus. She is a good woman.

      (d)   Neut.; refers to the fact given in the first sentence.

          Eunomia has a brother. There is no doubt.

      (e)   Masc.; refers to Euclio.

          Euclio loves his daughter. He is not a bad man.

      (f)   Neut.; refers to the fact given in the first sentence.

          Euclio is afraid. That is not doubtful.

      (g)   Neut.; refers to *consilium*.

          Staphyla hears Euclio's plan. It is a bad one.

      (h)   Fem.; refers to Staphyla.

          Staphyla goes back into the house. For she is full of care.

p.64 Reading exercise/Test exercise

Megadorus sees his neighbour Euclio. Euclio is leaving the forum. He is worried. For Euclio's mind is at home, because he doesn't see his gold, but Euclio himself is outside. Megadorus greets Euclio ingratiatingly, as a rich man greets a poor one. However Euclio is afraid, because Megadorus is a rich man. The reason is obvious. Megadorus wants Euclio's treasure. There is no doubt. Euclio goes into the house, he sees the gold, it is safe. He therefore leaves the house. Megadorus asks for the daughter of Euclio as his wife. Euclio promises his daughter, but without a dowry. For he is a poor man. He therefore has no dowry. Megadorus wants no dowry. He is a good man and rich enough. The marriage-rites are today. Megadorus therefore summons a cook into the house. However Staphyla is afraid, because Phaedra is pregnant by Lyconides. Megadorus marries a pregnant wife. That is a bad thing.

p.64 English–Latin

(a) Are you, a bad man, pouring scorn on me, a very good man?
    irridetne Euclionem, homo diues pauperem?

(b) That's bad. For Megadorus is making Euclio's daughter his wife.
    non dubium est. senex puellam filiam habet.

(c) Return to the Lar, slaves! Bring many garlands!
    i in aedis, serua. fer onera.

(d) What plan is there? Does Megadorus want a dowry? That's bad.
    quid noui? pecuniamne uis? non dubium est.

(e) Where are you going to? Are you going into the house? Are you preparing marriage-rites today? That's excellent.
    quid uolunt? domumne eunt? onerane ferunt? boni sunt.

(f) Cheer up, Megadorus. For the plan is a good one.
    bonum animun habe, domine. nam factum optimum est.

Section 1F

p.69 Exercise

habere	to have
explicare	to explain
celare	to hide
inuenire	to find
manere	to stay
*redire**	to return
ducere	to lead
dicere	to say
poscere	to demand
stare	to stand
rogare	to ask
fugere	to escape
amittere	to lose
*auferre**	to take away
facere	to make, do
*esse**	to be

* indicates an irregular verb. If you have made any mistakes, check the conjugation of the verb.

pp.71–2 Exercise

1
puer audax	*pueri audaces*
puerum audacem	*pueros audaces*
pueri audacis	*puerorum audacium*
puero audaci	*pueris audacibus*
puero audaci	*pueris audacibus*
omnis aqua	*omnes aquae*
omnem aquam	*omnes aquas*
omnis aquae	*omnium aquarum*
omni aquae	*omnibus aquis*
omni aqua	*omnibus aquis*

ingens periculum   *ingentia pericula*
ingens periculum   *ingentia pericula*
ingentis periculi   *ingentium periculorum*
ingenti periculo   *ingentibus periculis*
ingenti periculo   *ingentibus periculis*

2

Noun	Case	Num.	Gend.	*omnis*	*ingens*	*audax*
seruae	gen.	s.	f.	omnis	ingentis	audacis
	dat.	s.		omni	ingenti	audaci
	nom.	pl.		omnes	ingentes	audaces
thesauri	gen.	s.	m.	omnis	ingentis	audacis
	nom.	pl.		omnes	ingentes	audaces
oculos	acc.	pl.	m.	omnis(-es)	ingentis(-es)	audacis(-es)
dominus	nom.	s.	m.	omnis	ingens	audax
nominibus	dat.	pl.	n.	omnibus	ingentibus	audacibus
	abl.	pl.		omnibus	ingentibus	audacibus
consilium	nom.	s.	n.	omne	ingens	audax
	acc.	s.		omne	ingens	audax
cena	abl.	s.	f.	omni	ingenti	audaci
turbarum	gen.	pl.		omnium	ingentium	audacium
ciui	dat.	s.	m.	omni	ingenti	audaci
pecunias	acc.	pl.	f.	omnis(-es)	ingentis(-es)	audacis(-es)
puella	abl.	s.	f.	omni	ingenti	audaci
periculo	dat.	s.	n.	omni	ingenti	audaci
	abl.	s.		omni	ingenti	audaci
ignis	nom.	s.	m.	omnis	ingens	audax
	gen.	s.		omnis	ingentis	audacis
animis	dat.	pl.	m.	omnibus	ingentibus	audacibus
	abl.	pl.		omnibus	ingentibus	audacibus

3

ingentem	acc. sing. masc./fem.	*deum*	acc. sing. masc.
audax	nom. sing. masc./fem.	*consilium*	nom./acc. sing. neut.
	or nom./acc. sing. neut.	*homo*	nom. sing. masc.
		dominus	nom. sing. masc.
omnium	gen. pl. masc./fem./neut.	*coquorum*	gen. pl. masc.
tristes	nom./acc. pl. masc./fem.	*animos*	acc. pl. masc.
		domini	nom. pl. masc.
		filiae	nom. pl. fem.
		aedis	acc. pl. fem.
facilia	nom./acc./pl. neut.	*scelera*	nom./acc. pl. neut.
difficili	dat./abl. sing.	*coquo*	dat./abl. sing. masc.
	masc./fem./neut.	*filia*	abl. sing. fem.
		exitio	dat./abl. sing. neut.

p.73 Exercises

1   (a)   Therefore the bold cook wishes to cook a huge dinner.

    (b)   Why do you want to know all the names of the cooks?

    (c)   However you have a bold plan in mind.

    (d)   When you want to come into the house, call us at once.

    (e)   Every poor man wants to commit bold crimes.

    (f)   A huge crowd of bold men is approaching the house of Megadorus.

2   (a)   Many women neither sleep nor cook dinner.

    (b)   He is taking the goods away.

    (c)   You (pl.) want to know everything.

    (d)   Handsome men love beautiful women.

    (e)   Everyone wants to have money.

    (f)   Many men flee, but many stand firm.

    (g)   A rich man does not love a poor one.

    (h)   All good men care for citizens.

    (i)   Wicked men consider wicked deeds.

    (j)   Money worries everybody.

3   (a)   Every time of life is both short and frail.

    (b)   Old age is an incurable disease.

(c) Anger is a short madness.

(d) Man is an animal possessing reason.

(e) The way to a happy life is easy.

(f) It is difficult not to write satire.

(g) It is difficult suddenly to lay aside a long-lasting love.

(h) To change nature indeed is difficult.

(i) Woman is a fickle and changeable thing.

(j) An old man who is a soldier is a disgraceful thing; love in an old man is a disgraceful thing.

p.74 Reading exercises

2   (a) *uult*   Where does the poor man want to have a huge dinner?

(b) *uis*   Where do you wish to enter?

(c) *uult*   Every poor man wishes to bear the worries of a rich man.

(d) *uolumus* We slaves wish to love beautiful girls and to carry off our master's gold.

(e) *uolunt*   All citizens want to bear an easy burden.

(f) *uultis*   You never wish to cook dinner at Euclio's house.

pp.74–5 Reading exercise/Test exercise

Megadorus wants to hold marriage-rites. He therefore summons many cooks to the house. The task of the cooks is to cook a huge dinner. Megadorus is bringing home as his wife Phaedra, the daughter of Euclio. But the cooks consider Euclio a poor man and a gloomy one. For he wants to lose nothing. When he wishes to sleep, he places a huge bag over his mouth. In this way, he doesn't lose breath while he is sleeping. At the barber's because he wants to lose nothing, he collects all the nail-clippings and takes them home. He's not willing to give water. He's not willing to give fire, because he's afraid to lose (it). He's a gloomy man. Therefore the cooks want to enter the house of Megadorus, a rich and easy man. But there is much danger in Megadorus' house, huge silver pots, many clothes, much gold. If the slaves lose anything, they think the cooks (are) thieves and want to seize (them). But at Euclio's house cooks are safe. It is not easy to carry off silver pots from Euclio's house, because he has no pots!

English–Latin

(a)   Why do you (pl.) want to carry a load into the house of Megadorus, a rich man?

    cenamne in aedibus Euclionis, uiri pauperis, coquere uultis?

(b)   Every citizen wants (*or* all the citizens want) to get out of danger.

    serui audaces fugere ex aedibus uolunt.

(c)   Who wants to lose a huge (sum of) money?

    quae femina seruum audacem inuenire non uult?

(d)   When rich men hold marriage-rites, they summon cooks into the house.

    domini ubi cenam magnam uolunt, coquum bonum rogant.

(e)   All cooks carry huge knives.

    femina pulchra turbam magnam fert.

(f)   However at a poor man's house dinner is gloomy.

    apud diuitem cenae optimae sunt.

Section 1G

pp.79–80 Exercises

1   *seni misero*
     senibus miseris
     puellae audaci
     puellis audacibus
     puero ingenti
     pueris ingentibus
     onere multo
     oneribus multis
     consilio audaci
     consiliis audacibus

2   *animo, uirtuti, audaciae, diuitibus, oneri, filiis, aquae, domino, ignibus,*
     dis, feminis, coronae, consilio

3   *seruis ingentibus*
     mihi
     seni misero
     uxoribus malis
     nobis, tibi

4   (a)   Then the Lar of the household gives Euclio a pot full of
           gold.
     (b)   The wretched old man however entrusts all the gold to the
           shrine.
     (c)   But the bold slave wants to take the gold away from the
           wretched old man.
     (d)   However, Euclio shouts in this way to the wicked slave:
           'What business have you got in the shrine? What are you
           taking away from me?'
     (e)   Therefore the slave is afraid and doesn't take away the gold
           from Euclio.
     (f)   But Euclio takes away the pot from out of the shrine,
           because now he doesn't want to entrust the gold to the god.

pp.80–81 Exercises

2   *cura, animo, audaciis, homine, uxore, pecunia, filiis, domino, ignibus, honoribus, femina, coronis, consilio, scelere*

3   *in fano*
         a femina
         ex aquis
         in scelere
         ex animo
         in consiliis
         ex ignibus

4   (a) Euclio is a man of the utmost self-control.
     (b) Lyconides is a young man of the greatest beauty, but of no self-control.
     (c) Be of a calm frame of mind, my son.
     (d) You are a slave-woman of the greatest boldness and the greatest beauty, but of no self-control.
     (e) I am in a cheerful frame of mind, because I have as my daughter a girl of the greatest goodness.

5   (a) Fortune helps the brave.
     (b) No one is faithful in love.
     (c) All art is an imitation of nature.
     (d) Truth lies open for everyone.
     (e) Death is common to every age.
     (f) The gods care for great things, but do not bother with small ones.
     (g) The British have long hair, and have every part of their body shaved except their head and upper lip.

pp.81–2 Reading exercises

1   (a) The bold slave says many wicked things to the wretched old man.
     (b) Show me ointment (and) garlands and gold.
     (c) There is too much worry for my wife at home.
     (d) Why do you not give back my gold to me?

(e)   I promise my daughter to you because you are a good neighbour.

(f)   Beautiful wives always take away gold from rich men, because they want to give much money to the cooks.

(g)   I give you many slaves and much money.

(h)   I never entrust anything to a bold slave and a beautiful slave-woman.

(i)   I wish to promise my daughter to a rich man, because I have no dowry.

(j)   We have a garland at home, you (pl.) have ointment.

2   *(possible answers)*

(a)   *dant*   All citizens give money to good men.

(b)   *das*   Why do you give me gold?

(c)   *est*   We are in a cheerful frame of mind.

(d)   *credit*   Euclio entrusts the gold to the shrine, not to the bold man.

(e)   *aufers*   Why do you take away all the garlands and all the ointment from us?

(f)   *est*   Bold girls and handsome young men have no self-control.

(g)   *celo*   I hide from the man my daughter's dowry.

(h)   *promittis*   Why does your father not promise you as a wife to me?

(i)   *est*   You villain, what business do you have in my house?

(j)   *dat*   Boldness gives courage to every good young man.

p.82 Reading exercise/Test exercise

Euclio has a pot full of gold. Euclio carries the pot out of the house. For he is very afraid. For thieves always want to take all the gold away from every good man. Therefore he wants to hide the pot in the shrine. When Euclio hides the gold in the shrine, Strobilus sees. Euclio leaves the shrine. He is in a cheerful frame of mind, because he now fears no thief. Strobilus however creeps like a worm into the shrine. For he wishes to carry the pot off from the wretched Euclio. But Euclio sees the bold slave. He says many bad things to the bold slave, and demands his gold. But the slave doesn't want to give back the gold to the old man, because he doesn't have the gold. The slave shows his right hand to Euclio. Then he shows his left hand to the wretched old man. However Euclio asks for his third hand. The slave considers Euclio mad, and goes out. Euclio carries the pot out of the shrine and entrusts it secretly to another place.

p.83 English–Latin

(a) Euclio is a man of the greatest goodness.
     Phaedra puella summa pulchritudine est.

(b) Be cheerful and give me the money.
     aequo animo es et aurum seruo aufer.

(c) The wretched old man entrusts the pot full of gold to a wicked man.
     omnes senes ciuibus bonis aulas pecuniae plenas reddunt.

(d) But why do you not give back the gold to the old man?
     uos autem quare coronam iuueni aufertis?

(e) What business have you (s.) in the house of the wretched old man?
     quid uobis negoti est in fano Laris mei?

(f) I've an excellent father, a man of the greatest self-control.
     est mihi filius optimus, iuuenis summis uirtutibus.

Section Two

Section 2A

p.89 Exercises

1

celabunt	they will hide	*celabit*	1
inueniet	he will find	*inuenient*	4
amittes	you (s.) will lose	*amittetis*	3
habebimus	we shall have	*habebo*	2
coquent	they will cook	*coquet*	3
iubebit	he will order	*iubebunt*	2
uerberabis	you (s.) will beat	*uerberabitis*	1
credet	he will believe	*credent*	3
capietis	you (pl.) will capture	*capies*	3/4
scribam	I shall write	*scribemus*	3
facient	they will do	*faciet*	3/4
audietis	you (pl.) will hear	*audies*	4

2

credunt	*credent*	they will believe
salutat	*salutabit*	he will greet
scribit	*scribet*	he will write
fers	*feres*	you (s.) will bear
estis	*eritis*	you (pl.) will be
it	*ibit*	he will go
rogo	*rogabo*	I shall ask
curant	*curabunt*	they will take care of

3	*do*	*dabit*	he will give
		dabunt	they will give
	clamo	*clamabit*	he will shout
		clamabunt	they will shout
	maneo	*manebit*	he will wait
		manebunt	they will wait
	taceo	*tacebit*	he will be silent
		tacebunt	they will be silent
	duco	*ducet*	he will lead
		ducent	they will lead
	posco	*poscet*	he will demand
		poscent	they will demand
	dormio	*dormiet*	he will sleep
		dormient	they will sleep
	uincio	*uinciet*	he will bind
		uincient	they will bind
	capio	*capiet*	he will capture
		capient	they will capture
	fugio	*fugiet*	he will flee
		fugient	they will flee
	sum	*erit*	he will be
		erunt	they will be
	redeo	*redibit*	he will return
		redibunt	they will return

4	you (s.) will hear	*audies*
	they will call	*uocabunt*
	I shall make	*faciam*
	we will speak	*dicemus*
	you (pl.) will be silent	*tacebitis*
	he will lead	*ducet*
	we will love	*amabimus*

5	*ducent*	they will lead
	uerberabo	I shall beat
	duces	you (s.) will lead
	amabunt	they will like

fugiemus	we shall flee
mittes	you (s.) will send
decipies	you (s.) will deceive

All other verbs in this exercise are in the present tense.

If you have got the wrong answer in any of these exercises, check that you have identified the conjugation of the verb correctly, and check whether the verb is irregular.

p.90 Exercises

1 | | |
|---|---|
| you (s.) wish | *uis* |
| we prefer | *malumus* |
| they refuse | *nolunt* |
| he can | *potest* |
| we will prefer | *malemus* |
| you (pl.) do not wish | *non uultis* |
| you (s.) are able | *potes* |
| they will refuse | *nolent* |

2 | | | | |
|---|---|---|---|
| *est* | he is | *erit* | he will be |
| *possunt* | they can | *poterunt* | they will be able |
| *uoles* | you (s.) will wish | *uis* | you wish |
| *malent* | they will prefer | *malunt* | they prefer |
| *non uis* | you (s.) do not wish | *noles* | you (s.) will not wish |
| *erimus* | we shall be | *sumus* | we are |
| *nolumus* | we do not want | *nolemus* | we shall not want |

p.93 Exercises

1 | | |
|---|---|
| beautiful hand | *manus pulchra* |
| large hand | *manus magna* |
| my hand | *manus mea* |
| swift hand | *manus celeris* |

N.B. *manus – us* (4) is a feminine noun.

2 | | |
|---|---|
| *uia* | ablative sing. (without macron = nominative) |
| *amicae* | dative sing. (*or* gentive sing. *or* nominative pl.) |

nocte	ablative sing.
manui	dative sing.
celeri	dative *or* ablative sing.
officio facili	dative *or* ablative sing.
scelere audaci	ablative sing.
soli	dative sing.
nummis ducentis	dative *or* ablative pl.
astutiae tuae	dative sing. *or* gentive sing. *or* nominative pl.
sumptui magno	dative sing.

If you have made any mistakes, check the declension of the nouns and adjectives.

p.94 Exercises

1   (a)   Today our old man will give you two hundred coins into the hand.
     (b)   What do you want me to do? For I prefer to help rather than to do nothing.
     (c)   If the old man considers me a liar, I shall want to play many tricks.
     (d)   I shall do my duty; I prefer you to do yours.
     (e)   If I can remove the gold (away) from the old man, you will be able to give two hundred coins to your friends.
     (f)   Give me your hand, I beg you; I shall give you mine.
     (g)   If you wish to trust a woman, you are willing to write in running water.
     (h)   If you can get the gold away from the old man, Chrysalus, I shall consider you a slave of great astuteness.
     (i)   While the night is silent, thieves prefer to commit wicked crimes (rather) than to sleep.
     (j)   Take the wax, tablets and pen away from me; today I do not wish to write.

2   (a)   Experience is the best teacher.
     (b)   But who will guard the guards themselves?
     (c)   The deeds of mortals never fool the gods.

(d)   It is rage that helps lions, fear stags, vehemence the hawk
      and flight the dove.

(e)   Just as a great man can emerge from a hovel, so a beautiful and
      mighty soul can emerge from an ugly and lowly little body.

(f)   No man can be happy without virtue.

(g)   Without control no house nor state can survive.

pp.96–7 Reading exercise/Test exercise

Here is Chrysalus, the bold slave of Nicobulus, a man of great talent and
the utmost astuteness. Through Chrysalus, Mnesilochus wants to
deceive the old man a second time. Chrysalus has a difficult job. The old
man trusts neither Chrysalus nor his son. But Chrysalus adopts a bold
plan. He sends Pistoclerus, Mnesilochus' friend, into the house. He
orders Pistoclerus to bring wax, tablets, pen and thread. When the friend
returns, Chrysalus orders Mnesilochus to write a letter to his father. The
good son writes to his father in this way: 'Chrysalus is wicked, my (dear)
father. For today he will come to you and he will aim a great catapult at
you. For he considers you a town, old and full of gold. If he destroys your
tower and your ramparts, he will immediately assault you (coming)
through the gate into the town. Then he will order me to take away your
gold from the town in baskets and give it to my mistress. I am telling you
to be careful, my (dear) father. For the cost will be great, if he deceives
you a second time. Farewell.'

p.97 English–Latin

(a)   I order you to take my daughter home at once.
      Mnesilochus Chrysalum iterum senem miserum decipere uolet.

(b)   I always prefer the virtue of a poor man to the boldness of a rich man.
      audacis serui astutias quam mendacis amicae audaciam semper malet.

(c)   Nicobulus, a man of no astuteness, will never be able to remove
      the gold from the bold slave.
      Chrysalus, uir magna astutia, ducentos nummos senis facile auferre poterit.

(d)   The cost of a mistress is always great.
      furis manus semper celeris est.

(e)   The rich give no coins to the poor.
      senes iuuenibus pecuniam dabunt multam.

(f)   I shall have a lot of expense because I have a rich wife.
      erunt iuuenibus magni sumptus, quod amicas habent pulchras.

Section 2B

p.104 Exercises

For this exercise *-re* endings have been treated as indicative, though of course they could also be imperative singular.

1
precatur	he prays	*precantur*	they pray
mentiris	you (s.) lie	*mentimini*	you (pl.) lie
pollicemur	we promise	*polliceor*	I promise
sequuntur	they follow	*sequitur*	he follows
minaris	you (s.) threaten	*minamini*	you (pl.) threaten
loquimini	you (pl.) speak	*loqueris*	you (s.) speak
mentior	I lie	*mentimur*	we lie
opinare	you think (s.)	*opinamini*	you think (pl.)
progredimini	you (pl.) advance	*progrederis*	you (s.) advance
loqueris	you (s.) speak	*loquimini*	you (pl.) speak
pollicere	you promise (s.)	*pollicemini*	you promise (pl.)
minamur	we threaten	*minor*	I threaten

2
we threaten	*minamur*
he promises	*pollicetur*
they forget	*obliuiscuntur*
you (pl.) remember	*recordamini*
you (s.) speak	*loqueris*
I am following	*sequor*
advance! (s.)	*progredere*
beg! (s.)	*precare*
talk! (pl.)	*loquimini!*
promise! (s.)	*pollicere!*

3
Infinitives		**Imperatives**	
amare	to love	*minare*	threaten! (s.)
uocare	to call	*pollicere*	promise! (s.)
habere	to have	*sequere*	follow! (s.)
loqui	to speak	*audi*	listen! (s.)
inuenire	to find	*dormi*	sleep! (s.)
progredi	to advance	*precare*	pray! (s.)

mentiri	to lie	inueni	find! (s.)
opinari	to think	loquere	speak! (s.)
ducere	to lead	progredere	advance! (s.)
inire	to go in		
iubere	to order		

4

habeo	I have	habere	habe!
curo	I care for	curare	cura!
minor	I threaten	minari	minare!
loquor	I speak	loqui	loquere!
audio	I hear	audire	audi!
duco	I lead	ducere	duc! (irregular)
mitto	I send	mittere	mitte!
precor	I pray	precari	precare!
fugio	I flee	fugere	fuge!
credo	I trust	credere	crede!

p.105 Exercise

don't (s.) follow	noli sequi
don't (pl.) threaten me	nolite mihi minari
don't (s.) be stupid (m.)	noli stultus esse
don't (pl.) send the letter	nolite litteras mittere
don't (s.) hide the pot	noli aulam celare
don't (pl.) lead the slaves	nolite seruos ducere

p.105 Exercise

s.	pl.
omnis res	omnes res
omnem rem	omnis (-es) res
omnis rei	omnium rerum
omni rei	omnibus rebus
omni re	omnibus rebus

s.	pl.
pulcher dies	*pulchri dies*
pulchrum diem	*pulchros dies*
pulchri diei	*pulchrorum dierum*
pulchro diei	*pulchris diebus*
pulchro die	*pulchris diebus*
mea res	*meae res*
meam rem	*meas res*
meae rei	*mearum rerum*
meae rei	*meis rebus*
mea re	*meis rebus*
tristis dies	*tristes dies*
tristem diem	*tristis (-es) dies*
tristis diei	*tristium dierum*
tristi diei	*tristibus diebus*
tristi die	*tristibus diebus*

pp.106–7 Exercises

1
(a) Nicobulus: Don't threaten me, Chrysalus.

Chrysalus: But master, I'm telling you how it is. (*literally,* So I am telling you as the thing is.)

(b) The bold slave has a head full of tricks.

(c) The slaves soon leave the house and follow the old man.

(d) But who is speaking? It's Chrysalus, I think. (*literally,* As I think it's Chrysalus.)

(e) Look inside, my (dear) master. What do you see in the house? It's a bad thing I think.

(f) *Literally,* Chrysalus tells his master to take care and calls him ignorant of all things.

(g) Find out everything. I prefer you to remember (rather) than to forget.

(h) As you promise, so I want it (the thing) to be.

(i) What do you think? Look! The slaves threatens me, next he lies, then he begs and beseeches me.

(j) Advance, my (dear) Nicobulus, and threaten Chrysalus at once.

2 (a) Love is (an) unsuspecting (thing).
   (b) It is a great thing to be quiet.
   (c) There will be crimes as long as there are men.
   (d) Human affairs are frail and perishable.
   (e) It is sweet and honourable to die for one's country.
   (f) It is Roman to do and suffer brave deeds.

p.107 Reading

Literal translation only.

(a) Then you will find out everything, my (dear) master, if you want
     to know, when you see your son in the house of the Bacchides.
     (N.B. all the tenses in the Latin in this sentence are *future*, but
     need not be translated as such.)
(b) As you say the thing to me, so I think, because I trust you.
(c) Our old man is worth as much as a stinking mushroom, as
     Chrysalus thinks, because he is a slave of the utmost boldness.
(d) Because I want you to know everything, I will order you to look
     inside the house, where, if you have eyes, you will soon see your
     son with his girl friend.
(e) But if I can (shall be able to) give the old man the letter at the
     time when I want to, he will be as roasted as a roasted chick pea,
     as I think.

p.108 Reading exercise/Test exercise

Chrysalus pursues a mad business in his opinion (*literally*, as he
thinks) because he wants to deceive the old man a second time. Yet
the plan (he has) in mind is daring enough. For he will give the old
man Mnesilochus' letter. Chrysalus wants his master to be mad at
the time (*tum*) when he receives (*literally*, will receive) the letter,
because then he will be able to tell of Mnesilochus' bad character.
The bold slave gives the letter into the hands of the old man
(*literally, to* the old man – *dative*) at the time when he is coming out
of the house. The old man reads the letter, next he calls his slaves.
Then, when they are leaving the house, he orders the slaves to tie
up Chrysalus and (orders) Chrysalus to be quiet. But Chrysalus
laughs at the old man and says he is (*literally*, calls him) ignorant of
everything (of all things) and stupid. He considers his master, as he
says, (to be) worth as much as a stinking mushroom. The old man

becomes as angry as his slave wants. But then Chrysalus speaks of the danger of Mnesilochus (and) tells the old man to look inside the house of the Bacchides. The old man goes (*literally*, advances) to the house and looks inside. But he sees a dinner-party and a bad, sad affair.

p.108 English–Latin

(a) Don't approach my wife, Chrysalus.

noli seni misero (dative) *minari, serue.*

(b) When you write a letter, have the matter in mind; words soon follow.

ubi rem recordamini, pericula recordamini (or *in animo habete*); *animus numquam mentitur.*

N.B. *recordor* = recall *and* remember

(c) (But) the rich man, ignorant of virtue, threatens the poor man.

serui autem, omnium rerum nescii, periculi (genitive) *obliuiscuntur.*

(d) The good citizens are going (*literally*, advancing) into danger.

puellae omnes ex aedibus egrediuntur.

(e) I am not threatening you, but I am saying how the matter stands (*literally*, how the thing is).

nos non mentimur, sed ita tibi (or *uobis*) *loquimur ut res est.*

(f) Follow me, my slaves, and forget everything.

sequere me in aedis, mi fili, et deos precare.

Section 2C

pp.115–6 Exercises

1   **s.**   **pl.**

hic seruus   *hi serui*
hunc seruum   *hos seruos*
huius serui   *horum seruorum*
huic seruo   *his seruis*
hoc seruo   *his seruis*

ille miles   *illi milites*
illum militem   *illos milites*
illius militis   *illorum militum*
illi militi   *illis militibus*
illo milite   *illis militibus*

haec serua   *hae seruae*
hanc seruam   *has seruas*
huius seruae   *harum seruarum*
huic seruae   *his seruis*
hac serua   *his seruis*

illud periculum   *illa pericula*
illud periculum   *illa pericula*
illius periculi   *illorum periculorum*
illi periculo   *illis periculis*
illo periculo   *illis periculis*

hoc uerbum   *haec uerba*
hoc uerbum   *haec uerba*
huius uerbi   *horum uerborum*
huic uerbo   *his uerbis*
hoc uerbo   *his uerbis*

illa mulier   *illae mulieres*
illam mulierem   *illas mulieres*
illius mulieris   *illarum mulierum*
illi mulieri   *illis mulieribus*
illa muliere   *illis mulieribus*

2   genitive; ablative; nominative; dative; nominative *or* accusative; dative *or* ablative

3   *hunc militem; illi seni; huius puellae; illa consilia; haec pericula; illius feminae*

4

hi thesauri	nom. pl.	*illas mulieres*	acc. pl.
illius thesauri	gen. sing.	*hae mulieres*	nom. pl.
illas sorores	acc. pl.	*illi puero*	dat. sing.
hae sorores	nom. pl.	*hoc puero*	abl. sing.
illa res	nom. sing.	*illae feminae*	nom. pl.
has res	acc. pl.	*huic feminae*	dat. sing.
illae res	nom. pl.	*illius feminae*	gen. sing.
huius manus	gen. sing.	*hic dies*	nom. sing.
illae manus	nom. pl.	*illas dies*	acc. sing.
hae manus	nom. pl.	*hi dies*	nom. pl.

5

huius amici	this friend's	*gen. sing. masc./fem./neut.*
huius lunae	this moon's	
illum puerum	that boy	*acc. sing. masc.*
illum fratrem	that brother	
illa uxore	(by) that wife	*abl. sing. fem.*
illa manu	by that hand	
hoc officium	this duty	*nom./acc. sing. neut.*
hoc aurum	this gold	
hoc nomen	this name	
haec corona	this crown	*nom. sing. fem. (or nom./acc.*
haec negotia	these duties	*pl. neut.)*
haec res	this thing	
haec opera	these works	
haec manus	this hand	
illos ciuis	those citizens	*acc. pl. masc*
illos deos	those gods	

p.115 Optional revision

1	hide	1	*celare*
	tell	1	*explicare*
	find	4	*inuenire*
	hear	4	*audire*
	lead	3	*ducere*
	flee	3/4	*fugere*
	send	3	*mittere*
	bear	irreg.	*ferre*
	prefer	irreg.	*malle*
	be	irreg.	*esse*
	believe	3	*credere*
	write	4	*scribere*
	greet	1	*salutare*
	read	3	*legere*
	not to know	4	*nescire*

2	*amabis*	you will love	2nd person singular feature active	*amo*
	habere	to have	infinitive active	*habeo*
	duc	lead!	imperative singular active	*duco*
	minari	to threaten	infinitive deponent	*minor*
	dicet	he will say	3rd person singular future active	*scribo*
	uelle	to want	infinitive active	*uolo*
	scribitis	you write	2nd person plural present active	*scribo*
	potero	I shall be able	1st person singular future active	*possum*
	cape	take!	imperative singular active	*capio*
	dormiunt	they sleep	3rd person plural present active	*dormio*
	progredere	advance!	imperative singular deponent	*progredior*

defendis	you defend	2nd person singular present active	*defendo*
opprimes	you will surprise	2nd person singular future active	*opprimo*
neca	kill!	imperative singular active	*neco*
loqui	to speak	infinitive deponent	*loquor*
nolumus	we refuse	1st person plural present active	*nolo*
irridere	to laugh at	infinitive active	*irrideo*
state	stand!	imperative plural active	*sto*
rogas	you ask	2nd person singular present active	*rogo*

pp.116–8 Exercises

1   with these women
on that head
to this thing
through that crowd
with this prostitute
from that danger

2   *in hanc scaenam*
cum illa muliere
per haec incendia
cum illis fratribus
in hoc oculo
in illud oppidum

3   (a)   If that solider catches Mnesilochus with Bacchis, he will kill them.

      (b)   This Bacchis seems to be the girlfriend of Mnesilochus, that one of Pistoclerus.

      (c)   That young man loves this woman, and this one loves that one.

      (d)   Nicobulus hears the words of that soldier, then he clearly gets to know the character of his son.

(e)   All prostitutes seem evil to this slave and excellent to those young men.

(f)   That slave tries to deceive this old man.

4   (a)   The one salvation for the conquered is to hope for no salvation.

(b)   We cannot change the past.

(c)   We always strive towards the forbidden and yearn for what we have been denied.

(d)   Once spoken the word flies beyond recall.

pp.116–7 Reading

(a)   That soldier (subject) this woman (object) to/for this young man (dative) to believe.
ille miles hanc mulierem huic iuueni credere uult.
That soldier wants this woman to believe this young man.

(b)   that slaves (object) of this old man.
illum huius senis seruum uideo.
I see that slave of this old man.

(c)   this gold (object) to/for that soldier this slave (subject).
hoc aurum illi militi hic seruus dat.
this slave gives this gold to that soldier.

(d)   with this woman that young man (object) this soldier (subject) soon.
cum hac muliere illum iuuenem hic miles mox uidebit.
This soldier will soon see that young man with this woman.

(e)   to this woman he (subject) all these coins (object) to give.
huic ille feminae hos nummos omnis dare mauult.
He prefers to give all these coins to this woman.

p.117 Reading exercise/Test exercise

A literal analysis:

Nicobulus (subject) his son and Bacchis (object) in the house sees (*uidet*). The prostitute (subject) Bacchis (subject) is (*est*). To/for Chrysalus however a prostitute (subject) to be she (*illa*) does not seem. Now enters Cleomachus the soldier (subject) and of that prostitute (*meretricis*) the lover. Him (object) however Chrysalus (subject) of Bacchis the husband (*uirum*) calls. Of Chrysalus the master (subject) now fears greatly (*ualde*), because Bacchis (object) of the soldier wife (object) s/he thinks. Of Chrysalus the hands (object, subject *or* gen.) the slaves (object) immediately to release (*exsoluere*) he orders, Chrysalus (object) with this soldier (*milite*) to make a bargain, what he wants. To this soldier the slave (subject) immediately coins (object) many (*multos*) promises. But him (object) to be silent and evil words (subject) to hear (*audire*) he orders, because the old man (object) to deceive (*decipere*) he wants. Then the coins (object) to the soldier he (*ille*) promises, Chrysalus (subject) however to that soldier many false things he says about Mnesilochus (*de Mnesilocho*) and him (object) to the forum sends.

A more English version:

Nicobulus sees his son and Bacchis in the house. Bacchis is a prostitute. To Chrysalus however, she doesn't seem to be a prostitute. Now Cleomachus the soldier – that prostitute's lover – enters. Chrysalus however calls him the husband of Bacchis. The master of Chrysalus now fears greatly, because he thinks Bacchis is the wife of the soldier. He immediately orders the slaves to untie the hands of Chrysalus, and Chrysalus to make the bargain with this soldier which he wants. To this soldier the slave immediately promises many coins. But he orders him to be silent and to hear some bad words because he wants to deceive the old man. Then he promises the soldier the coins. Chrysalus however utters many insults to that soldier about Mnesilochus and sends him to the forum.

pp.117–8 English–Latin

1   (a)   *illius filiam hic amat.*
      (b)   *pater huius iuuenis diues esse uidetur.*
      (c)   *illas meretrices arbitror.*
      (d)   *hoc bonis ciuibus magnum officium est.*
      (e)   *ille miles hanc mulierem defendere uult.*
      (f)   *mores harum malos arbitror.*

2   CHR.   *quis est hic homo?*
      NIC.   *est filius meus Mnesilochus.*
      CHR.   *bella cum muliere esse uidetur. quid opinaris?*
      NIC.   *bella est, sed quis est? dic mihi, precor.*
      CHR.   *illumne uides?*

NIC.   *militemne illum dicis?*

CHR.   *ita.*

NIC.   *age nunc.*

CHR.   *ita faciam. huius mulieris uir est.*

NIC.   *quid dicis? sed haec mulier plane meretrix est.*

CHR.   *hocne arbitraris? scies mox omnia.*

NIC.   *quid? nuptane est illa? perii. me miserum! scelestum iuuenem!*

Section 2D

p.126 Exercises

All these verbs follow the patterns set out on p.122.

1	clamo	clamaui
		clamauisti etc.
	uideo	uidi
		uidisti etc.
	uinco	uici
		uicisti etc.
	uincio	uinxi
		uinxisti etc.
	abeo	abiui (or abii)
		abiuisti (or abiisti) etc.
	sum	fui
		fuisti etc.
	do	dedi
		dedisti etc.
	capio	cepi
		cepisti etc.
	fero	tuli
		tulisti etc.
	facio	feci
		fecisti etc.

If you made a mistake in forming these perfects, check the perfect stems on pp.123–6.

2	deleuisti	you (s.) destroyed	deleuistis
	gesserunt	they did, acted	gessit
	uicit	he conquered	uicerunt
	adfuistis	you (pl.) were present	adfuisti
	solui	I released	soluimus
	pugnauimus	we fought	pugnaui
	abiistis	you (pl.) went away	abiisti

3   *do*   you (s.) gave
    credo   he believed
    adfero   they brought
    sum   he was
    debeo   you (pl.) owed
    maneo   I remained
    opprimo   we surprised (etc.)
    scribo   they wrote
    adiuuo   you (pl.) helped
    tango   he touched
    amitto   you (s.) lost
    dico   we said
    exeo   he went out

4   *dedi; pugnauimus; deleuisti; amauit; adfuerunt; uicistis; exii;*
    necauerunt; respondit; gessisti; perfecimus; tulistis

5   **pres.**   **fut.**   **perf.**
s.   *dormit*   *dormiet*   *dormiuit*
pl. *dormiunt*   *dormient*   *dormiuerunt*
s.   *pugnat*   *pugnabit*   *pugnauit*
pl. *pugnant*   *pugnabunt*   *pugnauerunt*
s.   *delet*   *delebit*   *deleuit*
pl. *delent*   *delebunt*   *deleuerunt*
s.   *gerit*   *geret*   *gessit*
pl. *gerunt*   *gerent*   *gesserunt*
s.   *est*   *erit*   *fuit*
pl. *sunt*   *erunt*   *fuerunt*
s.   *aufert*   *auferet*   *abstulit*
pl. *auferunt*   *auferent*   *abstulerunt*
s.   *redit*   *redibit*   *rediit*
pl. *redeunt*   *redibunt*   *redierunt*
s.   *decipit*   *decipiet*   *decepit*
pl. *decipiunt*   *decipient*   *deceperunt*

6	*stabit*	future
	dederunt	they gave
	credet	future
	aderis	future
	uicisti	you conquered
	pugnabunt	future
	soluunt	present
	delent	present
	gerent	future
	mansi	I remained
	inuenistis	you found
	perficies	future
	diligis	present
	habes	present
	monuistis	you warned

p.127 Exercise

1 (a) Mnesilochus silently listened to the words of Chrysalus.
   (b) I fought with a soldier, now I shall fight with an old man, now however I am silent.
   (c) A long time afterwards the Greeks captured the city of Troy.
   (d) At this time of night everyone ought to be asleep.
   (e) Silently thieves enter the house secretly by night.
   (f) As the Greeks sent the horse against Troy at that time, so today Chrysalus will send writing tablets against his master.

2 (a) The defender of a fault says to me, 'We also did this as young men'.
   (b) Tell me, what have I done, except that I have not loved wisely?
   (c) We were Trojans: Troy was (Troy has existed, is a 'has been').
   (d) You have played enough, eaten and drunk enough; it is time for you to leave.
   (e) Nature has given us the seeds for knowledge; it has not given knowledge.

pp.127–8 Reading exercise

a very bold man (a); at that time (c); on this night (c); about your danger (b); in the silent night (c); by sad old men (b); a very astute slave (a); with me (b); in many hours (c); a long time afterwards (c); a very beautiful woman (a); out of the forum (b); at that time of night (c); with my wife (b); in ten years (c)

p.128 Reading exercise/Test exercise

The sons of Atreus a long time afterwards captured Ilium. For in the tenth year they at last stormed the city of Troy. For at the time the kings sent a wooden horse into the city. Epeus, a very astute man, built that horse. Armed soldiers were in the horse, very bold men. These men came out of the horse that night and soon destroyed the city. Thus on that day the city of Troy perished in one hour.

pp.128–9 English–Latin

1   (a)   *iuuenis in aedibus stetit tacitus.*

(b)   *senexne aurum militi dedit?*

(c)   *equos contra urbem Troiam miserunt.*

(d)   *hac nocte meum dominum uici et multam praedam cepi.*

(e)   *hoc anni tempore omnes domi manere debent.*

(f)   *milites signum uiderunt et mox contra oppidum progredientur.*

2   NIC.   *quid facere debeo, Chrysale? dic mihi.*

CHR.   *nolo.*

NIC.   *dic, quaeso. quid faciam? nam rem bene gerere uolo.*

CHR.   *rem bene geres, ut ego opinor, si aurum filio tuo dabis. sed ego non iubeo.*

NIC.   *nummos ei dabo. mane hic! mox huc reueniam. (Nicobulus in aedis intrat)*

CHR.   *adest exitium senis! ut eum decepi! nunc Mnesilochus amicae satis nummorum dare poterit.*

Section 2E

pp.135–6 Exercises

1
opinabor	*opinabimur*
opinaberis	*opinabimini*
opinabitur	*opinabuntur*
conspicabor	*conspicabimur*
conspicaberis	*conspicabimini*
conspicabitur	*conspicabuntur*
uidebor	*uidebimur*
uideberis	*uidebimini*
uidebitur	*uidebuntur*
irascar	*irascemur*
irasceris	*irascemini*
irascetur	*irascentur*
obliuiscar	*obliuiscemur*
obliuisceris	*obliuiscemini*
obliuiscetur	*obliuiscentur*
mentiar	*mentiemur*
mentieris	*mentiemini*
mentietur	*mentientur*
egrediar	*egrediemur*
egredieris	*egrediemini*
egredietur	*egredientur*
patiar	*patiemur*
patieris	*patiemini*
patietur	*patientur*

2
I shall think	*opinabimur*
you will lie	*mentiemini*
he/she will pray	*precabuntur*
you will seem	*uideberis* (or *idebere*)
you will speak	*loquemini*
we shall promise	*pollicebor*

3   *precaberis; minabitur; uidebuntur; loquemini; progrediar; opinabimur;*
     conabuntur; sequetur

4   *minabitur*   he/she will threaten
     precabuntur   they will pray
     opinabor   I shall think
     uidebimini   you will seem
     conspicabitur   he/she will catch sight of
     sequetur   he/she will follow
     loquentur   they will speak

5   *arbitraris*   you think
     conatur   he/she tries
     patiuntur   they suffer
     loquimini   you speak
     sequimur   we follow
     adgrederis   you go up to
     moror   I delay
     opinamur   we think
     progredimini   you advance
     uidetur   he/she seems
     mentior   I am lying

6   *dedit*   they like
     conaberis   they destroy
     mentitur   they will say
     uidebitur   you (s.) will speak
     fecerunt   you (s.) have carried
     amant   perfect
     delent   future
     dicent   present
     loqueris   future
     tulisti   perfect
     he gave   present
     you will try   present
     he lies   future
     he will seem   future
     they made   perfect

pp.136–7 Exercises

1 (a) Nicobulus called his son a worthless young man.

   (b) Philoxenus, however, considered mistresses nothing but good.

   (c) Nicobulus is threatening Bacchis with death if she will not release his son.

   (d) Because he is in love, Philoxenus seems to Nicobulus to be as valuable as a rotten mushroom.

   (e) Bacchis! I order you to embrace that old man. I shall embrace this one (note the mistake in *GVE* – *amplexor* is first conjugation and the future should be *amplexabor*).

   (f) Sister! I shall deal with the old man as you ordered, although it seems to me a great evil to embrace death.

   (g) In my opinion, both old men will soon advance to the doors.

   (h) It is just as I said. The old men are advancing to the doors.

2 (a) The humble have a hard time when the powerful disagree.

   (b) Divine nature gave the fields, human skill built the cities.

   (c) For I remember, I remember and I shall never forget that night.

   (d) Here, where Rome, the capital of the world, now is, was a tree, grass, a few cattle and the odd cottage.

   (e) Religion produced wicked and impious deeds.

   (f) Nobody was an utter scoundrel suddenly.

pp.137–8 Reading and Reading exercise/Test exercise

1 (a) + *quod amator* I consider you worthless, you rotten fellow, for this reason, because you dare to become a lover although you are an old man.

   (b) + *nisi bonum* I consider life nothing if not a good thing.

   (c) + *quam uitam* Old men always prefer death to life.

   (d) + *nisi nobis* I shall give you great trouble, Bacchis, if you do not return our sons to us.

   (e) + *quamquam Mnesilochum* Nicobulus however will receive gold and will enter the house of the Bacchises although he prefers to avenge Mnesilochus and Chrysalus.

(f) + *dum uiuis*   You must treat yourself well at this time while you live.

(g) + *ubi ad fores* You will then catch sight of your son when you approach the doors of the Bacchises and look inside.

2   Philoxenus, father of Pistoclerus, a man of outstanding goodness, came on to the stage. There he saw Nicobulus, father of Mnesilochus. Nicobulus told Philoxenus many bad things about their sons. At length they approached the house of the Bacchises, they beat on the doors and called the prostitutes. Then when those women had come out of the house, they demanded their sons. At length the prostitutes took the old men into their house.

p.138 English–Latin

1   (a) *nisi pecuniam (meam) mihi reddes, te necabo.*

(b) *nihil nisi seruus mendax me sollicitat.*

(c) *ille senex tanti est quanti seruus scelestus.*

(d) *filium meum, si ad me adgredi audebit, amplexabor/complectar.*

(e) *illo tempore nullam vocem nisi tuam audire poteram.*

(f) *quamquam vita bonum est, mors ad ianuas et divitum et pauperum adibit.*

Section Three

Section 3A

---

pp.144–5 Exercises

1
id bellum	*ea bella*	*bellum* is 2nd
id bellum	*ea bella*	declension neuter
eius belli	*eorum bellorum*	
ei bello	*eis bellis*	
eo bello	*eis bellis*	
ea urbs	*eae urbes*	*urbs* is 3rd
eam urbem	*eas urbes*	declension feminine
eius urbis	*earum urbium*	
ei urbi	*eis urbibus*	
ea urbe	*eis urbibus*	
is dux	*ei duces*	*dux* is 3rd declension
eum ducem	*eos duces*	masculine
eius ducis	*eorum ducum*	
ei duci	*eis ducibus*	
eo duce	*eis ducibus*	

2   gen. sing., nom. pl., dat. sing., dat./abl. pl., acc. sing., gen. pl., nom./acc. pl., nom. sing., acc. sing., acc. pl.

3   *(per) eos dies; eam uictoriam; eius belli; eis regibus; ea duces; id imperium; ei amicae; ei mores; eius; eis; eius; ei; ei; ea nocte*

4   *ei* is nom. pl. masc. *or*   nom. pl.   *uiri, patres*
      dat. sing. masc./fem./   dat. sing.   *feminae, exercitui, puero*
      neut.

      eae is nom. pl. fem.   nom. pl.   *amicae, res*

      ea is nom. fem. sing. *or* nom. pl.   *imperia, capita*
      nom./acc. neut. pl.   nom. sing.   *astutia, uirtus, urbs,*
                                                  manus

      eius is gen. sing. masc./   gen. sing.   *operis, pueri, rei, exercitus*
      fem./neut.

      eis is dat./abl. pl.   *signis, meretricibus, uiris,*
                                                  moribus

5   in that town
      because of that courage
      at their house
      at that time
      along/through that road
      with her
      on that night
      into that city
      for those hours
      towards those soldiers
      through that night
      for many days
      in that year
      that time

6   *cum eis feminis*
      ea hora
      apud eum
      in eam scaenam
      in eis urbibus
      ob ea pericula
      eis noctibus
      propter id bellum
      per eas horas

7	(a)	*hae*	These women are beautiful.
	(b)	*illos*	Do you see those soldiers?
	(c)	*eius*	It's enough of that war.
	(d)	*illius*	That man's head is huge.
	(e)	*earum*	A crowd of those women is coming in.

p.147 Exercise

diem longiorem, longissimum; nocte longiore, longissima; milites celeriores, celerrimi (-os); oculo celeriori, celerrimo; aedes ingentiores, ingentissimae (-as); familiam ingentiorem, ingentissimam; manus pulchrioris (-es), pulcherrimae; mulierum pulchriorum, pulcherrimarum; consilia stultiora, stultissima; homini stultiori, stultissimo; operum stultiorum, stultissimorum.

pp.148–9 Exercises

1

liber	free	*liberior*	freer	*liberrimus*	freest, most free, very free etc.
fortis	brave	*fortior*	braver	*fortissimus*	very brave etc.
bonus	good	*melior*	better	*optimus*	best
niger	black	*nigrior*	blacker	*nigerrimus*	blackest
similis	like	*similior*	more like	*simillimus*	most like
magnus	big	*maior*	bigger	*maximus*	biggest
celer	quick	*celerior*	quicker	*celerrimus*	quickest
paruus	small	*minor*	smaller	*minimus*	smallest
scelestus	wicked	*scelestior*	more wicked	*scelestissimus*	most wicked
stultus	stupid	*stultior*	more stupid	*stultissimus*	most stupid
malus	bad	*peior*	worse	*pessimus*	worst
tristis	sad	*tristior*	sadder	*tristissimus*	saddest
facilis	easy	*facilior*	easier	*facillimus*	easiest
multus	much	*plus*	more	*plurimus*	most
ingens	huge	*ingentior*	huger	*ingentissimus*	hugest

2	(a)	For that night the king of gods and men stayed with that woman in the house.
	(b)	Her husband, Amphitruo, left home with a very strong army.
	(c)	She thinks Jupiter (is) Amphitruo because he made himself like Amphitruo.

(d) That god is loving her the whole night long because he has never seen a more beautiful woman than her.

(e) He made that night longer because of Alcumena.

(f) Or rather, he made that night the longest of all nights.

(g) Mercury, his son, is a god of the greatest cunning. In fact he is more cunning than all the gods and men.

(h) He made himself very like the slave Sosia.

(i) Amphitruo will return home this night because he has been successful in war and has carried off a very great victory.

(j) I have never seen a more stupid slave than Sosia, (or) a more wicked god than Mercury on the stage.

3   (a) Later thoughts, so they say, are usually wiser.

(b) Golden reins/a golden bridle doesn't make a horse better.

(c) I see better things and I approve of them, but I pursue worse things. (I realize the better way to act but I follow the worse way.)

(d) No slavery is more degrading than (a) voluntary (one). (*A premise of Stoic philosophy – free men could be dictated to by desire and physical passion.*)

(e) Love reason! Love of this will arm you against the most difficult situations/things.

p.149 Reading

(a) *quam hanc*   I have never seen a longer night than this.

(b) *quam ille*   This slave is bolder than that one.

(c) *quam huic*   I shall give that old man more gold than this one.

(d) *quam illo*   Night is blacker at this time than at that.

(e) *quam hic*   That man is more courageous than this one.

(f) *quam mendacem*   I prefer a very foolish slave to a deceitful one.

(g) *quam hoc*   I shall never be able to bear greater danger than this.

(h) *quam illi*   There were never braver soldiers than those.

(i) *quam eum*   Have you ever seen a man more like a god than him?

(j) *quam eas*   Shall I ever spot more beautiful women than those?

p.150 Reading exercise/Test exercise

Mercury, the craftiest of gods, comes to the city of Thebes with his father because he loves a very beautiful woman, the wife of the general of the Theban legions. Although that woman is married, Jupiter still wants to lie with her for the whole night. As we see, gods can be freer from these things (restrictions, scruples, problems) than men can, because they have very great power and never suffer death. However, Alcumena really loves her husband. Jupiter therefore brings Mercury with him because he knows the most/very many tricks and the best deceptions. Mercury therefore has made himself like Sosia, Amphitruo's slave, and Jupiter very like/the spitting image of Amphitruo. The gods have entered Amphitruo's house like this. Jupiter, king of gods and men, has loved Alcumena secretly all night long and has made her pregnant. In fact he has made her more pregnant, because Amphitruo also made her pregnant that night when he went off to war. Now the greatest god has made the night longer because he really loves Alcumena and has placed Mercury in front of the house. Soon Sosia will approach the house and try to enter, and Mercury will drive him away from the house.

pp.150–51 English–Latin

1 (a) *haec uictoria maior erat quam illa.*
   (b) *illis annis, multi milites fortissimi, propter imperium regis stultioris, bellum longissimum gerebant.*
   (c) *nihil melius est quam officium ciuium optimorum.*
   (d) *sapientia deorum maior est quam hominum.*
   (e) *frater meus similior est patri/patris quam ego.*
   (f) *nihil peius est quam hoc malum.*

2 SOS.   *quis est melior quam ego?*
   MERC. *quis turpior?*
   SOS.   *immo uero, ego optimus sum omnium seruorum, omnium hominum fortissimus.*
   MERC. *et stultissimus stultorum.*
   SOS.   *audacior sum quia, hac nocte longissima, per has uias solus ambulo neque certe nigriorem nec longiorem noctem quam hanc umquam uidi. cur luna non se mutat neque haec signa occidunt? numquamne dies apparebit?*
   MERC. *te, nox, ut nunc pergis, pergere uolo. numquam enim officium maius patri meo quam hoc exsequeris.*

Section 3B

pp.157–8 Exercises

2

locutus sum	I spoke	*locuti sumus*	we spoke
uisum est	it seemed	*uisa sunt*	they (n.) seemed
recordata est	she remembered	*recordatae sunt*	they (f.) remembered
mentiti sumus	we (m.) lied	*mentitus sum*	I (m.) lied
ingressae sunt	they (f.) entered	*ingressa est*	she entered
pollicita es	you (f.) promised	*pollicitae estis*	you (f.) promised
secuta sunt	they (n.) followed	*secutum est*	it followed
adeptus est	he got/obtained	*adepti sunt*	they (m.) got

3　　*uideor*　　　　　　　　　he seemed
　　　adipiscor　　　　　　　she got
　　　obliuiscor　　　　　　I forgot
　　　ingredior　　　　　　　we (women) entered
　　　loquor　　　　　　　　you (pl.) spoke
　　　proficiscor　　　　　　they set out
　　　fio (see p.157)　　　　it became

4　　*minata est*
　　　profecti sunt
　　　hortatus sum
　　　uisa es
　　　oblitae sumus
　　　pollicitus est (*promisit* exists too)
　　　factum est
　　　mentiti estis

5　　*irascitur*　　　　　　　he/she is angry
　　　irascuntur　　　　　　they are angry
　　　irascetur　　　　　　　he/she will be angry
　　　irascentur　　　　　　they will be angry
　　　iratus/a est　　　　　he/she was angry
　　　irati/ae sunt　　　　　they were angry

minatur	he/she threatens
minantur	they threaten
minabitur	he/she will threaten
minabuntur	they will threaten
minatus/a est	he/she threatened
minati/ae sunt	they threatened
pollicetur	he/she promises
pollicentur	they promise
pollicebitur	he/she will promise
pollicebuntur	they will promise
pollicitus/a est	he/she promised
polliciti/ae sunt	they promised
mentitur	he/she lies
mentiuntur	they lie
mentietur	he will lie
mentientur	they will lie
mentitus/a est	he/she lied
mentiti/ae sunt	they lied
patitur	he/she suffers
patiuntur	they suffer
patietur	he/she will suffer
patientur	they will suffer
passus/a est	he/she suffered
passi/ae sunt	they suffered

p.158 Exercises

1
locutus	having spoken	*loquor*
profectus	having set out	*proficiscor*
adeptus	having gained	*adipiscor*
iratus	having become angry	*irascor*
conatus	having tried	*conor*
precatus	having prayed	*precor*
suspicatus	having suspected	*suspicor*
pollicitus	having promised	*polliceor*

hortatus	having encouraged	*hortor*
visus	having seemed	*videor*
egressus	having gone out	*factus*
egredior	having become	*fio*

2   (a)   He caught the soldier after he (the soldier) entered.
     (b)   The men thought a little, then came (after thinking a little the men came).
     (c)   He told a lot of lies, then went (he left after telling a heap of lies).
     (d)   Having advanced quickly from the city, the army soon pitched camp.
     (e)   Having said this she went out.

p.160 Exercises

1	*audacter*	boldly
	male	wickedly
	bene	well
	libere	freely
	magnopere	greatly
	multum	much
	celeriter	fast
	pulchre	beautifully
	paulum	slightly

2	*stulte*	stupidly
	bene	well
	fortiter	bravely
	longe	far
	similiter	in the same way
	saeue	wildly
	tacite	silently
	magnopere	greatly
	celeriter	fast/swiftly
	multum	much
	misere	unhappily

3   (the successful orator) will speak ... seriously, sternly, fiercely, powerfully, passionately, plentifully, bitterly, affably, gently, precisely, appealingly, kindly, sweetly, briefly and wittily.

p.162 Exercises

1   (a) The bold soldier wildly attacked the enemy – even though the latter was angry and had made lots of threats (the enemy was angry and made many threats, but the bold soldier attacked him wildly).

     (b) The cavalry, after leaving their camp, quickly advanced to the city (leaving their camp, the cavalry quickly advanced to the city; the cavalry left their camp and quickly advanced to the city).

     (c) The king got hold of a fast ship and fled far from his land.

     (d) To his wife who had spoken much, her husband replied fiercely.

     (e) When the ambassadors had spoken to the enemy, having returned to the camp, they reported their words to our leader.

     (f) After encouraging his soldiers, the commander took himself boldly off to the battle.

     (g) After suffering the ferocity of our cavalry, the enemy fled into their town and hid themselves away there.

2   (a) It's not living that's good, but living well.

     (b) No one puts on a toga unless he's dead.

     (c) The wealth of many exceptionally powerful people rules out loyal friendships: it's not just that Fortune herself is blind – she also generally renders blind those she has embraced.

pp.162–3 Reading

1   (a) So Amphitruo, having encouraged the soldiers at that time, went off to the battle.

     (b) The commander spoke to the soldiers and, having promised (them) the plunder after the battle, gave the sign.

     (c) The wife of Amphitruo, when she saw her husband in the street, left her house.

(d)   To his wife, when she made many prayers and recalled the faithfulness of her husband, Amphitruo nevertheless made no reply.

(e)   But the slave, having told many lies, easily deceived his master.

2   (a)   ... to citizens who have gained leisure and peace.

(b)   ... to the ambassadors after they had spoken these words.

(c)   ... a band of slaves who had set out for the camp of the enemy.

(d)   ... to that woman who had secretly followed her husband into the war.

(e)   ... the commander, who had advanced to the enemy army.

(d)   The soldiers spoke foul words ...

(b)   The commander of the enemy uttered reproaches ...

(a)   War seems to be the greatest evil ...

(e)   The legions followed ...

(c)   The masters killed ...

pp.163–4 Reading exercise/Test exercise

As the Teleboae had gained very much plunder in our land, our commander wanted to take revenge on them. So he set out the army into the land of the Teleboae and waged war on them. But Amphitruo, a man of the utmost courage, speaking through representatives, instructed the Teleboae to give the plunder back. But the Teleboae, men of the utmost ferocity, saying much fiercely and threatening our army much, instructed Amphitruo to depart immediately. Accordingly a battle took place. Our commander, having prayed to the gods and having encouraged the army, led the soldiers into battle. The enemy advanced bravely, but at length we defeated them. However, Amphitruo received the enemy's representatives in the camp the following day, having achieved so famous a victory as this. The representatives of the enemy, when they had set out from the city and come to the camp, made a strong appeal to our commander and delivered themselves to his judgement.

p.164 English–Latin

1 (a) *dux noster, exercitum hortatus, signum dedit.*

   (b) *Amphitruo per legatos hostes allocutus est.*

   (c) *omnes sapientiam adepti pacem et otium quam bellum malunt.*

   (d) *ea hora hostes a castris profecti sunt.*

   (e) *plane mihi loqui conato hostes ferociter sunt minati.*

   (f) *hominem sic locutum necauerunt.*

2 *Teleboae Amphitruoni per legatos allocuto* (or: *ubi Amphitruo eos per legatos allocutus est*) *haec responderunt: 'terram nostram adgressi estis. statim abite. nisi abibitis, pugnabimus.' haec dixerunt. Amphitruo autem, uir summa uirtute, cum exercitu e castris progessus, suos hortatus est. deinde in proelium duxit. ingens erat pugna. dux autem noster, uictoriam adeptus illustrem, iam domum regressus est.*

Section 3C

p.172 Exercises

1 about to enter   *intro*
   about to shout   *clamo*
   about to do   *facio*
   about to have   *habeo*
   about to advise   *moneo*
   about to remain   *maneo*
   about to hear   *audio*
   about to lie   *mentior*
   about to go out   *egredior*
   about to lead   *duco*
   about to capture   *capio*

2 future, past, future, future, past, future, future, future, past, future, future, past, future, past

3 *iturus, facturus, defensurus, redditurus, risurus, positurus, uisurus, iussurus, decepturus*

pp.172–3 Exercises

1 (a) But the very bad man deceived me with tricks throughout all my most wretched life.
   (b) Why therefore did he beat her fiercely with his fists?
   (c) This year I finished this house with my (own) hands.
   (d) Neither by cunning nor with tricks will you ever deceive the citizens.
   (e) The utter scoundrel conducted the business very well for himself, with enormous misdeeds and very many crimes.
   (f) Alcumena outdid all wives in her goodness and restraint.

2 (a) That slave is about to go into the house, isn't he?
   (b) I am going to beat him with my fists at the same time.
   (c) That man Sosia is about to act most foolishly, isn't he, if he wishes to enter this house?

(d)   I very much want to deceive that slave for this night with my appearance.

(e)   Sosia will never conquer me with his courage.

(f)   What does he think is about to happen? For at this hour I am about to take his name away from him by my trickery.

p.174–5 Exercises

1   *stultius; melius; putidius; miserius; stultissime; optime; putidissime; miserrime; pulchrius; celerius; audacius; peius; pulcherrime; celerrime; audacissime; pessime*

2 | | |
|---|---|
| *facillime* | most/very easily |
| *astutius* | more cunningly |
| *optime* | very well, best |
| *fortius* | more bravely |
| *magis* | more |
| *minime* | least/very little |
| *pulcherrime* | most beautifully |

3   a man of the greatest courage
with the greatest courage
a slave of the greatest cunning
with the greatest cunning
with hands and feet
this year
with the same appearance
with my fists
at the same time

4   *eodem die*
uxor summa uirtute
summa uirtute
pugno meo
eodem anno
eisdem manibus
seruus summa audacia
dolo

5   (a)   All the future is uncertain.
      (b)   We live among things destined to die.
      (c)   It is always difficult to talk about future events.
      (d)   The same goodness is in man and god.
      (e)   A way is made by violence.

p.175 Reading exercise/Test exercise

(a)   My father has entrusted an enormous task to me at this time; for
      while he has decided to deceive Alcumena with Amphitruo's
      appearance, I am intending to drive the slave Sosia away from
      the house. I shall therefore go into the street, meaning to threaten
      that slave with destruction by my fists. I shall easily deceive him
      with my trickery because he seems to me to be a man of no
      intelligence. I shall therefore steal his name from him at the same
      time with my tricks. For it will please me to go up to him with
      the same appearance and the same voice.

(b)   With his tricks and his cunning Mercury tricked Sosia as he was
      about to go into his master's house. For he did not allow Sosia to
      enter, although Amphitruo ordered him to tell Alcumena
      everything at that time. For Mercury looks after his father – that
      is, Jupiter. For Jupiter tricked Alcumena with the appearance of
      her husband in this house during this night. However, Mercury
      made himself like Sosia and took his name, with the same
      appearance and the same voice. Sosia at the last hardly trusted
      Mercury since he thought the god very like himself. And the
      slave thought this more easily because the god had the same hat,
      the same clothing, the same height, the same feet, the same chin,
      the same cheeks, the same lips, the same beard, the same nose,
      the same neck. Finally Sosia decided to consider himself Sosia
      because he knew himself well.

p.176 English–Latin

1   (a)   *quid ille seruus acturus est?*
      (b)   *nonne proelium Alcumenae narraturus est?*
      (c)   *eodem tempore dolis et pugnis meis eum decepturus sum.*
      (d)   *huc enim ueni mortem ei minaturus.*
      (e)   *hoc dolio nomen ei auferre mihi placuit.*
      (f)   *ego nihil facilius, nihil melius, nihil celerius feci.*

2　　MERC.　　*quis loquitur? eum, si inueniam, pugnis meis aggressurus*
　　　　　　　sum.

　　　SOS.　　*mihi melius est tacere. si me illis pugnis tanget, certe tanti*
　　　　　　　ero quanti murena.

　　　MERC.　　*quo iturus es, sceleste? quis es tu? ciuisne es?*

　　　SOS.　　*seruus sum.*

　　　MERC.　　*plura quam haec mihi dicere te uolo. quid est nomen tibi?*

　　　SOS.　　*nomen mihi est Sosia.*

　　　MERC.　　*tu mentiris. mene doliis tuis decepturus es? nisi celeriter*
　　　　　　　abibis, ego his pugnis te necabo.

Section 3D

pp.183–4 Revision exercises

1   household   *famili-ae, -is*
    eye   *ocul-o, -is*
    plan/advice/judgement   *consili-o, -is*
    mind/spirit/heart   *anim-o, -is*
    dinner   *cen-ae, -is*
    war   *bell-o, -is*
    god   *de-o, -is*
    crowd/mob   *turb-ae, -is*
    victory   *uictori-ae, -is*
    town   *oppid-o, -is*
    booty   *praed-ae, -is*
    father   *patr-i, -ibus*
    respect   *honor-i, -ibus*
    house/mansion   *aed-ibus*
    brother   *fratr-i, -ibus*
    wife   *uxor-i, -ibus*
    sister   *soror-i, -ibus*
    man   *homin-i, -ibus*
    load/burden   *oner-i, ibus*
    hand/band   *man-ui, -ibus*
    citizen   *ciu-i, -ibus*
    night   *noct-i, -ibus*
    day   *di-ei, -ebus*
    head/source/fount   *capit-i, -ibus*
    work   *oper-i, -ibus*

2   much   *mult-o, -ae, -o; -is*

much	*mult-o, -ae, -o; -is*		
unhappy/wretched	*miser-o, -ae, -o; -is*		
bad/evil	*mal-o, -ae, -o; -is*		
my	*me-o, -ae, -o; -is*		
your (s.)	*tu-o, -ae, -o; -is*		
our	*nostr-o, -ae, -o; -is*		
your (pl.)	*uestr-o, -ae, -o; -is*		
every/all	*omn-i, -ibus*		
sad/gloomy	*trist-i, -ibus*		
huge	*ingent-i, -ibus*		
short/brief	*breu-i, -ibus*		
bold/brave	*audac-i, -ibus*		
this	*huic, his*		

3

give	*do*	*dare*	*dedi*	*datus*
stand	*sto*	*stare*	*steti*	*statum*
order	*iubeo*	*iubere*	*iussi*	*iussus*
possess/hold	*possideo*	*possidere*	*possedi*	*possessus*
be	*sum*	*esse*	*fui*	fut. part.: *futurus*
go/come	*eo*	*ire*	*ii*	*itum*
bear/carry	*fero*	*ferre*	*tuli*	*latum*
wish	*uolo*	*uelle*	*uolui*	—
say/speak	*dico*	*dicere*	*dixi*	*dictus*
lead/consider	*duco*	*ducere*	*duxi*	*ductus*
take/capture	*capio*	*capere*	*cepi*	*captus*
conduct	*gero*	*gerere*	*gessi*	*gestus*
come	*uenio*	*uenire*	*ueni*	*uentum*
defeat/conquer	*uinco*	*uincere*	*uici*	*uictus*

get/gain/acquire	*adipiscor*	*adipisci*	*adeptus*
go up to/attack	*adgredior*	*adgredi*	*adgressus*
speak	*loquor*	*loqui*	*locutus*
follow	*sequor*	*sequi*	*secutus*
set out	*proficiscor*	*proficisci*	*profectus*
encourage	*hortor*	*hortari*	*hortatus*

promise	*polliceor*	*polliceri*	*pollicitus*
lie	*mentior*	*mentiri*	*mentitus*
catch sight of	*conspicor*	*conspicari*	*conspicatus*
think/judge	*arbitror*	*arbitrari*	*arbitratus*
try	*conor*	*conari*	*conatus*

pp.184–5 Exercises

1 (a) *mihi*   I may leave the house.

   (b) *seruum*   Mercury (has) attacked the slave with his fists.

   (c) *huic*   The slave obstructed this man (*or* got in his way).

   (d) *tibi*   I don't believe you.

   (e) *illam*   The man (*or*: her husband) loves her enormously.

   (f) *uobis*   That slave is threatening you.
                    (*You threaten someone in the dative* – p.183)

   (g) *patri*   A good son always obeys his father. (p.182)

   (h) *cenam*   The cook is at present preparing dinner.

   (i) *exercitui* My master is in charge of the army.

   (j) *te*   I instruct you to enter the house.

   (k) *ei*   The commander gave him this order ('ordered
                    this to him').

   (a) The cavalry are a hindrance to the legion.

   (b) Alcumena is a major concern of Jupiter's. ('Alcumena is a
        great care to Jupiter.')

   (c) This bad citizen is loathed by all decent people. ('... is an
        object of loathing to all good men.')

   (d) Amphitruo was the salvation of his citizens.

   (e) I will be a help to this city (*or*: I will go to the assistance of
        this city).

   (f) This duty is a pleasure to me.

   (g) This is your duty (this is something you are required to do).

   (h) Alas! I will bring destruction upon all my family.

   (i) This will do you no good (you'll regret this).

   (j) The victory of Amphitruo benefits all citizens.

3 (a) I had a good son.
   (b) My wife has a very large dowry.
   (c) Our citizens had no help.
   (d) No-one has a good mistress.
   (e) They have a son and a daughter.

4 (a) For a learned and educated man, living is thinking.
   (b) No road to Virtue is impassable.
   (c) Injustice cannot befall (be done to) the Wise Man.
   (d) Men believe their eyes more than their ears.
   (e) The man who mixes (Latin says 'mixed') useful with
        pleasant, wins ('won') every vote.

pp.185–6 Reading exercise/Test exercise

N.B. The key words that explain the dative have been italicized.

Sosia, when he comes to his (his master's) ship, will then *speak* to his master Amphitruo like this: 'I could not *report* your words to your wife, my lord, because a huge slave *threatened* me with his fists ('*threatened* fists to me'). He *obstructed* me fiercely. So *it was not possible* for me to go into the house. For that slave *was a very great hindrance* to your slave. So *it was necessary* for me to go back to you and *obey* his orders immediately, because I like how I look now ('my appearance is *pleasing* to me in this way, (namely) as it is'). This duty *was* not, as you promised, a *pleasure*, but a *great burden* to me.'

And Amphitruo will *reply* like this to his slave: 'What is that huge slave called (what *is the name* to that huge slave, what name does he have – dative of possession)?

Then Sosia (says): 'His name is Sosia ('to him the name is Sosia' – with Sosia attracted into the same case, dative, as 'him', see p.181. Strictly speaking Sosia complements the information about the name but 'Sosia' is so closely identified with the word 'him', it ends up in the same case as him not in the same nominative case as *nomen*). For that slave *took from* me my name, my appearance, my voice, everything. I now have no name, except "Nobody".'

p.186 English–Latin

1 (a) *maximus mihi seruus obstitit.*
   (b) *pulchra seni est filia/seni pulchra est filia/habet filiam pulchram*
        senex/senex pulchram habet filiam/ ...

(c)   *militibus meis licet mihi imperare/militibus meis mihi imperare licet.*

(d)   *Euclioni pecunia magnae uoluptati est/Euclioni pecunia ualde placet.*

(e)   *malus ciuis omnibus odio est.*

(f)   *omnes uolo imperiis meis parere/omnes imperiis meis parere mihi placet.*

(g)   *hoc officium uxori oneri (magno) erit.*

(h)   *dux, non milites, exercitui praeest.*

(i)   *celerrime tibi in patriam regredi necesse est/necesse est tibi celerrime in patriam regredi.*

(j)   *amantibus ita placet.*

2   JUP.   *uale, uxor. necesse enim est mihi ad copias regredi.*

    ALC.   *quid tibi negoti est? tibine sum iam taedio?*

    JUP.   *immo, magnae mihi es uoluptati. sed ubi dux exercitui non praeest, milites officiis operam non dant.*

    ALC.   *noli abire, mi uir, plus te amare potero, si mihi parebis.*

    JUP.   *noli mihi obstare. mox regrediar ita ut uis. nunc tamen mihi abire placet. uale.*

Section Four

Section 4A

p.196 Exercises

1.

uideor	*uidebar*	I was seeming	(like *pollicebar* – p.195)
expugno	*expugnabam*	I was storming	(like *amabam* – p.194)
fio	*fiebam*	I was being made	(like *capiebam* – p.194)
peruenio	*perueniebam*	I was reaching	(like *audiebam* – p.194)
sum	*eram*	I was	
conor	*conabar*	I was trying	(like *minabar* – p.195)
iubeo	*iubebam*	I was ordering	(like *habebam* – p.194)
reduco	*reducebam*	I was leading back	(like *dicebam* – p.194)
irascor	*irascebar*	I was getting angry	(like *loquebar* – p.195)
facio	*faciebam*	I was making	(like *capiebam* – p.194)

2.

tenebas	you (s.) were holding	*tenebatis*
loquebantur	they were speaking	*loquebatur*
praeerat	he was in charge	*praeerant*
minabamini	you (pl.) were threatening	*minabaris*
imperabam	I was ordering	*imperabamus*
ueniebatis	you (pl.) were coming	*ueniebas*

audebant	they were daring	*audebat*
obliuiscebaris	you (s.) were forgetting	*obliuiscebamini*
audiebat	he was listening	*audiebant*
patiebamur	we were suffering	*patiebar*
auferebamus	we were taking away	*auferebam*
sequebar	I was following	*sequebamur*

3   I used to think   *arbitrabar*
    he was abandoning   *relinquebat*
    they were throwing   *coniciebant*
    we used to follow   *sequebamur*
    you (s.) were reporting   *deferebas*
    she was going out   *exibat*
    they were accustomed   *solebant*
    you (pl.) were   *eratis*
    we were stating strongly   *affirmabamus*

4	**Present**	**Future**	**Imperfect**	**Perfect**
sentio	*sentit*	*sentiet*	*sentiebat*	*sensit*
	sentiunt	*sentient*	*sentiebant*	*senserunt*
minor	*minatur*	*minabitur*	*minabatur*	*minatus est*
	minantur	*minabuntur*	*minabantur*	*minati sunt*
ueto	*uetat*	*uetabit*	*uetabat*	*uetuit*
	uetant	*uetabunt*	*uetabant*	*uetuerunt*
tollo	*tollit*	*tollet*	*tollebat*	*sustulit*
	tollunt	*tollent*	*tollebant*	*sustulerunt*
eo	*it*	*ibit*	*ibat*	*iuit (or iit)*
	eunt	*ibunt*	*ibant*	*iuerunt (or ierunt)*
sum	*est*	*erit*	*erat*	*fuit*
	sunt	*erunt*	*erant*	*fuerunt*
audeo	*audet*	*audebit*	*audebat*	*ausus est*
	audent	*audebunt*	*audebant*	*ausi sunt*
adipiscor	*adipiscitur*	*adipiscetur*	*adipiscebatur*	*adipiscebatur*
	adipiscuntur	*adipiscentur*	*adipiscebantur*	*adepti sunt*
uideor	*uidetur*	*uidebitur*	*uidebatur*	*uisus est*
	uidentur	*uidebuntur*	*uidebantur*	*uisi sunt*
teneo	*tenet*	*tenebit*	*tenebat*	*tenuit*
	tenent	*tenebunt*	*tenebant*	*tenuerunt*

	Present	**Future**	**Imperfect**	**Perfect**
adgredior	*adgreditur*	*adgredietur*	*adgrediebatur*	*adgressus est*
	adgrediuntur	*adgredientur*	*adgrediebantur*	*adgressi sunt*
mentior	*mentitur*	*mentietur*	*mentiebatur*	*mentitus est*
	mentiuntur	*mentientur*	*mentiebantur*	*mentiti sunt*
accuso	*accusat*	*accusabit*	*acussabat*	*accusauit*
	accusant	*accusabunt*	*accusabant*	*accusauerunt*
colo	*colit*	*colet*	*colebat*	*coluit*
	colunt	*colent*	*colebant*	*coluerunt*

5   Imperfects are underlined.

loquar	future
sentiebat	he was feeling
amabit	future
negabat	he was denying
solebunt	future
audebant	they were daring
ponam	future
tollebatis	you (pl.) were removing
reliquit	perfect
habebit	future
tacebant	they were silent
opinaberis	future
arbitrabaris	you (s.) were thinking
expugnant	present
repellebas	you (s.) were driving back
iudicabatis	you were judging
coniecistis	perfect

If you got any of these wrong, check which conjugation the verb
belongs to.

Exercises p.197

1   *istius:*   *serui, feminae, templi, manus, rei, custodis, impetus*
              (gen. sing. masc./fem./neut.)

     ista: *lege, sacerdote* (*sacerdos,* priest, can be fem.)
              (abl. sing. fem.)

isti: *serui, uirtuti, manui, negotio, milites*
            (dat. sing. masc./fem./neut. *or* nom. pl. masc.)

ista: *femina res simulacra*
            (nom. sing. fem. *or* nom./acc. pl. neut.)

2   *serui*   *istius* (gen. sing.); *isti* (nom. pl.)

     negotio   *isti* (dat. sing.); *isto* (abl. sing.)

     uirtuti   *isti* (dat. sing.)

     custodibus   *istis* (dat./abl. pl.)

     manus   *istius* (gen. sing.); *istae* (nom. pl.); *istas* (acc. pl.)

p.198 Exercises

1   *seruorum quorundam*   gen. pl.   or certain slaves

     custodi cuidam   dat. sing.   to a certain guard

     signa quaedam   nom./acc. pl.   certain statues
                            (neuter)

     clamores quosdam   acc. pl.   certain shouts

     dolo quodam   abl. sing.   by a certain trick

     iudicibus quibusdam   dat. pl. *or* abl. pl. for certain judges
                                         or by, with, from

2   *cuiusdam:*   *templi sacerdotis manus*
                  (gen. sing. masc./fem./neut.)

     quaedam: *femina res negotia leges loca*
                  (nom. sing./pl. fem. *or* nom./acc. pl. neut.)

     quidam: *custos nuntius pueri milites magistratus iudices*
                  (nom. sing./pl. masc.)

p.201 Exercises

1
	Present	**Perfect**	**Future**
sum	*esse*	*fuisse*	*futurus esse*
accuso	*accusare*	*accusauisse*	*accusaturus esse*
expugno	*expugnare*	*expugnauisse*	*expugnaturus esse*
confirmo	*confirmare*	*confirmauisse*	*confirmaturus esse*
iubeo	*iubere*	*iussisse*	*iussurus esse*
reduco	*reducere*	*reduxisse*	*reducturus esse*
tollo	*tollere*	*sustulisse*	*sublaturus esse*
conicio	*conicere*	*coniecisse*	*coniecturus esse*
egredior	*egredi*	*egressus esse*	*egressurus esse*
mentior	*mentiri*	*mentitus esse*	*mentiturus esse*
uenio	*uenire*	*uenisse*	*uenturus esse*
eo	*ire*	*iuisse* (or *iisse*)	*iturus esse*

2
passurus esse	future	*patior*
loqui	present	*loquor*
amauisse	perfect	*amo*
sentire	present	*sentio*
habiturus esse	future	*habeo*
sustulisse	perfect	*tollo*
minatus esse	perfect	*minor*
uelle	present	*uolo*
iturus esse	future	*eo*
expugnare	present	*expugno*
secutus esse	perfect	*sequor*
poscere	present	*posco*
posuisse	perfect	*pono*
adeptus esse	perfect	*adipiscor*
iudicasse	perfect	*iudico*
reperturus esse	future	*reperio*
deferre	present	*defero*

3   to seem   *uideri*
      to have forbidden   *uetuisse*
      to be about to think   *arbitraturus esse*
      to report   *deferre*
      to have found   *inuenisse*
      to be about to remove   *ablaturus esse*
      to follow   *sequi*
      to have remembered   *meminisse*
      to be about to lie   *mentiturus esse*
      to promise   *promittere*
      to have spoken   *locutus esse*
      to be about to forget   *obliturus esse*

4   *solitus es*   2nd sing. perf.   *solere*
      detulistis   2nd pl. perf.   *deferre*
      confirmauere (= confirmauerunt)   3rd pl. perf.   *confirmare*
      affirmare   present infinitive
      sequere   imperative   *sequi (or
                                                                 sequeris)*

      coluisse   perfect infinitive
      puta   imperative   *putare*
      hortatus esse   perfect infinitive
      reperire   present infinitive
      mentire   imperative   *mentiri*
      accusaturus esse   future infinitive
      ausus est   3rd sing. perf.   *audere*
      repellere   present infinitive
      loquere   imperative   *loqui (or
                                                                 loqueris)*

      expugnauisse   perfect infinitive
      auditurus esse   future infinitive
      deferebat   3rd sing. imperf.   *deferre*
      iudicaturus esse   future infinitive

p.203 Exercises

1   (a)   Cicero states strongly that the people of Agrigentum have a statue of Hercules.

     (b)   The people of Agrigentum were saying that Verres had not been a good praetor.

     (c)   The story was that the man's slaves had entered the temple and had removed the statue.

     (d)   Cicero said that a certain messenger had announced all of this to the people of Agrigentum.

     (e)   I think that that man will always lie to you.

     (f)   Cicero was of the opinion that no one would ever commit worse crimes than that man.

     (g)   Verres used to send his slaves to the temples, take gold from citizens by force, show favour to his friends, even against the law, and embrace all crimes.

     (h)   I hear that Verres will report the name of a certain slave.

     (i)   Verres, because he did not want to be incriminated, ordered a certain friend to lie.

     (j)   I know that Verres was accustomed to accuse innocent men.

     (k)   Surely you have never heard more wicked crimes, gentlemen of the jury?

     (l)   Verres is a most wicked man, is he not?

     (m)   I heard that the people of Agrigentum made an attack on Verres' slaves.

2   (a)   Reason tells us that the gods exist.

     (b)   The outcome taught (us) that fortune favours the brave.

     (c)   I am a human being: I think there is nothing to do with humanity that does not concern me.

     (d)   They say that Democritus was never seen in public without a smile.

     (e)   A young man hopes that he will live for a long time.

     (f)   Renown is a fickle and unstable thing.

     (g)   Recently the illness of a certain friend of mine reminded me that we are at our best when we are ill. For what sick man does avarice or lust ever trouble?

     (h)   Here, where Rome now stands, an uncut wood used to grow green; such a great undertaking was pasture for a few oxen.

pp.204–6 Reading exercises

Translations only. Where there is ambiguity, the more likely translation is given first.

1   (a)   ... that the slaves will storm the temple.
   (b)   ... that Verres has sent the slaves to the temple.
         (*or*: ... that the slaves have sent Verres to the temple.)
   (c)   ... that the people of Assorus worship Chrysas (the river-god).
         (*or*: ... that Chrysas worships the people of Assorus.)
   (d)   ... that Verres will accuse me.
         (*or*: ... that I will accuse Verres.)
   (e)   ... that they (he, she, *or* it) love the statues.
         (*or*: ... that the statues love themselves.)
   (f)   ... that Scipio was a man of the greatest kindness.
   (g)   ... that the women have spotted everything.
   (h)   ... that that man will leave the city by night.
   (i)   ... that a great uproar had taken place.
   (j)   ... that he is going home.

2   The controlling verb is in **bold**; the accusative and infinitive is underlined.

   Cicero <u>templum esse</u> *apud Agrigentinos* **dixit**. <u>id</u> **affirmauit** *non longe a foro* <u>esse</u>. *in hoc templum* <u>intrauisse</u> **dixit** *Verris* <u>seruos</u>. <u>eos Verrem misisse</u> *Cicero* **opinatus est**. *Verres autem* <u>se hoc fecisse</u> **negabat**. *fama* **percrebrescebat** *Verris* <u>seruos</u> *in templum* <u>ingressos esse</u> *et* <u>custodes</u> *templum defendere* <u>conatos esse</u>. *magnum clamorem* <u>custodes fecisse</u> **putauit** *Cicero*; <u>Agrigentinos</u> *igitur ex urbe* <u>progressos esse</u> *et ad templum* <u>uenisse</u>. <u>fugisse</u> *tum* <u>seruos</u> *Verris* **affirmauit**. *Cicero* **negabat** *umquam* <u>se scelera peiora</u> <u>auditurum esse</u>.

   Translation
   Cicero said that there was a temple belonging to (amongst) the people of Agrigentum. He declared that it was not far from the forum. He said it was this temple Verres' slave had entered. Cicero was of the opinion that Verres had sent them. Verres however denied that he had done so. The story spread abroad that Verres' slaves had gone into the temple and that the guards had tried to defend the temple. Cicero thought that the guards

had caused a great commotion; and that the people of Agrigentum had therefore come forth from the city and had come to the temple. He declared that, at that point, the slaves of Verres had fled. Cicero said that he would never hear worse crimes.

3   (a)   acc. + infin.   They said that this could not happen.

   (b)   prolative infin.   He did not want you to do this.

   (c)   prolative infin.   I order you to remove the statue of Chrysas.

   (d)   acc. + infin.   He was declaring that the slaves had tried to kill him.

   (e)   acc. + infin.   The story was that Verres had removed the statue.

   (f)   prolative infin.   Gentlemen of the jury, all the people of Agrigentum were wanting me to prosecute Verres.

4   *Cicero dicit templum apud Agrigentinos esse non longe a foro. affirmat ibi esse simulacrum Herculis pulcherrimum. negat se pulchrius simulacrum quam illud umquam conspicatum esse. fama est ad hoc templum Verrem repente nocte seruos quosdam armatos misisse. dicit hos concurrisse et templum expugnauisse. affirmat custodes templi clamauisse et seruis obsistere templumque defendere conatos esse. dicit eos mox et peiora et scelestiora audituros esse.*

p.206 Reading exercise/Test exercise

I hear that there is a shrine of Ceres belonging to the people of Catina. Everyone knows that men are not allowed to enter that shrine. The story goes that women and young girls usually carry out the sacrifices there. Many people declare that in that shrine there used to be a very ancient statue of Ceres. Cicero said that Verres' slaves had removed this statue from that place at night; and that it had seemed to everybody to be a most dreadful business. Cicero said that Verres had then ordered a certain friend to find and accuse someone. For he (Cicero) said that he (Verres) had not wanted to be incriminated. Cicero declared that the friend had put forward the name of a certain slave, had accused the slave, and had provided false witnesses against him. However, he also stated that the senate of the people of Catina had called the priestesses and had asked them about the whole affair. Cicero said that all the priestesses had seen everything, and that the senate had said the slave was innocent. Cicero thought that the members of the jury had never heard worse crimes, but that soon they would hear worse.

p.206 English–Latin

1   (a)   *arbitror Verrem hoc fecisse.*

(b)   *Cicero dixit seruos in templum intrauisse.*

(c)   *multi ciues ad urbem ueniebant, negotium faciebant, domum regrediebantur.*

(d)   *amicus Verris nomen cuiusdam serui detulit.*

(e)   *nos omnes scimus istum scelestum esse.*

(f)   *num arbitraris seruos simulacrum sustulisse?*

(g)   *Cicero uir optimus erat, amicos libenter defendebat, numquam scelerum hostium nostrum obliuiscebatur.*

(h)   *Cicero arbitratur iudices numquam peius scelus audituros esse.*

2   *Syracusanis lex est de sacerdotio Iouis. Cicero dicit hanc legem Syracusanos iubere tres uiros creare; Syracusanis sortiri necesse esse; unum ex tribus sacerdotem fieri. affirmat Verrem amico cuidam, Theomnasto nomine, sacerdotium dare uoluisse; Syracusanos negauisse; Verrem dolo rem perfecisse.*

Section 4B

p.216 Exercises

1   (a)   *comite claro*   *comitibus claris*

             calamitate magna   *calamitatibus magnis*

             conuiuio Graeco   *conuiuiis Graecis*

             amico nobili   *amicis nobilibus*

             magistratu innocenti   *magistratibus innocentibus*

             forma turpi   *formis turpibus*

             re Romana   *rebus Romanis*

  (b)   The ablatives are: *comitibus, Asia, conuiuiis, sermone, ui, amico, diebus, homine turpi, uiro nobili, manu celeri*

  (c)   *ingenti*   dat./abl. sing.   *templo, uirgine, cura*

        audacibus dat./abl. pl.   *feminis, sacerdotibus*

        sola   abl. sing. fem.   *uirtute*

        magnis   dat./abl. pl.   *pueris, manibus*

        tanto   dat./abl. sing. masc./neut. *proelio, praetore*

        longiore   abl. sing.   *periculo, uia*

N.B. Most third declension nouns have ablative singular ending in *-e*. If you have made any mistakes, check carefully the declension of the nouns and adjectives.

2   N.B. The underlined words below relate to the Reading exercise on *GVE* pp.219–20, which you will come to later.

  (a)   The man was <u>much</u> better <u>than all the others</u>.

  (b)   He said that he had not killed the man <u>with the utmost force</u>.

       (*literally*, He denied himself to have killed ...)

  (c)   That man beat the door <u>with rocks</u>.

  (d)   Cicero asserted that the Agrigentini were brave men.

       (*literally*, men of great courage)

  (e)   Praetors, very serious men (*literally*, men <u>of the utmost seriousness</u>), do not enjoy parties.

  (f)   The Lampsaceni used to conduct their business <u>in the Greek manner</u>.

(g) Greeks prefer to spend their life <u>in leisure and peace</u> (rather) than <u>in war and disasters</u>.

(h) Cicero thought that Verres was worse <u>than the other praetors</u>.
(*literally*, ... thought Verres to be...)

(i) The story was that Verres' slaves had used <u>the greatest violence</u>.
(*utor* takes the ablative)

(j) <u>At that time</u> Ianitor came to Verres <u>with all speed</u> and tried to detain him <u>with many words</u>.

pp.217–8 Exercises

1 *alius*   nom. sing. masc./gen. sing. masc./fem./neut.   *comes, hospitis, calamitatis*

   alii   dat. sing./nom. pl. masc.   *Lampsaceno, sermones, ianuae*

   alia   nom. sing. fem. *or* nom./acc. pl. neut.   *conuiuia, uirgo*

   alia   abl. sing. fem.   *calamitate*

   aliqua   nom. sing. fem.   *mulier*

   aliqua   abl. sing. fem.   *re, serua*

2 (a) Different people say different things. (*Note 1 p.217*)
   (b) Some were Lampsaceni, the others were Agrigentini.
   (c) Different people are making an attack on the town in different places.
   (d) Some ran from the fields, others from the town. (*Note 2 p.217*)
   (e) Someone will say something.
   (f) But who is calling? Some magistrate? No one.
   (g) Catiline, are you hesitating to go away to some country?
   (h) Verres left the house with some companion.

p.219 Exercises

1 *ipsi*   dat. sing./masc. pl. nom.   *calamitati, consules, conuiuio, nuntii*

   ipsa   nom. sing. fem. *or* nom./acc. pl. neut.   *grauitas, signa, simulacra*

   ipsa   abl. sing. fem.   *grauitate*

2   *ipsi uoluere (= erunt)*   they themselves wanted

     signum ipsum   the statue itself

     ipsae clamarunt (= auerunt)   the women themselves shouted

     consilio ipso   by the plan itself

     ipsi homini pepercerunt   they themselves spared the man

                                  or they spared the man himself

                                  (*parco* takes the dative; *ipsi* = dat. sing. *or* nom. pl. masc.)

     ipsa laetitia   the joy itself

     obsecrarunt ipsi oraruntque   they themselves begged and prayed

     noli ipsam retinere   *literally,* don't keep the girl herself

3   (a)   No-one can be with a calm mind.

     (b)   The wise man conquers Fortune with courage.

     (c)   Alas, Fortune, who is a more cruel god to us than you? (*te* = ablative of comparison)

     (d)   That man enjoys riches the most who least need riches. (*fruor* takes the ablative)

     (e)   Alas, how difficult it is not to betray a crime by one's expression.

     (f)   Silver is cheaper than gold, gold is cheaper than virtue.

     (g)   An honourable death is better than a shameful life.

     (h)   Always something new out of Africa.

     (i)   The whole life of man is nothing other than the journey to death.

     (j)   Nature shows different routes to different people (*or* ... one route to one man, a different one to another)

p.219 Reading

The ablative phrases are indicated by the underlining in the answers to p.216 question 2 given on p.163 above.

(a)   *multo*   ablative of measure of difference

     omnibus aliis   comparison after *melior*

(b)   *summa ui*   describing how (ablative of manner)

(c)   *saxis*   instrument – 'with which'

(d)   no ablative phrase

(e)	*summa grauitate*	describing the praetors (ablative of description)
	conuiuiis	*fruor* takes the ablative
(f)	*more Graeco*	describing how they acted
(g)	*otio et pace* and *bello et calamitatibus*	describing how they prefer to live
(h)	*ceteris praetoribus*	comparison after *peiorem*
(i)	*summa ui*	*utor* takes the ablative
(j)	*eo tempore*	time when
	summa celeritate	describes how he came (ablative of manner)
	multis uerbis	instrument – 'with which'

p.220 Reading exercise/Test exercise

In the Hellespont, judges, you know that there is a town more famous and more noble than the other towns of Asia, called Lampsacus (Lampsacus by name). I assert that the Lampsaceni themselves are peaceful (quiet) men. They spend their life in the Greek manner. For they prefer to make use of leisure and peace (rather) than to spend their life in wars and disasters. That man arrived at Lampsacus at a certain time (on one occasion). The Lampsaceni took him to Ianitor, a very important man. That man however soon said that he would move to a certain Philodamus. For Philodamus had at home a very beautiful daughter. Judges, you know that Verres always strongly pursued beautiful women in all ways and at all times. Ianitor thought that he had offended Verres in some way and began to detain him with the utmost force. Verres therefore sent Rubrius to Philodamus, using a very bad (wicked) plan, because Philodamus was a man of great repute among the Lampsaceni and was used to receiving praetors and consuls, not their friends. But Verres ordered Rubrius to bring Philodamus by force. Philodamus, because he did not want to appear unwilling, prepared a party (and) ordered Rubrius to invite all his friends. They came with all speed; they reclined at table; at first they drank in the Greek manner (but) soon in larger goblets. They enjoyed the party at this time with happy conversations (with joy and conversations). But soon Rubrius said, 'Philodamus, call your daughter'. But he, a man of the utmost rectitude, was angry. He said that women should not recline at a party with men. An enormous uproar occurred through the house. When the Lampsaceni heard the disorder, they gathered at night at Philodamus' house with the utmost speed.

Next day, however, they set out to Verres' lodging. They began to attack (beat) the door with swords (iron) and rocks (and) at the same time to put fire around it. But the Lampsaceni spared Verres because some citizens said that this would be better for them than to kill a Roman praetor.

pp.220–21 English–Latin

1   (a)   *Verres Rubrio peior erat.*

     (b)   *Lampsaceni pace et otio fruebantur.*

     (c)   *Philodamus erat uir summae grauitatis* (gen.)*, Verres summa cupiditate* (abl.)*.*

     (d)   *coqui conuiuium sermone et laetitia parabant.*

     (e)   *Verres et comites more Graeco bibebant.*

     (f)   *Lampsaceni ianuam pugnis pulsabant et eodem tempore summa uoce clamabant.*

2   *Philodamus erat uir summa grauitate, aliis tamen semper multo hospitalior. Rubrium et comites ad conuiuium inuitauit. omnes summa celeritate peruenerunt. sermone et laetitia bibebant. subito autem Rubrius Philodamum iussit filiam uocare. Philodamus autem negabat se eam uocaturum esse. tumultus tum erat.*

Section 4C

pp.228–9 Exercises

1   *conatus/-a/-um eram*   I had tried
    excogitaueram   I had devised
    uisus/-a/-um eram   I had seemed
    monueram   I had warned
    usus/-a/-um eram   I had used
    feceram   I had made
    afueram   I had been away
    collegeram   I had collected

2   you (pl.) had begged   *oraueras*
    you (s.) had caught sight of   *conspicati eratis*
    he had moved   *commouerant*
    they had urged   *hortata erat*
    I had spared   *peperceramus*
    she had remembered   *recordatae erant*
    we had welcomed   *receperam*
    I had embraced   *amplexi eramus*
    you (s.) had cut down   *cecideratis*
    we had forgotten   *oblitus eram*
    they had ignored   *neglexerat*
    you (pl.) had advanced   *progressus eras*

3   *constitueram*
    passus eras
    reuocauerant
    recordati erant
    cognouerat
    adepta erat
    excogitaueramus
    complexi eratis
    collegeramus
    commoueras

4

Pres.	Fut.	Imperf.	Perf.	Pluperf.
reuocat	*reuocabit*	*reuocabat*	*reuocauit*	*reuocauerat*
reuocant	*reuocabunt*	*reuocabant*	*reuocauerunt*	*reuocauerant*
tenet	*tenebit*	*tenebat*	*tenuit*	*tenuerat*
tenent	*tenebunt*	*tenebant*	*tenuerunt*	*tenuerant*
arbitratur	*arbitrabitur*	*arbitrabatur*	*arbitratus/-a/-um est*	*arbitrantus/-a/-um erat*
arbitrantur	*arbitrabuntur*	*arbitrabantur*	*arbitrati/-ae/-a sunt*	*arbitrati/-ae/-a erant*
uidetur	*uidebitur*	*uidebatur*	*uisus/-a/-um est*	*uisus/-a/-um erat*
uidentur	*uidebuntur*	*uidebantur*	*uisi/-ae/-a sunt*	*uisi/-ae/-a erant*
neglegit	*negleget*	*neglegebat*	*neglexit*	*neglexerat*
neglegunt	*neglegent*	*neglegebant*	*neglexerunt*	*neglexerant*
sentit	*sentiet*	*sentiebat*	*sensit*	*senserat*
sentiunt	*sentient*	*sentiebant*	*senserunt*	*senserant*
utitur	*utetur*	*utebatur*	*usus/-a/-um est*	*usus/-a/-um*
utuntur	*utentur*	*utebantur*	*usi/-ae/-a sunt*	*erat usi/-ae/-a erant*
patitur	*patietur*	*patiebatur*	*passus/-a/-um est*	*passus/-a/-um erat*
patiuntur	*patientur*	*patiebantur*	*passi/-ae/-a sunt*	*passi/-ae/-a erant*
fit	*fiet*	*fiebat*	*factus/-a/-um est*	*factus/-a/-um erat*
fiunt	*fient*	*fiebant*	*facti/-ae/-a sunt*	*facti/-ae/-a erant*
non uult	*nolent*	*nolebat*	*noluit*	*noluerat*
nolunt	*nolet*	*nolebant*	*noluerunt*	*noluerant*
est	*erit*	*erat*	*fuit*	*fuerat*
sunt	*erunt*	*erant*	*fuerunt*	*fuerant*
colligit	*collegit*	*colligebat*	*colliget*	*collegerat*
colligunt	*colligent*	*colligebant*	*collegerunt*	*collegerant*
constituit	*constituet*	*constituebat*	*constituit*	*constituerat*
constituunt	*constituent*	*constituebant*	*constituerunt*	*constituerant*

5   impf; he had called back; perf; you (s.) had collected; fut; pres; they had read through; fut; you (s.) had tried; perf; you (pl.) had been; perf; they had gone out; perf; pres; fut; we had killed.

pp.231–2 Exercises

1   The antecedent is underlined.

    (a)   Diodorus used to have small <u>cups</u>, which Mentor had made.

    (b)   <u>The letter</u>, which he had written, soon arrived in Sicily.

    (c)   He was calling back <u>the men</u> who had asserted that they were in Rome.

    (d)   <u>The thing</u> which you have devised is criminal.

    (e)   <u>Diodorus</u>, whom Verres knew had certain very beautiful cups, had gone away.

    (f)   Diodorus was born from a noble <u>family</u> which had never become well-known.

2   (a)   *quem:*   He was a man whom all the women used to love.

    (b)   *cui:*   She was a woman to whom every man was pleasing.

    (c)   *quam:*   The young girl, whom Verres had wanted to love, was noble.

    (d)   *qui:*   Many men, who had become the companions of Verres, were the sons of noblemen.

    (e)   *quae:*   Mentor had made the small cups which the companions of Verres had caught sight of.

    (f)   *quorum:*   Many men, whose greed the good citizens had thought was very great, were going to Verres.

    (g)   *quod:*   The companions of Verres removed from the temple the statue which that man had dared to desire. (Note misprint *cupire* for *cupere* in the Latin in *GVE.*)

    (h)   *quos:*   The companions whom Verres had brought away with him to Lilybaeum, had caught sight of the cups of Diodorus.

3   *quae: poculis* (neut. pl.)

    quem: seruus (masc. sing.)

    cuius: genus (neut. sing.)

    cui: filio (masc. sing.)

    quibus: fana (neut. pl.)

4   (a)   and when he had heard it ...
     (b)   and when he had told these things ...
     (c)   and when they had recalled these women ...
     (d)   and when they had caught sight of them ...
     (e)   and when he had threatened him ...

pp.234–5 Exercises

1   (a)   A young girl of excellent reputation
     (b)   When Cicero and Antonius were consuls
     (c)   Under my leadership
     (d)   Young girls born from a noble family
     (e)   He removed the gold out of boldness and greed
     (f)   From Rome
     (g)   At home
     (h)   From Lilybaeum
     (i)   In the whole province
     (j)   In the absence of the praetors

2   (a)   *uir magnae uirtutis/uir magna uirtute*
     (b)   *Verre praetore*
     (c)   *te duce*
     (d)   *puer genere nobili natus*
     (e)   *hoc modo cupiditate*
     (f)   *Romae*
     (g)   *domo*
     (h)   *Lilybaeum*
     (i)   *tota Sicilia*
     (j)   *ceteris absentibus*

3   (a)   He who has much desires more.
     (b)   The poor man is not he who has too little but he who
           desires more.
     (c)   He who begins (it) has half the deed (i.e. is half-way there).
     (d)   Fortune snatches nothing away except what she has given.
     (e)   It is sweet to remember what was hard to endure.
     (f)   Diaulus was recently a doctor, now he's an undertaker; what
           he does as an undertaker, he had also done as a doctor.

p.235 Reading exercise/Test exercise

That man by his greed drove out from the province Diodorus of Malta, who had left Malta long before and at that time was living in Lilybaeum. He had been a man of great respect among the people of Lilybaeum, who had got to know that he was a man of the greatest goodness. But in Verres' praetorship, he lacked a home for a period of almost three years because of certain beautiful cups which he used to have. For the companions which that man had brought with him when he came to the province, had announced to him that Diodorus had these cups; and when he had got to know this, inflamed by greed, he had summoned Diodorus to him and had demanded the cups. However, Diodorus, who was unwilling to lose the cups, had asserted that they were in Malta in the hands of a close relative. But when Verres had written a letter to that relative, in which he kept on demanding the cups, the man had said that he had sent them to Lilybaeum within the last few days. Meanwhile Diodorus had departed from Lilybaeum.

pp.235–6 English–Latin

1   (a)   *Diodorus, qui multa pocula pulchra habebat, Lilybaeo Roman abierat.*

(b)   *Verre praetore, tota prouincia uiri facta scelesta excogitare poterant.*

(c)   *Verres, qui genere nobili natus erat, semper cupiditate potius quam uirtute agebat.*

(d)   *comites, quos Verres secum ad prouinciam duxerat, erant scelesti.*

2   *quae ubi Verres audiuit, insania Diodorum absentem accusare constituit. tota prouincia res clara erat. fama erat Verrem cupiditate argenti uirum innocentem absentem accusauisse. Diodorus, qui hoc tempore Romae erat, omnia quae audiuerat suis patronis narrauit. quae ubi pater Verris audiuit, litteras isti misit. quibus in litteris narrabat omnes tota urbe scire Verrem esse scelestum. quae ubi Verres perlegit, cupiditatem timore potius quam pudore repressit.*

Section 4D

pp.247–8 Exercises

1   *captum iri*   to be about to be (to be going to be) captured
     liberatum iri   to be about to be (to be going to be) set free
     iussum iri   to be about to be (to be going to be) ordered
     ablatum iri   to be about to be (to be going to be) taken away
     repertum iri   to be about to be (to be going to be) found

2   (a)   Verres said the robbers would be captured.
     (b)   Verres said that the Roman citizens would not be freed.
     (c)   Verres asserts that the cups of Diodorus will be taken away.
     (d)   Diodorus says that the cups will not be found by Verres.
     (e)   Verres said that his friends would be ordered to find the cups.
     (f)   I shall go to see if he is at home.
     (g)   Maecenas goes to play, Virgil and I to sleep.

pp.249–51 Exercises

1   *liberor*   *liberamur*   I am freed etc.
     liberaris   *liberamini*
     liberatur   *liberantur*

     adiuuabar   *adiuuabamur*   I was being helped etc.
     adiuuabaris   *adiuuabamini*
     adiuuabatur   *adiuuabantur*

     iubebor   *iubebimur*   I shall be ordered etc.
     iubeberis   *iubebimini*
     iubebitur   *iubebuntur*

     uideor   *uidemur*   I am seen/I seem etc.
     uideris   *uidemini*
     uidetur   *uidentur*

     latus eram   *lati eramus*   I had been carried etc.
     latus eras   *lati eratis*
     latus erat   *lati erant*

caesus sum	*caesi sumus*	I have been killed/
caesus es	*caesi estis*	I was killed etc.
caesus est	*caesi sunt*	

reuocari   to be called back

confirmatus esse   to have been confirmed

recipior	*recipimur*	I am received etc.
reciperis	*recipimini*	
recipitur	*recipiuntur*	

dicar	*dicemur*	I shall be said etc.
diceris	*dicemini*	
dicetur	*dicentur*	

2   she followed (deponent)
he is accused (passive)
they were taken away (passive)
he was left (passive)
he is carried (passive)
he speaks (deponent)
he lied (deponent)
he used to catch sight of (deponent)
he will consider (deponent)
he will try (deponent)
it will be told (passive)
it was announced (passive)
it was seen (passive)
it dared (deponent)

3   *capietur*
liberari
feriebantur
ablatum erat
reuocatus esse
perlectum est

4   (a)   The ship was not captured by our fleet.
     (b)   The news was announced to Verres by a messenger.
     (c)   The ship was brought to Syracuse by the sailors.
     (d)   The craftsmen were taken away by Verres.
     (e)   The pirates were executed with an axe by the Romans.

5   (a)   Nothing was said by Verres.
     (b)   The ship was captured by a pirate.
     (c)   Young men are sent by Verres to Rome.
     (d)   The pirates' ship was taken away by our men.
     (e)   My treasure will be given to the friends.
     (f)   It was announced to Verres that the ship had been captured and that the pirates were being killed with an axe.

6   (a)   *homines a Romanis defendebantur.*
     (b)   *numerus praedonum a te cognitus est.*
     (c)   *pecunia a Verre data est.*
     (d)   *ciues Romani a Verres securi feriuntur.*
     (e)   *nautae ab illo liberabuntur.*
     (f)   *pocula a Diodoro ablata erant.*

p.251 Reading exercise/Test exercise

It was announced to Verres that, with Publius Caesetius and Publius Tadius in command, a certain pirate ship had been captured, and that the ship was full of very handsome young men, silver and clothes. Verres ordered the ship to be brought to Syracuse by the sailors. Then punishment was expected by everyone. But although the old men were executed immediately, the handsome young men however were taken away by him and given to his friends. Nobody had thought the pirates would be freed. However this was done by Verres.

But afterwards a much more wicked deed was done by him. For in the place of the pirates who had been freed, Verres began to substitute Roman citizens, who had previously been thrown into prison. Although they were known by many, they were still killed with an axe.

p.251 English–Latin

1 (a) *nauis a Romanis inuenta est.*

(b) *pecunia Verri a praedonibus dabatur.*

(c) *iuuenes Romam mittuntur.*

(d) *nuntiatum erat nauem captam esse et Syracusas appelli.*

(e) *nemo praedones captum iri senserat.*

(f) *Verres Romae accusabitur.*

2 *Syracusani rationem habebant praedonum qui necati erant. quae ratio habita erat ex numero remorum qui capti erant. magnus numerus praedonum deerat, quod multi a Verre liberati erant. ciues autem Romani in praedonum locum substituti sunt. Verres illos milites Sertorianos fuisse arguit. quamquam a multis Syracusanis cogniti erant securi percussi sunt.*

Section 4E

pp.262–3 Exercises

1
reuocans, reuocantis	calling back
incendens, incendentis	setting fire to
accipiens, accipientis	receiving
sentiens, sentientis	feeling
iubens, iubentis	ordering
adipiscens, adipiscentis	getting
egrediens, egredientis	going out
fruens, fruentis	enjoying
recordans, recordantis	remembering
exiens, exeuntis	going out

2
inspicienti:	*seruae, uiro*	(dat. sing.)
	muliere	(abl. sing.)
accedentem:	*principem*	(acc. sing.)
nitente:	*serua*	(abl. sing.)
commorantum:	*mulierum*	(gen. pl.)
conflagrantibus:	*moenibus, ceteris*	(dat./abl. pl.)
circumiens:	*Cicero, mulier*	(nom. sing.)

3
(a) Verres was standing on the shore, leaning on a woman.

(b) (*Literally*) The pirate replied to them asking that he had seen the ships fleeing.

(*English*) When they asked him, the pirate replied that he had seen the ships fleeing.

(c) (*Literally*) The sailors being in need of food...

(*English*) Although the sailors were in need of food, Cleomenes did nothing.

(d) While Verres was making love to a woman, it was announced that the ship had been captured.

(e) You can see the ship ablaze with fire.

(f) They caught sight of the rest following a little more slowly.

(g) While waiting in Syracuse, the pirates saw the walls of the city.

(h)   Verres said that he had not seen the ships approaching the harbour.

(i)   No day is long for a busy man.

(j)   Nothing is difficult for someone in love.

4   *Verre absente*
nautis sequentibus
populo inspiciente
nauibus ardentibus
Cleomene commorante
multitudine principem hortante

pp.265–6 Exercises

1   *eguissem etc.*
conflagrauissem
commoratus essem
secutus essem
acceptus essem
incensus essem
nisus/nixus essem
occidissem
sensissem
liberatus essem
accessissem

2   (a)   Since Cleomenes had fled, the others followed.

(b)   Since the pirates had advanced very quickly, the last ships of the Romans were the first in danger.

(c)   Although the commander had reached the shore quickly, the rest however were sailing more slowly.

(d)   When Cleomenes had reached the shore with his ship, he hid (himself) at home.

(e)   The rest also abandoned their ships since they had not been able to escape from the pirates by sea in any way.

(f)   The leader of the pirates ordered the ships to be burned* when they had been captured.

* *incendi* = present infinitive passive – see *GVE* p.246.

3   (a)   *cum imperator ad litus nauigauisset.*
    (b)   *cum naues incensae essent.*
    (c)   *cum praedones Syracusis commorati essent.*
    (d)   *cum moenia inspecta essent.*
    (e)   *cum multitudo incendium conspicata esset.*
    (f)   *cum nautae cibo eguissent.*

4   *eguit*   indicative perfect
    conflagrasset   subjunctive pluperfect
    tulerat   indicative pluperfect
    recordatus esses   subjunctive pluperfect
    constituisse   infinitive perfect
    excogitaueras   indicative pluperfect
    accepissent   subjunctive pluperfect
    captus esse   infinitive perfect
    occisi essent   subjunctive pluperfect
    conspicati sunt   indicative perfect

p.267 Reading exercise/Test exercise

Thus the first ship to be captured was one belonging to the people of
Haluntium. (*Literally,* a ship of the Haluntines was captured first.) In
command of it was a nobleman from Haluntium, Phylarchus, whom
the people of Locri afterwards ransomed from those pirates at public
expense. Next a ship from Apollonia was captured and its captain
Anthropinus killed. While these events were taking place, Cleomenes
meanwhile had already reached the shore of Helorus. He had already
rushed out of the ship on to land and had left his quadrireme bobbing
on the sea. Since their commander had disembarked onto dry land, the
rest of the ships' captains followed Cleomenes closely.

p.267 English–Latin

1   (a)   *multitudo naues ardentes conspicata est.*
    (b)   *reliqui praefecti nauium Cleomenem, cum in terram exiisset,
          secuti sunt.*
    (c)   *Cleomenes, cuius uxor in litore cum Verre erat, nauibus
          sequentibus e portu egressus est.*
    (d)   *praefecti nauium, cum mari praedones effugere non potuissent,
          principem secuti e nauibus egressi sunt.*

2   *praedones nauibus incensis Syracusas accedere constituerunt.*
     audiuerant enim portum Syracusanorum pulcherrimum esse et
     sciebant se numquam nisi Verre praetore eum uisuros esse. quod cum
     statuissent Syracusas nauigauerant. piratica nauis Verre praetore,
     nostris nauibus ardentibus, usque ad portum Syracusanorum accessit.
     pro di immortales! o factum turpissimum!

Section 4F

p.279 Exercises

1

Verb	Pres. subj.	Impf. subj.
concido	*concidam*	*conciderem*
hortor	*horter*	*hortarer*
morior	*moriar*	*morerer*
sum	*sim*	*essem*
timeo	*timeam*	*timerem*
aufero	*auferam*	*auferrem*
passive	*auferar*	*auferrer*
reuoco	*reuocem*	*reuocarem*
passive	*reuocer*	*reuocarer*
nauigo	*nauigem*	*nauigarem*

2

clamet	pres. subj.
amat	pres. indic.
dormiret	imp. subj.
auferret	impf. subj.
conspicatus esse	perf. infin. (deponent)
conati essent	pluperf. subj. (dep.)
dat	pres. indic.
dicetur	fut. indic. (passive)
excogitat	pres. indic.
curet	pres. subj.
nescirem	impf. subj.
cupiuisse	perf. infin.
loquitur	pres. indic. (dep.)
abstulisset	pluperf. subj.
monearis	pres. subj. (pass.)
accidat	pres. subj.
aget	fut. indic.
persuadet	pres. indic.
perficias	pres. subj.

3   **Indicative**

Verb	Present	Imperfect	Pluperfect
ago	*agit*	*agebat*	*egerat*
passive	*agitur*	*agebatur*	*actus erat*
perficio	*perficit*	*perficiebat*	*perfecerat*
commoror	*commoratur*	*commorabatur*	*commoratus erat*
libero	*liberat*	*liberabat*	*liberauerat*
passive	*liberatur*	*liberabatur*	*liberatus erat*
iaceo	*iacet*	*iacebat*	*iacuerat*
sequor	*sequitur*	*sequebatur*	*secutus erat*
nolo	*non uult*	*nolebat*	*noluerat*
accidit	*accidit*	*accidebat*	*acciderat*

Subjunctive

Verb	Present	Imperfect	Pluperfect
ago	*agat*	*agere*	*egisset*
passive	*agatur*	*ageretur*	*actus essat*
perficio	*perficiat*	*perficeret*	*perfecisset*
commoror	*commoretur*	*commoraretur*	*commoratus esset*
libero	*liberet*	*liberaret*	*liberauisset*
passive	*liberetur*	*liberaretur*	*liberatus esset*
iaceo	*iaceat*	*iaceret*	*iacuisset*
sequor	*sequatur*	*sequeretur*	*secutus esset*
nolo	*nolit*	*nollet*	*noluisset*
accidit	*accidat*	*accideret*	*accidisset*

p.281 Exercises

1   (a) Verres persuaded Servilius that he should go to Lilybaeum
         (to go to Lilybaeum).
     (b) When he came to Lilybaeum, Servilius was flogged by the
         lictors.
     (c) Verres had ordered the lictors to flog the man.
     (d) Servilius, as a Roman citizen, begs Verres not to flog him
         nor to kill him.
     (e) Just as Verres flogs Roman citizens, so I assert that he will
         be flogged by Roman citizens.
     (f) Verres urges certain slaves not to spare Servilius nor to give
         help to him begging (when he begs for it).

2   (a)   *ut Lilybaeum adeat*
      (b)   *ne abeatis*
      (c)   *ut Seruilium caederent*
      (d)   *ne taceret*
      (e)   *ut mihi credas*
      (f)   *ne quis fugiat neue abeatis*

p.282 Exercises

1   (a)   It happens that Servilius speaks slightly too freely about the wickedness of Verres.
      (b)   Verres brought it about that Servilius came to Lilybaeum.
      (c)   It happened that Servilius, when he had come to Lilybaeum, was flogged by the lictors.
      (d)   Gavius, when he was in chains at Syracuse, said that he would bring it about that he would escape and come to Messana.
      (e)   Verres will bring it about that Roman citizens are killed.

2	*perficiam ut:*	**I shall bring it about that** (or **I shall manage to do):**
(a)	*Verres Lilybaeum adeat.*	Verres comes to Lilybaeum.
(b)	*uir a lictoribus caedatur.*	The man is flogged by the lictors.
(c)	*serui eum ad terram adiciant.*	The slaves throw him to the ground.
(d)	*uerberibus moriatur.*	He dies from the blows.
(e)	*socii Romam profugiant.*	The friends escape to Rome.
	accidit ut:	**It happened that:**
(a)	*Verres Lilybaeum adiret.*	Verres came to Lilybaeum.
(b)	*uir a lictoribus caederetur.*	The man was flogged by the lictors.
(c)	*serui eum ad terram adicerent.*	The slaves threw him to the ground.
(d)	*uerberibus moreretur.*	He died from the blows.
(e)	*socii Romam profugerent.*	The friends escaped to Rome.

pp.283–4 Reading exercise/Test exercise

This Gavius from Consa, of whom I speak, when he had been thrown into chains by this man among that number of Roman citizens and had escaped secretly by some method from the mines and had come to Messana, since he saw Italy and the walls of the people of Rhegium, Roman citizens, so near now, and since he had come back to life as if renewed from that fear of death and darkness by the light of liberty and some scent of the laws, began to speak at Messana and to complain that he, a Roman citizen, had been thrown into chains, that his route was directly to Rome and that he would face Verres as he arrived.

p.284 English–Latin

Verres uirum, cui Gauio erat nomen, in uincla coniecerat. qui perfecerat ut profugeret Messanamque perueniret. affirmauit se Verrem Romae delaturum esse. Verres autem, cum hoc audiuisset, seruis suis imperauit ut uirum caperent. illi in nauem ingredientem retraxerunt et ad magistratum duxerunt. Verres cum Messanam peruenisset, imperauit ut Gauius medio in foro nudaretur et caederetur. lictores ei oranti clamitantique se esse ciuem Romanum non pepercerunt. itaque accidit ut ciuis Romanus a Verre necaretur.

Section 4G

p.292–3 Exercises

1   (a)   If Verres' father were here, he would judge his son to be an enemy of our state.

(If Verres' father had been here, he would have judged his son to be an enemy of our state.)

    (b)   If we were to pardon Verres, we should be stupid.

    (c)   If Verres were to demand my cups, I should send a letter to him without delay.

    (d)   Even animals if they heard these things would be moved.

(Even animals if they had heard these things would have been moved.)

    (e)   Unless you kept on shouting that you are a Roman citizen, you would be killed.

    (f)   If you had this protection, even the enemy would spare you.

(If you had had this protection, even the enemy would have spared you.)

    (g)   If there were foresight, there would be no evil.

    (h)   Wine prepares the mind (gets you in the mood) for lovemaking, unless you have too much.

2   (a)   *si ciuis Romanus essem ...*

    (b)   *si praesidium postulet ...*

    (c)   *si mora non esset ...*

    (d)   *si amici commoueantur ...*

    (e)   *si praesidium postularemus ...*

    (f)   *si clamitem ...*

    (g)   *uelim dicere ...*

    (h)   *uellem rogare ...*

    (i)   *postularem ...*

    (j)   *commouear ...*

p.297 English–Latin

*Quamquam Gauius Raecium cognitorem nominauerat (cum ...
nominauisset), litteras ei non misisti. uelim, Verres, te hoc mihi dicere. cur
moratus es? cur statim litteras non misisti? nonne Gauius 'si litteras ad
Raecium mittas' inquit 'me ciuem Romanum esse dicat. si adesset, me quem
accuses innocentem esse affirmaret.' sed tu, Verres, summa Gauii neglegentia
crucem parauisti. si bestiis hanc rem narrarem hae etiam commouerentur.*

For Alison and Lydia

'If Winter comes, can Spring be far behind?'

Shelley, *Ode to the West Wind*

Chapter 1

Guinness in plastic pints, pool players angling back into their shot, a DJ playing novelty records from the seventies, white walls which appear as if they are sweating, a hanging cloud of cigarette smoke: Kerry Scott feels for her bag with her feet and contemplates her departure from the college bar. As this thought crosses her mind, however, Matilda arrives with another tray of drinks, neatly swaying her hips to avoid the pool cue jabbing back into her.

'Guinness, was it, Kerry?'

And Kerry nods, even though the three pints she has already drunk are swelling her stomach against the top button of her jeans. She is hungry, needs something to mop up the beer. Matilda squeezes in and settles down next to her.

'We deserve this,' she remarks, sipping at her pint and extracting a cigarette from her packet. 'Well, *I* certainly deserve it, that seminar was a nightmare.'

Matilda had been presenting a seminar on Joseph Conrad that afternoon and had been completely winging it, a fact which had been as obvious to the lecturer as it was to the students. It had got embarrassing after a while, and in the end the lecturer had just sighed and told her to sit down and try and read the book in question next time. Kerry likes Matilda, she has an appealingly lazy contempt for almost every aspect of college life. Matilda always teases Kerry good-naturedly for being hard-working and getting good marks, and Kerry hopes that Matilda does not get kicked out at the end of the year – an event which appears to be becoming increasingly likely. Although they are not friends exactly, Kerry enjoys meeting Matilda in the bar and listening to her irreverent slagging off of lecturers and students alike.

1

'I feel like I'm going to give birth.' Kerry puts her hands to either side of her stomach. 'I'm going to call it Guinness.'

Matilda laughs. 'You could do with putting on a bit of weight, Kerry. It's all that studying you do, you'll waste away. I've seen you in the library, you're like its ghost late at night . . .'

'Don't lie. You can't have seen me 'cause you don't even know where the library is.'

'Ah, that's where you're wrong, Kerry. I got off with some third-year when I first started here and as there was nowhere else to go . . .'

Kerry puts her hands over her ears. 'No, no, I don't want to hear about it . . .'

'He was lovely. The problem was that he knew it. Politics student, I think.'

The noise in the bar is getting louder, the space increasingly restricted, the music more and more unbearable. Some of the students are singing along drunkenly in an attempt to demonstrate their acquaintance with songs which are no less terrible now than they were twenty years ago.

'How many Essex girls does it take to screw in a lightbulb?' somebody is shouting next to her. She can almost feel their spittle hitting her ear.

Kerry slides her foot through the strap of her bag under the table and sips at the bitter Guinness. Essex is Gary. There is no getting around it. The word came like an unexpected slap across the face, triggering – as it always does – the acid memories, the awful stomach-clenching pain of him. Why had he gone there? Why had he gone to Essex? Why that particular journey? She has never worked that one out, never been able to fit it into the overall story: an awkward piece in an already troublesome jigsaw. It wasn't in Gary's nature to be mysterious: Essex, Essex, Essex . . . The word becomes meaningless in her head, the way words did when she was a child, losing all cohesion after constant scrutiny, like tube-station names curving around grimed platforms.

'What's up, Kerry?' Matilda shouts above the noise. 'You look terrible all of a sudden.'

'I can't take much more of this. I should be going.'

'Kerry, babe, don't leave me with this rabble. I need someone human with me.'

A group on the table next to theirs are singing along to 'Tiger Feet' and banging the table, making the pints pogo alarmingly in front of them.

'Why do Essex girls get their periods?'

Oh no, Kerry thinks. Just get me out of here. Away. Gone. Space. Move, Kerry, move.

'I've gotta go, Matilda. I'll see you tomorrow.'

Simon Davis from the Revolutionary Students' Group leers at her as she tries to squeeze past him.

'Kerry,' he says holding his hands together in front of him as if praying. 'Kerry, Kerry, Kerry. You cannot go. I absolutely forbid it. I order you to enjoy yourself. What else did you come to college for?'

His intervention, however, brings down the wrath of Matilda upon him.

'Move your leg and let her out. If she wants to go it's certainly none of your business. Go and sell some of your papers or hold a meeting or something. Kerry, I might see you in the cafeteria tomorrow, yeah?'

Kerry waves goodbye and as she is leaving turns back for a second. Simon Davis is saying something about her to the boy next to him and they are both laughing.

She walks up the white stairs which lead away from the bar, feeling the welcome freshness of the air and the noise receding. The corridors of the college are quiet, the walls plastered with notices from societies and the political meetings of rival groups advertised by rhetorical questions to which the correct answer would always appear to be no. *Is Socialism dead? Is the Labour Party the only alternative to the Tories?* There are notices for the canoeing club, the parachute society, the Tequila appreciation society, an invitation to discover the real truth about Islam. Simon's mocking question echoes in her head. *What did you come to college for?*

Kerry goes into the toilets and rinses her face, feeling the relief of cold water against it. She looks at herself in the mirror, drops of water still clinging to her cheeks. Her face gazes solemnly back at her: black shoulder-length hair, dark round eyes, a regular face, eyebrows slightly suggesting a frown. Sometimes, when she is drunk, she talks to herself in mirrors, asks questions of herself, but there is somebody in the cubicle so she just hums as she flicks her hair behind her ears.

She is walking down the steps of the college when somebody calls her name. She turns to see Robin, a student from her course. Like Kerry, Robin is a mature student, and Kerry guesses they must be about the same age. He is aloof with the rest of the group and always hands in work on time. The story is that Robin is rich, having inherited a large sum of money and a house after the death of his father. He is tall and very good-looking, with a well-defined face; delicate high cheek bones framed by soft curly hair. There is something puzzling about him which Kerry cannot pinpoint exactly. It might be his curious detachment, as if he is constantly observing, judging, weighing things up. He has a lugubrious laugh and an upper-class accent which he does not bother to attempt to disguise. Brushing a strand of curly hair out of his eyes, he smiles a crooked half-smile.

'Hi, Kerry, I thought I saw you down there. You going home?'

'Yes.'

'I'll walk with you to the tube. I've just been in the library.'

As they make their way towards Kentish Town tube, past the windows of McDonalds with kids hunched over milk-shakes and burger wrappers, Robin says: 'How's the seminar coming along?'

'Slowly.'

'Yeeess,' he says meditatively as if he has known this all along. 'You're doing *The Wasteland*, aren't you?'

'Yes.'

'Isn't it just the best poem ever? It's the best poem ever written. Isn't it?'

'No,' says Kerry, startled into honesty by his sudden excitement.

4

'You don't think so?'

'No.'

'OK,' he says and then falls silent. Kerry feels awkward and trys to explain herself.

'I mean, I like it and everything . . . I like the way it sounds and stuff, but you know . . . it doesn't really . . . I mean, I do like it but it doesn't really . . . have a big effect on me,' she concludes lamely.

Robin lopes along in silence. His height and long legs mean that he walks faster than Kerry so that she is having almost to jog to keep up. He doesn't seem to notice. She tries to think of something else to say but can't and they carry on in silence. When they arrive at the tube station, Kerry doesn't have a ticket and stops to buy one. She hopes that Robin will just carry on through the ticket barrier but he stands and waits for her as she queues for the machine.

He rests against the barrier, one long leg in front of the other, still half smiling at her. A dosser lurches up to him, hunched inside a tatty black coat, with his filthy beard and dirt tan. Robin glances at the man and glances away again. The dosser clutches at his arm and Robin looks down at his hand briefly before swiftly, skilfully, brushing it off him like a fallen leaf. The man begins to hurl furious abuse at him. He is hunched up in his black coat and shaking his fist so that he looks like Rumpelstiltskin on a bad day. Kerry half expects him to begin stamping his foot. She struggles to drop the remaining coins as quickly as possible into the machine and puts her hand through the Perspex flap to catch the ticket as it screeches out. The man has now worked himself up into a violent rage but Robin does not move, just stands still half smiling and waiting for Kerry. The dosser's partner, a red-faced woman carrying a can of Tennants Extra, limps over to join in the screaming.

'All right,' says Robin placidly as she approaches.

'Yes,' says Kerry quickly as the couple stumble towards them, slipping her ticket into the machine.

'Slag!' screams the woman at her. 'Fur coat and no fuckin' knickers, ya slag!'

'Fur coat?' exclaims Kerry when they are safely on the escalator. 'What's she on about?'

'So you didn't mind the bit about the knickers?' says Robin, and Kerry laughs.

When they reach the bottom of the escalator, they pause as they are going to different platforms.

'Well, 'bye then,' says Kerry.

'Listen, Kerry, what are you doing next week?'

She blushes. It sounds as if he is going to ask her out. Thankfully he doesn't give her time to answer.

'Because some friends and I are going to Ireland for a few days. You know, just travelling about a bit. There's a cottage – in Galway, I think. We're going to stay there for a few days. Do you want to come? It should be fun.'

'Oh, thanks, but I couldn't,' she says, grateful that the sheer scale of the invitation makes it possible for her to decline.

'Why not?'

'I just couldn't afford it, I've got a massive overdraft.'

'I'll pay for you.'

She stares at him. He smiles at her calmly. 'I mean so that there's nothing in the way of your going . . . unless you don't want to, of course?'

'No, I'd like to, it's just that . . .'

'If you want to do something, you should do it,' announces Robin in the same calm judicious manner. 'Don't you think? You haven't got the money. OK, but I have. And I'd like you to come.'

'Well, it's not always that straightforward.'

'I think it is.'

'Look, I'd really like to, it's just . . .'

'No. You don't want to then.' He doesn't appear to be angry, just perfectly matter of fact. 'You can't want to or you'd go. Anyway . . .' he waves his hand vaguely ' . . . be seeing you then.' And he walks away. Kerry realises that she hasn't even said thank you for the offer. She doesn't feel grateful, though, she feels as if she has been tested and doesn't like it.

There are no via Bank trains on the indicator board so she

sits and watches the yellow dotted minutes of the Charing Cross branch trains ticking down, and the sliding horizontal messages reminding customers that there is no smoking on London Underground. There is something light and cheerful about Kennington via Charing Cross, something rather sinister about Morden via Bank. Perhaps it is the dark and portentous procession of names: Old Street, Moorgate (tube disaster), Bank (change for Monument), London Bridge (is falling down), Borough. Kerry begins to invent other names that would be appropriate for the loop: Abattoir, Charnel House, Mortuary Street. She is getting bored and when a via Charing Cross train arrives, she catches it and changes at Camden Town.

Kerry gets off the train at Old Street, the tube station an underground parody of the roundabout with its confusion of numbered exits leading from the hub of the ticket area. Even after having lived here for some years, Kerry finds the one-way systems and turn-offs confusing – the City Road, the New North Road, Great Eastern Street, Old Street – round and round and never sure which road is which, the turning that will lead to the desired destination. It sometimes makes her uneasy, being a mature student living in a place called Old Street. It isn't even really an area in itself; the roundabout is like a dirty, expired Catherine wheel throwing out its roads to neighbouring areas: Islington, Clerkenwell, Shoreditch, Hoxton, Spitalfields. There is something tired about Old Street itself, some colourless quality, too many dreary shops selling office equipment.

Kerry walks west down Old Street towards Clerkenwell. It is a lonely walk with the curious deadness of the road at night, and she sings quietly to herself, checking the shadows behind her so that nobody catches her doing it. When the footsteps quicken and shadows lengthen behind her, her voice drops to a whisper but she does not stop singing. She wonders if Marco will be at home when she gets in. Marco started off staying with her when he got thrown out of his last house and has lived there ever since. He has a series of floating casual jobs and is currently working in a delicatessen in Finsbury Park. Kerry does not really mind the fact that the living arrangement

7

has become more or less permanent. He is often not there so that she almost looks forward to the times when he is.

He cooks meals for her sometimes. Marco is a good cook; he used to be a chef until he got sacked for fighting with the restaurant owner over unpaid wages. He is particularly good at fish and seafood and Kerry loves it when he brings home swordfish or fresh tuna or squid, watching him chop off the latters' beady-eyed heads and briskly wash his hands in lemon juice after cleaning them out. Once he even triumphantly bought home something which he claimed was shark steak. Marco has a strange fascination with and fear of sharks, and it gave him enormous pleasure to be prodding one with his fork. Marco had been Gary's friend. He sometimes introduces Kerry as his sister.

Kerry's block of flats is set back from Old Street, nestling alongside a giant estate which is almost invisible from the main road and which slides into the other estates as far back as the City Road. She turns down a narrow bench-lined walkway which runs alongside an abandoned church, its white weather-vaned spire like a beacon signalling her home. It is just the shell of a church now, open to the elements, overgrown with rose bay willow herb and draped in shadows. Its windows, which must once have been jewelled with stained glass, now frame the sky and trees on the other side. A group of boys – thin-faced white kids – are sitting on two facing benches tapping a ball across the walkway to each other. As Kerry passes, one of the boys passes the ball across. It hits her ankle and spins away in front of her. She stops the ball and taps it awkwardly back to them and they shove each other and whistle at her. Gary was always terrible when things like that happened, Kerry had to stop him from starting fights. It didn't matter how outnumbered he was, he did not understand the principle of a dignified retreat.

'You what? Nah, Kerry, that cunt said something. Come on, Mr Mouth what did you fuckin' say?' That was before he stopped going out altogether.

At the bottom of Kerry's flats there are five-a-side football pitches belonging to the Leisure Centre, little kids in blue away or red home Arsenal shirts kicking balls to each other; the crop-haired men they will grow up to resemble are carrying sports bags and heading into the tiny Five Crowns pub, with its TV set up for horse-racing and its lunatic karaoke on Friday nights. Kerry pauses to fish for her keys, opens the heavy door to the block, and pushes the button for the lift. It is a cold-silver lift with little indentations like scales that hurt the eyes. The only way that you can tell if it is moving is by the red lights changing between floors, and she always gets nervous between the third and fifth floors because the number four light never comes on. There is a terrifying pause between arriving at the ninth floor and the door opening which makes her stomach churn. Sometimes she trudges up the stairs just to avoid it.

She can hear voices and smell dope as she opens the door to her flat. Marco is sitting on the sofa sharing a joint with his friend Danny. 'Hi,' says Kerry dumping her bag on the sofa and walking straight into the kitchen. She is not too thrilled that Marco has brought Danny back to the flat. Danny works as a despatch rider. His bike helmet lies by his feet with a sticker across it which reads I LOVE SATAN. When Danny is not chasing across the city on his bike, he is getting wasted and trying to get laid. These are Danny's only activities, apart from occasional pauses to shovel junk food into his mouth. Danny is good-looking but not in a way that has ever interested Kerry. He once tried to kiss her at a party. Generously, she did not tell Gary about this.

'Great view, Kerry,' he mumbles as she emerges from the kitchen with a cup of tea.

Kerry is used to the view by now but she turns and walks to the window. It *is* a great view, especially at night, the glittering city laid out below: the orange and white lights of offices, Canary Wharf with its ruby belt and point of electric snow, the elegant angles of the Barbican's towers, the Nat West building like Darth Vader, sometimes a strange laser sweeping across the dark sky. One of the office blocks has a helicopter pad. Kerry hates helicopters. Sometimes, the police arrive looking for someone on the neighbouring estate, circling and circling, the different sounds of the motor whining and clattering, the spotlight probing the shadows of the walkways below. Marco is planning to buy a giant rocket so that the next time it comes they can fire it at the helicopter. The boys are still out sitting on the benches in the shadow of the old church, tapping the ball to and fro across the path, hunched forward in their Ralph Lauren shirts and baggy jeans.

Kerry sits down and accepts the joint this time, still staring down out of the window at the dark corridor of tree-tops below leading to the shattered church.

'This skunk's really trippy,' says Marco, examining the glowing red tip as Kerry passes it back to him.

'Have you . . .' Danny starts, and then pauses to stare out of the window again.

'Have I what?' Marco replies after a long pause.

'What's that?'

'Have I what?'

'Have you what what?'

'No. You started to ask me something. You said "Have you . . ." and then just stopped.'

'Did I?'

'Yeah.'

Danny frowns, scrunching his face in the effort of remembering. Marco and Kerry watch him expectantly. Danny looks at his feet. 'No, it's gone.'

'*Lost and gone forever . . .*'

'Goodnight,' says Kerry. 'There's some sheets in the cupboard for . . .' She waves her hand at Danny.

'Danny,' says Danny. 'I'm Danny. Have you got any Pot Noodles in the house?'

'Was that it?' Marco asks.

'What?'

'Have you got any Pot Noodles? Was that what you was going to ask earlier?'

'When?'

'Goodnight,' says Kerry.

Don't Step on the Lines

She lies in bed. She is going to dream about Gary again, she just knows it. Fatal, treacherous dreams that undermine every effort she makes in her waking life to get things in some kind of order. Maybe if she says to herself that she is going to dream about him then she won't. An ordinary nightmare would be fine, just to wake up nervously in the blackness, scared of some strange unknown image before colliding with sleep again. 'Weialala,' she murmurs to herself, pulling the duvet around her head like a hood. It is a better poem when you are stoned because then it doesn't matter so much that it doesn't really say anything particularly important. Robin would probably despise her for saying that. But why does it matter what he thinks? She can imagine him and his friends in their Irish cottage, sarcastic and intelligent, playing little word games, drinking Jameson's, going for walks. They can't be friends from college though because Robin hasn't got any. But then has Kerry any real friends from college? She begins to feel sorry for herself and then remembers that she has other friends. Could you see Essex from her window? Probably not, probably you could only see as far as East Ham where her friend John lives with his baby. Don't think about that though, don't dream about the last time you saw Gary, his face contorted with rage, his foot bloody because he had smashed a glass on the floor and stamped on it, wanting – but unable – to hurt Kerry and turning on himself instead. He had screamed though, screamed blue murder, screamed and howled and broken things: 'Murdering bitch, you fucking murdering bitch!' And then burst – with the released energy of a champagne cork flying from its bottle – out of the flat he had not left for months previously, slamming the door so hard that the walls had shaken, before jumping in his car and driving – for a reason Kerry did not know, perhaps there was no reason at all – to Essex.

Kerry wakes up at five o'clock in the morning. Has she been asleep? Has she been dreaming? Yes, she has been asleep because she can remember a dream and not about Gary but rather a stupid anxiety dream about leaving her bag on a train.

11

She gets up and goes to the bathroom, sitting bleary-eyed on the toilet, looking at Marco's collection of prostitutes' phone-booth cards. He has stopped collecting them now because everyone is doing it. There are more people collecting the cards than there are prostitutes, and someone has even held an exhibition, or published a coffee table book of them, much to Marco's disgust.

Gary used to laugh watching Kerry on the toilet because she did not put her feet on the ground. 'You're a midget, Kerry,' he would say. 'How tall are you?' And she would always reply, 'I'm five foot four, and that's average actually.'

They hadn't lived here then. Gary had a flat on an estate off the Essex Road, where he had lived with his grandfather until the old man died. It was an estate with a twisted geography of walkways and stairs, the architect having been inspired by Italian hill villages. You would have had to possess an advanced qualification in navigation skills to find your way around the estate, which had upper and lower walkways running around it with little indication as to when the names changed. The stairways were choked with rubbish and stank of piss, swollen flies buzzing heavily around the dull red-brick walls. The bit they had lived on hadn't been that bad, at least it wasn't right in the middle or by one of the stairways where the gangs used to hang about. The flat itself had been strange: the front door was the highest bit, and you had to go downstairs to get into the living room. It was disorientating, as if the flat were sunken, and Kerry sometimes got nervous at night thinking of the people outside and above them on the walkway, as if they could look down and see them sleeping. She is much happier now living high above the city.

Towards the end, the sunken flat had seemed wholly appropriate for Gary's mood. He cut off more and more, not just from Kerry but from everything. She would come home from work and find him exactly where she had left him, staring at – but not watching – the television. She knew that he had spent the entire day there, gazing at the whole depressing spectrum of daytime TV; a dumb witness to its unchanging tedium. He would not move when she came in.

Gary had been an actor, had ridden briefly on the wave during the early-eighties which had carried boys and girls with the right accents into films and TV. Only for some reason Gary had not stayed on the wave, he had taken a dive – a dive he did not, could not, understand properly – and had remained far from the shore. Perhaps there was no reason, perhaps he was just unlucky, but Gary refused to accept it as such. He had been shown briefly a world which had then been denied to him and this inspired first anger and then a deep depression. Even the tiny parts dried up. He had gone to work in the post office, but since he had been sacked for hitting a supervisor he had just hunched into the sunken living room, sometimes forgetting even to go and sign on.

Gary was funny, quick-witted, a mimic – he could catch a gesture, an expression, a laugh. Gary's mimicry was what had made Kerry love him. He had a gift, people sometimes tried to join him but they were never as good. He was so sharp, so quick-witted, he had a genius sense of timing. He played with words, either to charm or to mock. In his depression, this talent decayed into a cruelty which he would also direct at himself, a sterile cynicism. And sometimes they would have terrible fights, especially when Kerry was tired from work and returned home to find the air thick with stale cigarette smoke and clothes all over the floor. Fighting was a relief, restoring some kind of energy to the dead air of the flat, her tongue still capable of stinging him out of his stupor, his dull hurt.

'You're gonna leave me, aren't you?' he said once.

'No,' she said.

But then she nearly did. One night, she had persuaded Gary that they should go out for a drink. She had invited Marco because Marco was one of the few people that Gary would allow in the flat. Marco didn't care whether Gary liked him being there or not, and she would sometimes turn up to find them both sitting in the living room, morosely watching *London Tonight* or *A Question of Sport*.

13

Marco had descended the steps into the living room, shaking his head. 'Fucking kids, unbelievable.'

'What?' said Kerry.

'There's about four cars burning out there. Trendy Islington, eh?'

Gary moved his head. He was drinking a bottle of Beck's which Kerry had brought home for him. He was in a terrible mood.

'So what?'

Marco looked back at him steadily. 'So nothing. I'm just saying, that's all.'

Gary snorted. 'Just saying! What else are they meant to do?'

Kerry stood in the doorway. 'Yeah, come on, Marco, it's not as if there's a lot for them to do around here.'

Gary swivelled around to her as if he had just been waiting for the opportunity. 'What are you on about, you stupid cow. What are you gonna do, build them a leisure centre? It's got fuck all to do with whether they've got something to do or not. They just like burning cars and that's it. End of. Good luck to 'em.'

Marco glanced at Kerry who went back into the kitchen. She was surprised because Gary didn't normally abuse her directly like that – whether people were there or not. She heard *EastEnders* starting. Marco said to Gary, 'This is your soap, man. It could have been written for you. Misery Square in Walford. You should write to the BBC and apply for a walk-on part.'

Kerry walked back into the living room. 'Walk? Write a letter?' she said bitterly. 'That's a bit ambitious, isn't it?'

Gary laughed drily. He held the bridge of his nose between his forefinger and thumb. 'Oh, you're a brilliant double act,' he said.

'Come on,' said Marco slapping his shoulder. 'Let's not sit here digging all night. We'll go to the pub.'

'I'll just get my coat,' said Kerry. She went into the bedroom and picked up her coat. It was new, she had bought it that day at lunchtime. She liked it because it was bright red. She stood in front of the mirror and flicked her hair out from under the collar. Red suited her because of her black hair. She put on some red lipstick, pursed her lips, and smiled at herself in the mirror. When she came back into the living room, Marco was leaning forward in his seat as if bursting to go, but Gary was still sprawled in the chair, eyes fixed on the TV.

'Are you gonna put a jacket on?' asked Kerry, wondering whether he would notice the new coat.

'No.'

'It's freezing out,' said Marco.

'I ain't goin' out.'

They stared at him. 'Oh, come on,' exclaimed Marco in exasperation. 'This is too much. We'll get pissed, have a laugh.'

'I ain't goin'.'

'Gary,' Kerry wailed. 'You said, come on . . .'

Gary did not answer but picked up the remote control from the arm of the chair and flicked channels. What happened next was so quick that she can hardly picture it in her mind any longer. She went to take the remote control from his hand and suddenly he was out of his chair, his face contorted with hatred, holding the remote high in his clenched fist as if he were going to strike her with it. She stared numbly at his bared teeth, waiting for the blow, but then Marco was between them, pushing Gary back down into the seat.

'Come on, Marco,' she said dully, still clinging to the lapels of her coat. 'Let's go. Leave him.'

Marco stood up and looked at Gary, shaking his head. 'I feel sorry for you,' he said.

'Don't,' Kerry snapped. 'He's got enough self-pity to last a lifetime anyway.'

As Marco went up the stairs she turned back to Gary. 'Don't wait up for me 'cause I won't be coming back.' He flinched slightly as if he had been struck and then pointed the remote control at the TV and turned up the volume.

They walked down the Essex Road in silence. Kerry wasn't really thinking about where they were going. Her face felt swollen but she had no urge to cry. She could feel each footstep that she was taking, the air on her face, a sudden acute awareness of everything around her: fly-posters for boxing matches and new record releases peeling from corrugated iron hoardings. They passed the fishmonger's where Marco would sometimes buy mussels and squid, the pub on the corner of New North Road which was always changing its name, the estate whose gangs would come up and fight the gangs from their estate in the summer. They continued walking down to Upper Street even though several buses passed them, and entered one of the nondescript pubs just off Islington Green. Marco went to the bar and Kerry stared at her reflection in a mirror that had flowers carved on it.

'He's in a bad way,' said Marco as he sat down and placed a pint and a short in front of her. He knocked back his short in one gulp and sprinkled the drops on the head of his Guinness. Kerry did the same, even though it brought tears to her eyes, watching the way the drops of whisky fizzed gently on the creamy top.

'I know,' she said when she could speak again. 'He's losing it completely. The thing is, it sounds selfish and everything, but why should *I* have to deal with it all the time? I've got my own problems, I've got to keep the money coming in. It used just to come in spells but now it's all the time he's like this. And it's such a shame because he can be one of the best, one of the funniest . . .'

Marco gulped back his pint. 'Oh, yeah, I know that. Otherwise I'd have given up on him months ago.'

'Everyone else has,' said Kerry sadly.

He looked at her sharply. 'Except you.'

Kerry stared at the flowers curling their way around the mirror. What were they meant to be? Foxgloves? Daffodils? She didn't know the names of flowers. Or rather, she knew names but couldn't match them to actual plants. Somebody had made that mirror somewhere, had the idea to decorate it with flowers. And now it was hanging in a pub in the Angel and two people were sitting under it having a conversation about another person who had decided that his life had become a complete waste of time, and other people were passing to and fro between seats and bar, and somebody was laughing loudly in the mirror and in mock offence pushing the shoulder of the person who had just made some cutting remark.

'I'm thinking of going to college,' said Kerry suddenly.

'College?' Marco looked puzzled. 'But it'll be full of students.'

'You do tend to find them hanging about there,' Kerry agreed.

'It don't make no difference now, though, does it? A degree or whatever. Degrees get you nowhere.'

'I wouldn't be doing it for that.'

'Why then?'

''Cause I like reading. I want to study English Literature.'

'Well,' said Marco, 'you don't have to go to college to read.'

'No,' said Kerry. 'But I just want to do it, just for doing it. I wanted to do it when I was younger but . . . well, it just didn't happen. But now I want to do it.'

'I suppose,' Marco replied, 'it would be pretty cool just to doss about for three years on a grant.'

'I don't want to doss about.'

They bought more drinks and more chasers and Kerry was dreading the bell because then she'd have to decide. She knew, though, that she was going to go back.

'Hurry up now. Come on, drink up, haven't you got homes to go to? Here, is that dead, mate?' The barman's hand hovered over Marco's half-full glass.

'Well, what does it look like to you, mate? Does it look dead?'

The barman scowled at him. 'Don't get lippy with me, son. Now drink up and get out.'

'Listen, mate, I've been paying your wages all night so go and annoy someone else for a few minutes.'

The barman gestured to somebody behind the bar. Marco was about to get both a slap and yet another pub ban. Kerry was sometimes amazed that there were any pubs in London he could still go into. He was half rising from his seat and the other barman was moving out from behind the bar. Kerry got up. 'It's OK,' she said, 'we're going. But you don't need to be so rude about it, do you?'

'Just get out, you stupid bitch.'

17

Kerry's reaction was unexpected – even to her – and instant-aneous. She picked up the glass that Marco had not finished drinking and threw the remaining beer in the barman's face. 'There you go,' she said, 'you can take the glass away now.' The bar staff rushed towards them like a pack of rugby players and bundled them towards the door. One of them punched Marco around the ear as they were ejected into the street.

'You're barred!' yelled the barman from the door, a dark stain over his brewer's t-shirt, as if he had been shot in the chest.

'I wouldn't come in your poxy pub again anyway,' shouted Marco, holding his ear. The barman made towards him but the others held him back.

'Leave it, Dave, they ain't worth it. Go on, you slags, fuck off out of here and don't come back.'

They crossed the road. 'I want some chips,' said Marco, still rubbing his ear. 'Kerry, you're a nutter. Do you know that?'

'I'm just sick of being talked to like that. Work, home, and now even the pub . . . I've never been barred from a pub before,' she answered.

'It's addictive. Just say no.'

They wandered back up the Essex Road eating chips. 'Well,' said Marco suddenly, 'what are you gonna do?'

Kerry thought for a while. 'I'm going home.'

'Do you want me to come with you?'

'No.'

Kerry walked steadily towards the flat, singing gently to herself. She climbed the stairs to their walkway nervously. The long path leading to the flat was quiet and empty. She avoided walking on the lines of the paving stones, taking quick jerky steps every so often to land safely in the squares. *Or else the wolf will come and eat you*, she remembered her mum saying. Why did her mum say that and not the one about breaking your granny's back? Far away she could hear shouting but couldn't tell from where the noise was coming. She could see the big bowl of flowers that belonged to their next-door neighbour. What type of flowers were they? Kerry arrived at the front door.

The TV wasn't on. She noticed the unfamiliar silence straight away. She went quietly down the stairs into the sunken flat. The living room was empty and the ash-tray was on the floor some way from the sofa. Butts and ash littered the carpet and Kerry picked up the ash-tray and put it on the ugly sideboard that had belonged to Gary's grandad. Gary wasn't in the bedroom either. She took off the red coat and threw it on the bed. Then she went into the bathroom. When she switched the light on, she jumped. Gary was lying naked in the bath. There was no water in it, but there must have been at some point because the mirror was still lightly steamed over with condensation. When Gary turned his face to her she yelped because she thought it was covered in blood, but it was her lipstick. He had smeared his face with her lipstick. 'I had a bath,' he said, and began to cry. His face was streaked with tears and lipstick.

Kerry knelt down by the bathside. 'Gary,' she whispered. 'Gary, you've got to do something.'

He grabbed her hand squeezing it very tightly. 'Kerry, don't leave me. I'm sorry, don't leave me. I'm sorry.'

She tried to lift him out of the bath. 'Come on,' she said. 'Come on, let's get to bed.' He stood up and she looked at him naked, the thin line of hair down to his flat stomach, his penis flopping between his legs, his lipsticked face like a child's gone mad with his mother's make-up. She took a flannel and wiped his face, smudging off the lipstick. 'You've got to get help,' she repeated uselessly, knowing that he wouldn't ever do that.

'Yes,' he agreed numbly, allowing her to lead him from the bathroom, clinging to her tightly as if he were blind and she were guiding him away from some danger, some imminent fall.

Chapter 2

'Do you want half an E?' says the girl to Marco.

Marco weighs things up. Of course he wants the pill but he knows that there is more to the offer than that, and if he takes it off her he will be stuck with her for the rest of the evening because she will feel that she has some kind of claim on him. He looks across the bar table at her. He definitely doesn't want anything to happen with her, but the more alarming possibility is that he might end up wanting it to if he shares her pill. Which would be bad news because he has taken the piss ruthlessly out of Danny for doing just that one night in the bogs of this very same bar.

He looks at her across the bar table. It isn't that she is unattractive, it is just that he can almost smell her insecurity, her need to feel that she isn't missing out on anything. And she is from Wolverhampton. None of which would stop Danny who would take her drugs and then laugh at her with his mates afterwards and call her a loser. Marco sips at his pint. Lorna has the pill between forefinger and thumb and is neatly biting it in half with little sharp teeth. She washes it down and puts the remaining half to Marco's lips. He hesitates and then opens like a child. She smiles at him, popping it in his mouth, and he looks around the bar to see if anyone has witnessed this transaction.

Marco wishes that Kerry was with him. Then it would be easy to get rid of Lorna. But when he went back to the flat after work, there was nobody there, just Kerry's books spread out on the desk by the window. Somebody had phoned for her, a guy with a posh voice. He had forgotten to write the message down, what was the name again – Roger? Rupert? Definitely a student.

Marco remembers when Kerry told him that she was going to study, one night when Gary had been really out of order. He hadn't been too supportive, partly because the thought of somebody suddenly changing the structure of their life had unnerved him and made him envious. Not of studying particularly, which is something that Marco considers a total waste of time, but of breaking out of a routine. Now, though, he likes Kerry studying, enjoys watching her reading, her eyes moving across pages; occasionally marking passages of the book with a pencil. She is doing it because she likes it, not because she thinks it is a rung on society's ladder, not because she thinks it is a passport to a better life. Marco is not sure whether Kerry is particularly happy, but she is strong, she didn't let Gary drag her down with him, she is getting on with things. She has backbone. He wonders what would happen if he suddenly had the money to get his own place. He would miss living with Kerry. How much would she miss him? What if she got a new boyfriend and wanted him to move in with her? There would be no room for Marco and he shudders at the thought of dossing down on the floor of Danny's disgusting wreck of a flat.

Lorna takes his hand. 'Are you getting anything off this yet?'

'No.'

'I am. I got a little rush just then.'

'Right. Listen, Lorna, I'm just going for a piss, I'll see you in a bit.' And he removes his hand. Marco squeezes through the bodies towards the back of the bar. Arnold is standing by the door to the bogs, his bulging eyes nervously scanning the bar.

'How you doin', Marco?'

'All right, Arnold.'

'Where you livin' now?'

'Up at Kerry's. You know Kerry, don't you?'

'The little bird with black hair who's in with you sometimes? Quite nice-looking?'

'Yeah.'

'I know her sister better. She knows a mate of mine.'

'Yeah?'

Arnold nods wisely as if this conversation means something

important, but like most conversations in this bar it means very little. Some people appear to live their lives in the place; Marco wonders if they ever go home since he has never been in and not found them there, standing at the end of the bar with their drinks and Marlboro Lights. Still, he has had some good nights in here. Everybody slags it off but they still come back. Marco looks down the long bar at the hands offering notes, the bottles of flavoured Absolut, the occasional mobile phone lurking on a table.

Sometimes Arnold moans to Marco about the fact that people only give him respect when they want their drugs from him, are only glad to see him arrive anywhere because they know it means the drugs have arrived. And usually Marco is grateful enough for Arnold's presence that he clutches him to him during these outbursts and says that he understands and that he loves him and that these people are wankers anyway. Instead of saying: What do you expect, Arnold? You're a dealer, of course they see drugs walking in the door when they see you. If you didn't want to be miserable, paranoid and friendless, you should have gone to see a different careers adviser. But then Marco does genuinely like Arnold. Sometimes when he tells him he loves him, he actually means it. Because seeing Arnold is reassuring, whether he's buying drugs from him or not. Just the sight of him there at the door with his constantly shifting eyes, his overemphasised geezerness, his white Patrick Cox shoes, means that all is normal, everything's OK. Like walking into the pub and seeing Danny already at the pool table, cue in hand, shooting his big mouth off, bantering with his pool-addict Glaswegian mates about whether you get two shots on the black.

As if he knows what Marco is thinking, Arnold grins at him and follows him into the bogs, pushing him gently into the cubicle and locking the door. Marco watches his little origami negotiations, the cashpoint card switching quantities until the two lines are even, the final teasing rolling of the note. Somebody tries the door, there are voices outside as Marco bends down. Because of the small size of the cubicle, he has to kneel by the side of the toilet, trying not to let his knee touch the ground. The line is fat and he has to pause and take another shot at it, dabbing at the leftover fragments with his finger. As he moves to get up, his knee scrapes the ground, leaving a dirty wet patch on his jeans.

'Shit!' Marco leans back and waits for Arnold. 'Thanks, man.'

'No worries, Marco. You're the best of this fucking dross. You're different. You're an original.'

'Thanks, Arnold. I love you.'

Outside, somebody rattles the door. 'When you two have finished shagging each other up the arse in there, do you think you could open the fucking door?'

Arnold deftly finishes wrapping his coke and opens the door.

'I didn't realise it was a full moon tonight. Learn some manners.' He grins at Sid who is waiting outside accompanied by a scowling cocaine-clone with sideburns to match his attitude, the kind of sub-species that Marco cannot imagine in any other situation than queuing for the cubicles in clubs. Marco's conception of hell, his room 101, is a giant Gents filled with people exactly like the pair in front of him, shirts hanging out, standing in an eternal queue for the cubicles.

'Fuck me,' says Sid as he sees Marco, 'the whole of the Islington A-list in one cubicle.'

'Flush yourself away when you've finished, Sid.'

The bar is completely mobbed now. The music is loud and Marco pauses, letting it fill him up, rise through his throat and his eyeballs. Lorna is sitting at the table talking to a skinny guy who is obviously trying to chat her up but she has put her jacket on Marco's chair, keeping it for him. Marco had half hoped that somebody would take his seat while he was away.

'Hi,' she smiles as he collapses into his seat. 'You've been ages. This is Mark. Mark, this is Marco.'

'All right, Mark,' says Marco, putting back his head and staring out at the faces, the mouths working.

'Hey we've got the same name . . .' says Mark with a stupid grin.

'What?'

'The same name. We're the same. Mark, Marco. Same thing really.'

Marco stares at him and then looks away. He leans his head back and puts his hand on Lorna's leg under the table. She shifts it towards him. He strokes it just above the knee. She continues talking to Mark but she is smiling faintly. His hand is inside her thigh. Mark gets up and goes to the bar. Uncontrollable, contemptuous thoughts course through Marco's mind. I'm going to fuck you, he thinks. You're a stupid bitch, he thinks. I don't even fancy you but I'm going to fuck you anyway just because you've made it perfectly clear that you will. Either here in the same cubicle that you fucked Danny in, or back in your flat that you probably share with some other loser, and I'll enjoy it but then I'll walk out and I'll laugh at the slagging I'll get off Danny for it and I'll say I just did it for half a pill.

And suddenly Marco hates these thoughts that are like some kind of poisonous treacle and he knows that he can't do it. He can't go back to her flat and use her bathroom and see her stuff by the side of the bath, the shampoos that she uses, the bath oils, all the Body Shop bottles. He can't watch her sifting her record collection, skipping quickly over the older albums; he can't look at the pictures she has on the wall, maybe even photos, her address book on the table. He can't just fuck her contemptuously and walk out of the door. He pulls his hand away from her and she turns to him, smiling.

'Shall we go?'

'Look, Lorna, sorry, I can't.'

Her smile fades. 'What do you mean?'

'I've got to go . . . I've got to meet somebody. . . I'm sorry.'

'What's the matter? I thought . . .'

'Look,' he says, feeling a sudden rush of honesty, 'it's not you, it's me. I've got to be straight up here. I could go back with you and that would be all very well and everything . . . you know . . . but it would be kind of a crap thing to do as well.'

'A crap thing to do?'

'Yeah, you know, like Danny and everything . . .'

'Like Danny?' Her face is tightening, hardening. She is scrunching her jacket into her hand.

'Yeah, I don't wanna be like that.'

'No,' she says quietly. Then she laughs suddenly. She looks down at her Absolut and cranberry juice for a moment and clinks the ice against the side. When she looks up at him, her face has a strange expression on it. 'Go away, Marco. Go on, go away, just go away.'

Once when Marco and Gary were slumped in front of the TV at three o'clock in the afternoon they watched a kids' programme which involved a voyage into a brain that was staffed by white-coated boffins, a kind of cerebral Mission Control, issuing instructions to all the senses. Marco imagines now that, inside his head, his own overworked team are slumped around despairingly, some lighting fags and cracking open bottles of whisky after yet another abject failure to control tongue.

'Listen . . .'

'No, you listen, you patronising bastard. Don't ever come near me again. What I wanted was quite simple. But not . . . not *ever*. . . for you to take pity on me. And certainly not for you to tell me. Now get lost.'

'Lorna, I'm sorry. No, really, you're right, I was stupid . . .'

She casts him a look of contempt and gets up from the table, joining Mark up at the bar and keeping her back ostentatiously to him. Marco sighs. Poor performance really. He gets up to go for a piss and in the toilets finds the bouncer dressing down two boys he has just hauled out of the cubicle. Ludicrously, they are trying to claim that they were just having a chat. Marco knows that this will cut no ice with the bouncer who derives all his job satisfaction from hauling couples out of cubicles; who has taken the art of spying over toilet doors to new levels.

'What does it say on my forehead?' demands the bouncer.

'What?'

Marco knows the answer to this one as it has been directed at him by the same bouncer on a couple of occasions.

'Does it . . .' the bouncer steps forward a little ' . . . does it say CUNT on my forehead?'

Marco tries not to giggle, looking down at the urinal.

'Er . . . no. No it doesn't.'

'Well, why are you talking to me like one then? Eh?'

'No, mate. Sorry, mate. It's just . . .'

''Cause if you'd held your hands up and apologised and said you wouldn't do it again, I might have let you stay. But no. You started talking to me like a cunt, giving it the we-was-just-havin'-a-chat bollocks.'

'Sorry, mate, seriously . . .'

'I'll "sorry, mate" you if you're not out of here in one minute.'

'OK, we're going.'

The bouncer adjusts his collar. 'Where do these people come from?' he says to nobody in particular. Two more boys come laughing into the bogs, see the bouncer and pause for a minute before quickly adopting positions at the urinals. 'Smart move, boys,' says the bouncer.

Coming out of the toilets, Marco spots Danny at the bar.

Danny hugs Marco. 'Marco, Marco, I'm so gone, man. Let me get you a pint.'

'Where've you been?'

'Here, there and everywhere . . . there you go.' He hands Marco a pint of Guinness. 'Miaooow,' he murmurs just loud enough for the girl passing him to hear. She smiles awkwardly and blushes slightly. Marco laughs.

Danny sees Lorna up at the bar and raises his pint to her. She stares at him for a second and then looks away angrily. Danny is puzzled, clearly trying to remember what he might have done to her. 'What's the matter with her then?'

Marco shifts uncomfortably. 'No idea. What are you doing now anyway?'

'I'm gonna have a little chat with Arnold. Then I'm going home. Do you wanna come up?'

'There's some party in Dalston . . .'

'Yeah, we could check that out. It's near the house . . . we've got time for one more anyway.' He grins at the girl who had passed him earlier. 'Hiya, do you want to come to a party?' To

Marco's disappointment, instead of telling Danny to get lost, she pauses.

'And where is this party then?' She is wearing a long skirt and black trainers. She has a detached elegance, smooth skin. Her eyes are long, amused, languid. The problem with Danny is that he has the looks to back up his shamelessness. The girl is smiling at him, flirting with him. 'And what about my boyfriend? Is he included in this invitation?'

'Of course. Bring him along. No problem.' Danny is leaning towards her confidentially. 'Is that him over there? The speccy one . . . I mean, the one with glasses?' he changes tack quickly, as the girl's face registers that she is not prepared to accept any insults directed at her boyfriend. The boy is glancing at them now and makes his way over. He looks quizzically at his girlfriend, waiting for an introduction.

'Jeremy, this is . . . well, I don't actually know your names yet . . . they've invited us to a party. In Dalston.'

'I'm Danny,' says Danny extending his hand. 'And this is Marco.'

'What do you do, Danny?' asks Jeremy, which is number one on Marco's list of boring pointless questions.

'Do?'

'You know, your job . . .'

'Oh, right, I'm with you now. Well, Jeremy . . .'

Marco looks across at his reflection in the mirror. Danny is about to start bullshitting. True to form, he starts a lengthy monologue about his job as a promoter of DJs, how he has just flown back from the Miami music conference, how he will shortly be off to Italy to check on new DJing talent there, and about a totally slamming club where he might be able to get them VIP passes for the Benji Candelario night. Marco can see that Danny might as well be speaking in Serbo-Croat for all the impression that these lies are having on Jeremy, but he is nodding and murmuring politely while keeping one arm uncomfortably round the girl's waist like a seat-belt.

Amazing how you can make time for your despatch riding, thinks Marco, and is almost tempted to say it. But he can't help admiring Danny for ripping off the patter of Dale, who does promote DJs and fortunately isn't in the bar tonight. In the mirror he can see Lorna and Mark getting ready to leave. You try and be a bit decent and you end up feeling like the biggest low-life. Still, it was pretty stupid to have brought Danny into it. In the giant gold-embossed mirror he can see Arnold slipping a wrap to somebody and turning his hand over to receive the money, like shy basketball players quietly slapping palms.

The lights in the bar flicker on and off to announce imminent closure, Mark holds the door open for Lorna, a girl at the bar falls over. 'She got hit by a motorcycle earlier,' explains her friend to the people around, 'she must be concussed.' And the smirks from everybody who had assumed that it must be a drug/drink-related tumble turn into expressions of concern and murmurs about calling an ambulance.

'Marina, I think we should go.' Jeremy is looking at Danny as if he were a stoat advancing on an egg-filled nest.

'Don't fancy this party then? Oh, well, give us your number. We're having a big party for some of these Italian DJs soon. You should come. It will be mental.'

Marina is smiling at Danny in an openly flirtatious way and giving him her phone number. Marco feels a bit sorry for the boyfriend who now looks clumsily helpless. He can tell that they are going to have an argument later on and that Marina is going to tell him not to be so uptight and paranoid when in fact he has an excellent reason for being both. Two-faced bitch. She wouldn't just be standing by grinning stupidly if some girl was making a big play for Jeremy. Danny is just lucky that it is a Jeremy and not a Gary who is the spectator in this sketch, or by now people would be leaping out of the way as Danny went flying across the bar. Gary was a Class A nutter when it came to Kerry. Somebody only had to hold the door open for her and smile to be putting himself at imminent physical risk. And suddenly Marco feels a pang of missing Gary which almost makes him wince. Gary before he got really bad; the stupid mad bastard, the only person who could make Marco laugh until he had to plead with him to stop, the genius mimic who could not only imitate Arnold's voice but his face at the same time, could assume his posture.

Danny is complacently tucking Marina's number into his jacket pocket.

'Cabbin' it?' he asks Marco.

'Got any money?'

'Yeah. Here . . .' he passes Marco a pint with about half a Guinness in that somebody has left on the bar while they go to the toilet ' . . . drink that while I go and sort us out.'

They stagger out on to Upper Street, walking up towards Highbury Corner in search of a cab. Over the Town Hall, a pink and green light display glows surreally in the night sky where once there was a board announcing the number of unemployed in the borough. Marco finally flags down a cab and warns Danny not to get them chucked out by getting cheeky with the driver. They pass Marina and Jeremy on the way home. They are standing in the street arguing; Jeremy is gesticulating and finally Marina turns on her heel and walks away. Jeremy stares after her, not sure whether to let her go, and then his weakly flickering pride is extinguished completely and he jogs after her, catching at her arm while she brushes him off. Women, thinks Marco, are without a doubt superior to men in this sort of situation. Just give up, Jeremy, she'll always outsulk you.

Danny giggles. 'I am definitely gonna shag that one.'

'Yeah, I think you're made for each other.'

'I never said I wanted to marry her, Marco. Here, give us your thumb nail, he ain't gonna see anything.'

Marco can see no end to it, sitting in a taxi beneath a cloud-streaked London sky, past the estate where Kerry and Gary used to live, a plane light winking like a flashing star. The night stretches on, morning will come, other nights will arrive. It just goes on and on, standing in bars, taking drugs, moving on somewhere else in cabs across the time and space of the city, waiting outside parties for the rest of the group to arrive, misbehaving, getting kicked out. They joke about it, they talk about reconquering the night, but sometimes, Marco thinks, they're not conquering anything except their own consciousness of the boredom of it all, supported – well, it must be admitted – by things up the nose and down the throat; pissed up, E'd up, charlied up, onwards and upwards, gulping and snorting and swallowing and dabbing, and on and on and on, because what would they do if they didn't do this, who would they be, how would they assemble their lives? How would they respond to that boring and pointless question: What do you do? Do? Yes, apart from working in a delicatessen or riding around the City on a bike or driving a van or waiting on tables cash in hand so that they can also sign on? I do . . . this and that. What is there to do? What is to be done? As a hero of Marco's dad's once asked. On and on and further still, until night and day blur together. Like a bicycle that has to keep moving to stay upright because otherwise it starts to wobble, to lurch dangerously, it comes crashing down on to the concrete. Marco is in a cab heading towards the Kingsland Road with Danny who, if we're going to be really honest, is shallow, amoral and not too bright, but good company sometimes, plus he's got the drugs. On and on up the Kingsland Road and he doesn't know why and he suddenly thinks of Kerry and wonders if she is sitting at home reading with a bottle of wine, and envy gives him a good sharp slap and he'd better snap out of it, SNAP OUT OF IT, MARCO, so he turns and grins at Danny and says, 'Yeah, that Marina . . . she was nice, man.'

Chapter 3

But Marco is wrong. Kerry is not sitting in her flat reading while he is dabbing his way down the Kingsland Road with Danny. She is instead sitting in the living room of Mrs Gordon, her formidable old English teacher from school, who is explaining why *The Wasteland* is not the greatest poem ever written.

'Prissy, desiccated and sexless,' she announces firmly as she clears away the remains of a broccoli and salmon quiche and refills Kerry's glass with Armagnac. 'Think about Ezra Pound who became a fascist and had to take the consequences for it, but who at least looked critically at the post-war settlement.' She pauses in the doorway, the plates still in her hand. ' "... *For an old bitch gone in the teeth, for a botched civilisation ...*" ' Could Eliot have written that? I don't think so. I find Eliot's politics so much more offensive than Pound's.'

She disappears into the kitchen and begins to rinse the plates under the tap. Kerry picks up her glass and follows her in but Sylvia Gordon waves her away.

'I shan't be a second, I just can't stand leaving it until morning. You go and make yourself comfortable, Kerry dear ... oh, Christ, we've run out of washing-up liquid. Honestly, darling, I'll get it done so much quicker if you just go and sit down, take the bottle over to the sofa ...'

Kerry sips at her Armagnac and watches her old teacher whose hair is going grey and whose eyesight is ... well, just going. She scrubs ferociously at a bit of quiche stuck on the plate. Kerry smiles and walks backwards out of the kitchen and then over to the huge sofa. She gazes slightly drunkenly at a print on the wall. It has always been there. It is called 'The Meeting of Dante and Beatrice'. Dante is standing on a bridge watching three young women approaching. One of the girls is straining around the eldest and sternest-looking of her companions to get a second look at Dante. In doing so, her dress is pulled tight across her figure, emphasising the curve of her breasts.

At school, Kerry was Sylvia Gordon's favourite. Sylvia had a few favourites, but Kerry was her special one, her cause célèbre. It was Sylvia who had insisted that Kerry should do the Oxbridge entrance exam, coaching her after school in this house, teaching her about Shakespeare and Blake. And how Kerry had loved it, how she had allowed herself to be exercised, how she had opened up for the first time to the sweet seduction of being made to feel clever. In the evenings, they would talk until the light began its soft fade then Kerry would sit down to eat with the Gordon family who would finally be allowed to come in from wherever they had been banished to. There was Mr Gordon, the quietly balding advertising executive, and the Gordon sons in their scruffy t-shirts and little round glasses, clever and sarcastic, trying to impress Kerry. Those evenings are always evoked for her by the taste of fennel; she remembers biting into it for the first time here and exclaiming at its curious taste, an aniseedy filament lodging in her teeth. 'Don't you like it?' Mrs Gordon had asked, and Kerry had paused before replying, 'Yes. Yes, I do.'

Sylvia Gordon had insisted that Kerry mark one of the more prestigious colleges at Oxford as her first choice, and she had allowed herself to be swept along by her teacher's enthusiasm, sitting the entrance exam and getting an interview. 'Oh, the fools, the damn' stupid fools!' Sylvia had almost sobbed when the rejection letter arrived later. Kerry herself had not been greatly surprised. The interview had been a disaster; all she could really remember of it was the colour of the wet stone of the colleges, a great tree brushing the window of the book-lined study, and that voice, its soft bullying modulations in the dusty air.

'Kerry, believe me, you are ten times more worthwhile than any of these saps.' Sylvia had glared at Cressida McFarlane, daughter of a well-known political analyst, who was celebrating her acceptance by New College. 'We'll just have to try again.'

But not only had Kerry not tried again, she had rejected the idea of going to university altogether. This had led to a fantastic, sometimes vicious, battle with Sylvia. 'You, Kerry Scott, were made for better than being a bloody secretary and living with some yob!' she cried, not above a little snobbery herself. 'What a waste, what a terrible waste! For Christ's sake, here are all these nice little Emmas and Mirandas who are going to university because it's expected of them, because they're middle-class, while you, Kerry Scott, who could do so well . . .'

But Kerry had been determined. She just wanted to leave and start working. It wasn't simply because Oxford had rejected her – as being rejected had filled some of Cressida McFarlane's friends with a depression whose lingering sense of failure they would never really shake off for the rest of their lives – but simply that she *had* been rejected. It was not meant to be. She had never really had any doubts that she was not like them and now it had been confirmed. Her moments of happiness had been spent in Sylvia Gordon's book-lined living room, she had been awakened to something. But because she had never seen Oxford or Cambridge or any particular university as her birthright, the disappointment of rejection did not plunge her into any kind of desperation, any flurry of reapplications, second choices or crammers. She had just started seeing Gary; he was doing film-work still and they had gone out all the time – a summer of pubs and parties and nights at his flat which was new and exciting. She simply wanted to leave school after that. It was finished and there was nothing more to be said.

After winning that battle with Sylvia and leaving school, relations between them had almost died away to nothing. There had been a long silence, punctuated only by the odd Christmas card, then the silence had become total. Kerry had thought that that was it, her teacher was just part of that strange world of characters who had once been very important but were now just vague forms – recognisable despite their lack of proper faces – in sometimes troubling dreams. But then Gary. *You bitch, you fucking murdering bitch*! Slamming out of the sunken flat and on to first the Essex Road and then the Road to Essex, the A whatever it was, and then running down some other road whose name or initial she never knew, and then – she could only think of it like a film – a brilliant glare of light and then blackness.

Several months afterwards, she had phoned Sylvia Gordon to ask her for a reference for her college application. 'I'm not sure if you'll remember me . . .'

'Kerry? Kerry Scott . . . my goodness, how lovely to hear from you. Don't be silly, of course I remember you . . .'

So Kerry had returned to the living room where she had been taught Shakespeare and Blake – '*Pale thro' pathless ways, The fancied image strays*' – and once again she had sat down at Mrs Gordon's old heavy table and listened to her husky laugh, her self-assured prejudices, and had resisted her blandishments to go to a proper university and not just an ex-polytechnic. But this time Sylvia Gordon had managed to surrender with something like goodwill.

In nearly every other way, however, old age has not mellowed her at all. She comes back into the living room wiping her hands on a dish cloth, sits down and adjusts the light away from her eyes. She tells Kerry about an argument that she has just had with her son John and how he – outrageously – had told her that if she continued behaving badly, he wouldn't let her see his new baby any longer. Kerry likes John and knows that Sylvia must have been at her most exasperating to force him into a wild threat so lacking in credibility, given that he would never implement it.

Kerry does not, however, feel like delivering home truths to Sylvia tonight, especially with the Armagnac warming her veins. There is little point anyway since Sylvia has an impressive defensive armoury with which to deal with truths she does not particularly welcome. Kerry remembers their own arguments, especially when she had declared with adolescent bravado that she was not going to be Sylvia's puppet and that she should sponsor a child in Africa if she wanted to interfere in somebody's life. She still feels a whisper of shame about this when she remembers that Sylvia had been giving up her free time to teach her.

'Just give John a ring,' Kerry urges now. 'You're both as bad as each other when it comes to a row. In my family nobody can remember to sulk. There are so many rows they just get forgotten five minutes later.' She grins as she remembers her last conversation with her sister Jeanette: *You ain't better than me. You better remember that, you stuck up cow, just 'cause you're at college, Miss fuckin' Goody Two Shoes.'* Jeanette who has always moaned about Kerry being the favourite, and yet who always phones Kerry first when she gets sacked (again), pregnant (again), or is definitely – *No, I mean it this time, Kerry* – going to leave Darren (again).

'Well, you know, Kerry . . .' says Sylvia Gordon, reaching for the bottle of Armagnac, 'I totally disagree with your analysis. We are certainly not "just as bad as each other". And I'm his mother anyway so I'm entitled to make my opinions known whether he . . .' she splashes a generous amount of Armagnac into their glasses ' . . . likes it or not.' And she settles back in her chair, regally triumphant, and Kerry knows that she has clinched it with this appeal to motherhood and the rights which it bestows. Because, while it may be true that it is *both* your mum and dad who fuck you up, dads usually peak early, inflicting most of their damage in the formative years when you still care enough about them to allow it to happen. But mums tend to retain the power to carry on doing so and, however spirited the resistance, there is usually only one loser. Kerry knows that John is probably miserable for allowing himself to get sucked into another argument with his mum. And she knows that he is asking himself these questions: Could I have avoided it? Was it my fault really? Was I out of order? The problem for John is that in the Appeals Court of the Conscience there is no jury and just a single judge who also happens to be the plaintiff, her arms folded neatly beneath her gold brocade, pronouncing the only possible verdict. Guilty. *'Bound and weary I thought best . . .'*

Sylvia Gordon tries to hide a yawn and Kerry can see that she is fading. 'Sylvia, do you have a cab number?'

'Oh, but, Kerry darling, you mustn't go now. Look, you haven't finished your drink.'

'Honestly, I couldn't. I'm already quite drunk actually.'

'Well, don't leave it so long next time. And just remember to give Eliot a hard time. Nasty little elitist . . .' She yawns again.

'The cab number?'

'Ah, yes. In the kitchen by the phone there are a couple of cards.'

Kerry sits in the back of a cab, heading towards Old Street. The cabbie is a silent African who keeps switching radio channels. His seat is covered with brown and white wooden beads, a Christmas tree deodorant jigging by the rear-view mirror. He does not take the right turn-off and they have to go around the roundabout twice. Kerry looks out at the two strange whale-ribs which arc over it, and the useless white structure like an elongated bus shelter rippling along the pavement as if it has been melted by some fierce heat. All around, she can hear the dull boom of fireworks, the occasional shriek of a rocket. From time to time she sees them burst, a temporary flurry of light on the November sky, falling back towards earth and then sucked in by the darkness – golden ink flicked across black water. She hopes that Marco will be in when she gets home but knows that he won't. He will be out with Danny misbehaving at some pub, club or party; he might not turn up again for a couple of days.

Kerry takes the silver-scaled lift to the ninth floor and she can hear her phone ringing. Hopefully, Marco will have remembered to leave the answerphone on. She makes her way quickly into the dark flat, switching on lights as quickly as possible on the way to the phone. There is the click of the answerphone kicking in and she waits to see if the person will talk or just put down the receiver in which case she will dial last number recall to identify the culprit. But somebody does start to speak and at first she cannot work out who it is. 'Hi, Kerry . . . well, I guess you're still out. It's Robin here. I stayed in to work on

the assignment but I think your strategy was probably better...'
She reaches down to the receiver but then removes her hand
again, listening for the end of the message. '... and, well, I
don't know really. Just give me a call ... whenever ... tomorrow
maybe ... OK?' Click.

Kerry lifts up the phone, listens to the dialling tone, and
puts it down again. She frowns slightly. What is it? What's he
up to? He is beginning to intrude on her. How did he get her
number anyway? She can't remember giving it to him. Kerry
cannot decide how she feels about what appears to be a growing
persistence on his part. Why should Robin, who seems to
luxuriate in his isolation, decide that there is something about
Kerry that interests him? It is a question that she would rather
not ask herself, she is not ready to start untangling motives.
Nor is she ready to ask herself how she really feels about it.

She plays back the messages. In the first one, she can hardly
hear the speaker for the sound of voices and music which means
that it is Marco.

'We're down ... where are we, Danny? No, you prick, the
name of the street ... I know we're in Dalston ... come
down ... tell bouncer to get me ...'

The second one is from a tearful Jeanette. 'Kerry? Kerry?
Are you there? Pick up the phone, please ...' Pause. Silence.
Sniff. 'OK, well, look, I'm gonna leave that bastard Darren,
and I think I'm pregnant which is all I need ... oh, and they've
only gone and sacked me at work just for being twenty minutes
late. I really need to speak to you.' Silence. Sigh. 'Oh, why
aren't you in? Phone me, please, KitKat. If I'm not here, I'll be
at mum's. Phone me, whatever time, yeah?'

Two more messages. 'Kerry ... it's really kickin' down
'ere ... magic party ... got some little treats ... bouncer's
cool ... he's called ...'

Then back to Robin again. 'Hi, Kerry ... well, I guess you're
still out ...'

She listens to the whole message again, frowning. She goes
into the kitchen and makes a cup of tea, staring down at the
tea-bag bloating under the boiling water like a blister. She needs

to speak to someone or at least hear somebody's voice. She starts to prepare herself, arranging cushions by the phone and checking to make sure that there are at least five cigarettes left in her packet. She turns the TV slightly so that she can see it and puts the volume down. Just before sitting down she remembers to go to the toilet. She may say that she needs the toilet later in order to get off the phone, but she doesn't want to actually need to go. OK, that's everything. Kerry sinks into the cushions, flicks the channel to a programme about prostitutes in Amsterdam and then settles down with the phone to speak – well, mostly listen – to Jeanette for an hour or so, while outside the fireworks continue their ceaseless screeching and banging.

In the morning, Kerry wakes to the sound of the phone ringing. She waits for the answerphone to click in but it doesn't. She remembers with annoyance that she unplugged it while she was on the phone to Jeanette last night so that she could carry the phone into the kitchen to get a glass of Ribena. She lies in bed looking at the ceiling, hoping that it will stop, but it continues ringing until it is as if the noise is with her in the room announcing its intention to continue until she does something about it. Kerry sighs and swings out of bed, pulling on a t-shirt and stumbling into the living room.

'Kerry?'

'Yes.'

'Hi, it's Robin from college. I've been trying to get in touch with you . . .'

'What time is it?'

'It's . . . it's about 11.30.'

'Oh, right.'

'Listen, Kerry, what are you doing today?'

Kerry pauses. What is she doing today? Nothing really. She had said to Jeanette that she might go for a drink with her in the evening, but Jeanette is about as reliable as the 55 bus – the phantom, as Marco calls it. In all probability Jeanette will be back with Darren this evening and will have forgotten altogether about last night's conversation with Kerry.

'Nothing in particular. Some work maybe.'

'OK, well, I just wondered if you had the time, whether we could meet up, talk about the assignment . . .'

'Aren't you meant to be in Ireland?'

'Ireland? Oh, right, yes, Ireland.'

Kerry waits for him to offer some further explanation but he doesn't.

'So? Can you make it?'

Kerry hesitates. 'Well . . . yes, all right then. Where?'

'The thing is, I've invited Susan to come round. You know, Susan McGuire? Why don't you come as well? To my house. I'll make something to eat and we can talk about . . . everything.'

'OK.'

'Here's the address . . .'

Kerry sits by the phone when she has replaced the receiver, regretting that she said she will go. At least there will be somebody else there. Susan McGuire is from Northern Ireland. A painfully shy and silent girl, she has the capacity to make herself almost invisible in classes. She is plain, small and slightly . . . shapeless. In fact, she is shapeless in almost every way. What is Robin doing hanging around with her? And, more worryingly, what does he think that they have in common? Kerry looks at the address she has written down. It is in a street around the back of London Fields.

Later that afternoon, as she is sitting reading, she hears the sound of a key in the door. It is a red-eyed Marco.

'God,' Kerry laughs, 'look at you.'

'I'm still buzzin'.' Marco slumps on to the sofa and puts his hand over his eyes.

'Where've you been?'

'We went to some party. That was OK. Then some girl started trailing after us 'cause she knew Danny had some charlie. Did you ever meet that girl Paula? The one who dyed her hair red and didn't like it, so she tried to peroxide it back and it all fell out?'

Kerry shakes her head.

'You're lucky. Anyway she was like chewing gum in our

41

hair so we dumped her and went back into town, to Charing
Cross Road . . .'

Kerry smiles. No wonder he is in a bad way if he ended up
with Danny in the one-room club in the Charing Cross Road
that she once accompanied him to. For Kerry, it was incon-
ceivable that anybody would be there voluntarily, still less pay
to get in. It was packed with the detritus of Saturday night so
that you could hardly breathe, there were only warm cans of
lager to drink, only one toilet that was quite impossible to get
into, only one stupid slide on the wall. The one thing that it
had a surplus of was dealers. 'It's OK when you're completely
off your face,' Marco had said as he registered Kerry's discomfort. Which was OK for Marco because he *was* completely
off his face, while Kerry still had enough purchase on reality
to feel that the club was a giant can of warm lager into which
she had been dropped along with two hundred other people,
floundering around for a small space in which to tread water
at least. And she had got sick of the sight of empty-eyed boys
with ruffled dirty peroxide hair and wraparound shades pushed
back on their heads. Marco might love the chaos, the degeneracy
of it, but she just wanted so badly to get out that it became a
pressing physical need. She remembered a guy who obviously
had the same feeling because he had managed to get the
window to the fire-escape open and was hanging out as far as
possible so that he could suck in the sweet fresh morning air
as it began to lift the city from the night.

Kerry watches Marco crumpled on the sofa. She knows that
she can't keep up with him, does not particularly want to any
more. She still likes going out, but after a while she gets bored
or tired or both and wants to come home, while Marco will go
on as if unable to stop, as if stopping is a concession, a weakness.
The one thing that she does miss about not staying out all night
with Marco any longer is going to Columbia Road in the early
morning with the sun still new in the sky, the flower stalls setting
up, drinking pints of Guinness and watching people laden with
plants struggling home. She never wants to reach a point where
she does not do that any longer.

Don't Step on the Lines

Later, Marco dozes while Kerry makes coffee and toast for them. Outside, the sky is exploring the part of the colour spectrum that lies between light and dark grey, the carpet of trees leading to the old church is copper-leaved, and high up above them all is a solitary kestrel, hanging on the air currents, its yellow bionic eyes trained down on the undergrowth for the faint flurry of mouse or vole. From the astroturf pitches come the cries and curses of the five-a-side footballers, and down on the benches the boys sit tapping a ball across to each other.

'What are you doing tonight?' asks Kerry, spreading peanut butter across a piece of toast, enjoying the texture of it under the knife.

'There's some Sunday thing starting up in a pub in Farringdon. Fancy it?' Marco yawns.

'I'm going out tonight, round to someone's house. Are you sure you're up for it?'

'Oh, yeah.' Marco stretches, wriggling his toes. 'It'll be a laugh . . .'

'You're working tomorrow?'

'Yeah, but I don't have to be in 'til ten.'

There is an easy silence. Kerry watches the half-moon shapes she is biting out of her toast.

'I don't really want to go to this person's house tonight,' she says.

'Don't go then.'

Yes, thinks Kerry, don't go then. Why am I going? Or why aren't I just going and not analysing it? It is boring, this constant questioning of motives and decisions. There is Marco stretching on the sofa, tired and hungover but still about to go out again. And maybe he will and maybe he won't, but whatever it is he ends up doing, he will just do it. While I will keep going round in circles. What do I want, what do I really want? What if I neither want to stay nor to go? What if I both fear loneliness and avoid company at the same time?

Kerry looks at red-eyed Marco on the sofa, thinks of Gary frozen by the headlights in his last desperate sprint, turns to her piled books by the side of the sofa where she has been working. It all seems so tiny sometimes, so ridiculous. No strategy is better than any other. She is a fragment, an insignificance, carrying her books home from her underfunded college on rainy autumn evenings, back to the neat isolation that she has spun around herself.

'. . . Kerry?'

'What?'

'I said, whose house are you going to?'

'Oh, right, sorry. Some guy from college, I don't know him that well, he wants to talk about the assignment.'

'Oh yeah?' says Marco mockingly.

Kerry frowns at him. 'And he's invited somebody else anyway.'

'Smokescreen. She won't turn up. You'll go in and he'll already have Barry White on the turntable, lights dimmed, oysters and champagne at the ready. Oh no, I forgot, he's a student. It'll be Blur and spaghetti Bolognese. One of those student spaghetti Bologneses, where they put sweetcorn in and leave lumps of tinned tomatoes and it's all watery and they don't cook the pasta properly. Never trust people who can't cook, Kerry.'

'You don't know he can't cook yet,' she replies.

'There are so many different kind of bad cooks,' muses Marco, ignoring her as he warms to one of his favourite themes. 'I reckon your admirer will be the spaghetti Bolognese cook, though . . .'

'He's not my admirer.'

'What's his name?'

'Robin.'

'Ohh,' mocks Marco affecting an upper-class accent. 'Robin. How perfectly spiffing.'

'Give it a rest, Marco,' says Kerry.

'Getting a bit sensitive, aren't we? I don't even know the geezer, I'm only kidding.'

'Do you see me laughing?'

Marco gets up and looks for a record and Kerry goes into

her room to get changed. She picks out tops and throws them on the bed, kicks shoes around, unable to find anything she wants to wear. She puts on a pair of black jeans and a black jumper. Too beatnik, too existentialist. She swaps the jeans for tights and a kilt, puts on some make-up and looks at herself in the mirror. Small, she thinks, I look small. She puts on some earrings, bares her teeth at the mirror.

Marco glances at her as she comes back into the living room but does not say anything. He is watching his favourite shark video with the volume turned down and DJ Krush on the record player.

'Bronze Whaler,' he murmurs as a shark swims lazily into view, 'a very eclectic shark. Can be trouble if they're in the wrong mood.'

'Have you seen my keys anywhere?'

'Kitchen.'

'Are you coming back tonight?'

'Dunno, are you?'

'Of course,' says Kerry impatiently. 'Well, if you do, I'll see you later.'

'See you.'

Kerry does not like moving about London on Sunday afternoons. She hates the uneasy stillness of the streets, the closed shops, the unpredictability of tubes and buses, the grey edginess of it all. She particularly hates Hackney on a Sunday, the criss-crossing railway lines carrying trains north and east, buses heading for Homerton or Stamford Hill. As she is walking up Mare Street, about to cut through the mazy streets around London Fields, a boy in a baseball cap holding one scruffy copy of the *Big Issue*, that he has clearly taken from a bin, steps out and starts walking with her. '*Big Issue*. Help the homeless,' he says. She glances at him. His clothes are stained, his hair under the baseball cap is matted, his pupils wide.

'No, thanks,' she says.

He continues to walk by her side and she quickens her pace. *Leave me alone, leave me alone.*

'Got a fag, darling?'

Maybe if she gives him a fag he will go away. She pulls her packet out and hands him two without stopping.

'Got a light?' He puts one of the fags behind his ear and touches her arm.

'Sorry.'

'What? You've got fags but no light. Come on, give me a light. Give me a light, come on. Give me a light.'

He is laughing as if they are sharing a joke.

'I haven't got one.'

'She hasn't got one. She doesn't have a light for me. Fags but no light. Strange that, very strange.'

He laughs again.

They have walked about fifty yards together. Somebody watching might think they know each other, or at least see the boy's laughter and think that it is all light-hearted. Kerry hopes that he will soon be further from his normal territory than he will want to go. She walks faster, ignoring him. No way is she going to turn off now into the back streets and dead-ends around London Fields. He will drop away soon.

'I bet you've got a house. We could go back to your house. Come on then, let's go somewhere. Together. You're cute, you know that? You must know that. You're cute, aren't you? Big time. Yeah, come on, baby, I want you to suck my cock . . .'

He is holding her arm now, actively trying to detain her. She spins around. 'Fuck off, you little shit! I mean it, don't touch me.'

He steps back. They are facing each other. He has a tattoo on his neck, a broken line which says *Cut Here*. Kerry wishes she could. A couple walking along the road slow their pace. They are not going to intervene but they slow down, looking behind them, knowing that something is going on. The boy grins at Kerry and sticks his tongue out waggling it obscenely at her. Suddenly, the woman from the couple turns around and says, 'Are you OK, love? Is he bothering you?'

The man looks awkward, hanging on to his girlfriend's arm as if trying to turn her back round again.

'Yes, he is,' says Kerry.

'Leave her alone,' says the woman. 'Just leave her alone.' She breaks away from the man who is still looking resolutely in the other direction.

The boy stares at them for a minute and then laughs. 'Cunts!' He spits and turns to walk away.

The woman looks at Kerry. She has big eyes, heavy with mascara, and is wearing a thick gold chain over a red poloneck jumper.

'You OK?'

'Yeah,' Kerry replies, shaking.

'Scum.' The woman watches the boy's departing back.

'Thanks,' says Kerry. 'Thanks for stopping.'

'All right, love. Mind how you go.'

Kerry crosses London Fields, realising that she has taken the longest possible route to the house.

She finally takes the turning into Robin's road, feeling relief when her position is confirmed by the street-sign half hiding under an overgrown bush. Tall grey houses with basements and steps leading up to the front door face each over parked cars across the road. Most of the front doors have more than one bell now, and some of the houses are being slowly strangled by ivy which appears to be trying to enter through the paint-cracked sash-windows and to have already forced the brick-work into a crumbling surrender. Other houses are in a better state of repair, and Kerry glances surreptitiously through the windows at pine shelves neatly stacked with books and CDs, at paper globe-lanterns and framed pictures carefully positioned on the wall. When she arrives at Robin's house and climbs the steps to his front door, there is only one bell. She places her finger over it, hesitates, as if she might just turn and go back the way she came, and then presses it firmly, watching its signal produce a shadow through the thick glass which gets closer and then stretches a shadow-hand to open the door, revealing a smiling Robin and a smell from the kitchen which is certainly not spaghetti Bolognese.

The house is large and warm with a couple of bicycles in

the hall, and Robin leads Kerry through to the kitchen where Susan McGuire is already sitting at a large table. Kerry has always wanted to have the sort of house with a kitchen where you can have a large table, like Sylvia Gordon's. There is a half-finished bottle of white wine on the table, and several pots are on the stove. Robin gets Kerry a glass.

'White? Red? Beer?'

'White's fine.'

Kerry examines the kitchen. There are several cookery books, lots of piled copies of the *Guardian*, some postcards and a Steve Bell cartoon tacked on a large noticeboard. There is a long spice-rack with cumin, celery salt, turmeric, coriander seeds, Thai seven spices, chilli powder, paprika, saffron. Some of the spice bottles are open on the area in which Robin is cooking. A black cat with white paws slides into the kitchen, stares at Kerry impudently and tenses as if about to jump on to her lap. She stares back at it warning it not to. Kerry has little time for cats, and even less for their owners. The cat jerks forward slightly and then leaps. Kerry pushes it straight off back on to the floor. It glares at her and flicks its tail. Robin laughs.

'That's the way to treat it.'

'Is it your cat?' asks Susan.

'No, it's Jill's. One of the girls who lives here.'

'What's its name?'

'Izzy.'

'Izzy,' calls Susan, patting her lap encouragingly. 'C'mon, Izzy.'

The cat looks at her scornfully, rubs its back on the wall and stalks out of the room. Susan smiles an oh-well smile at Kerry, as if she is used to rejection, and sips at her wine. They begin to talk about people at college. Susan recounts a story about Simon Davis who called her a traitor to the Irish people because she refused to take out a subscription to *Revolutionary Marxist Journal* and join the Irish Support Movement.

'I was only asking him some questions about it,' she says in her gentle Irish accent, 'but he just started shouting at me. So I said, "Well, if you're just going to shout at me, then I certainly don't want to join your group." And you know what he said to me?'

Kerry shakes her head.

'He said, "The problem with you, Susan, is that you are completely stupid and everybody knows it." '

'What did you do?' Kerry asks.

Susan sighs. 'Well, I couldn't think of anything to say. That's my problem. I always think of things to say afterwards.' She laughs sorrowfully. 'Maybe because I *am* stupid.'

'You're not stupid,' says Robin, looking up from the pot he is gently stirring. Susan gives him a grateful adoring glance, and Kerry realises immediately that she is completely besotted by him.

'We're just waiting for the rice now,' Robin says, sitting down and pouring himself some wine. He is wearing a large Aran jumper and jeans. The simple style suits him, it looks easy and effortless. Kerry glances at his angular, almost aristocratic face, framed by softly curling hair. His nose is long and fine and Kerry almost shudders with a curiously violent image of a fist landing on it or a head flying towards it. Gary had had his nose broken three or four times, usually fighting against ridiculous odds in pubs. Marco always said that to stop Gary once he got started you would have to beat him unconscious, something which had happened on a couple of occasions. Kerry looks at Robin again, unable to imagine him even lifting his fists to defend himself. He is simply not made for physical violence.

'You shouldn't pay any attention,' he continues to Susan. 'What does it matter what anyone thinks of you anyway?'

'Everyone cares what people think of them,' Kerry replies. 'Not all the people obviously, but everybody cares in some way what people think of them.'

'I don't,' says Robin calmly, staring at her, 'I don't care what anybody thinks of me. I am completely indifferent to what people in that college and in general think of me. I couldn't change how I am anyway so what's the point in worrying about it?'

'That's great,' says Susan, 'I wish I could be more like that.'

'Except I don't believe it,' Kerry persists impatiently. 'Somebody who says "I don't care what people think of me", must care even to be able to say it. They must be thinking about what people think of them to make that statement. Perhaps they think that appearing not to care will make people think better of them.'

Susan frowns. 'I'm not sure if I follow . . .'

Robin smiles placidly. 'She's saying it's a pose. Perhaps you're right, you know. Perhaps I do care a little.' And he looks in an amused way at Kerry from beneath his hair until she turns her glance away, slightly embarrassed.

'This is a lovely house,' Susan remarks brightly. 'It's all yours, isn't it?'

'Yes. My father left it to me when he died a couple of years ago. But I share it with a couple of people. Jill, the girl whose cat it is, and her boyfriend Mac, and Olly and Ruth.'

Robin, Jill, Mac, Olly, Ruth, and Izzy the cat, thinks Kerry contemptuously, glad that Marco is not there. Then she regrets her contempt because she finds that kind of inverted snobbishness quite tedious. Marco is constantly classifying and judging people, especially friends of Kerry's. He is not quite so discriminating about his own acquaintances, though. It is a comfortable house, she likes the way the pans and grater and garlic crush are hanging on hooks from the wall, the sense of being lived in that the house gives off. And how lucky to have all this as a student – kitchen, garden, spacious rooms – without having to pay any rent.

A girl wanders into the kitchen. She is pretty and thin-faced with a nose ring and a brightly coloured jumper. She is smoking a roll-up. Her hair is tied back into a small pig-tail. Despite her prettiness there is something instantly off-putting about her to Kerry, something pinched and ungenerous, as if she would be incapable of a sudden howl of laughter. 'Hi,' she says, nodding vaguely around her.

'This is Jill,' Robin says, draining the rice into a colander, steam billowing around him, condensation clinging to the glass door leading to the dark garden. 'You going to eat?'

'Yeah, if there's enough.'

'I've made loads. Mac?'

'He's going out.'

Jill sits down at the table and studies Susan and Kerry. There is an awkward silence. Susan is clearly racking her brains for something to say, pained by the silence. Kerry does not like this kind of silence either but has learned that it is not always her responsibility to do anything about it. Jill pours herself some wine. The sound of the bottle being replaced on the table echoes noisily in the muteness of the room.

'What is it you do, Jill?' asks Susan finally.

'I'm a social worker.'

'That must be really. . .' Susan pauses, flounders for a word ' . . . really interesting.'

Jill relights her roll-up and sighs almost imperceptibly before replying with casual contempt, 'Not really.'

Susan blushes slightly and Kerry suddenly feels a protective warmth towards her. She was just trying to be polite, for God's sake. Social workers may have an undeserved reputation but Jill is not doing much to restore their image.

'Why do you do it then?' Kerry asks, allowing a slight sharpness into her voice.

'It's a job. Money.' She blows out smoke quickly through her nostrils.

'But it must still be interesting sometimes,' Susan persists, 'at least when you started and everything.'

Jill brushes her hair away from her forehead. 'Maybe, I can't really remember.'

Susan gives a brittle laugh. 'Well, I'm glad you're not *my* social worker.' Kerry smiles inside at Susan's statement, wondering if she meant it to sound that rude. She is beginning to warm to her.

'I mean,' Susan continues, two red spots appearing on her cheeks, 'what do you say in your case conferences or whatever they're called, when someone asks you whether you think some child is at risk? "Maybe. Dunno really." ' And she laughs harshly again.

'OK,' says Robin putting plates of food on the table. 'Here we are.'

Jill picks up her plate. 'I'm gonna eat upstairs,' she says, 'I've got a few things to sort out. See you later.'

Kerry is glad that she is not hanging around. She glances semi-conspiratorially at Susan who still has two bright red spots on her face and is tightly holding her knife and fork upright in each hand. Kerry enjoyed that bright little flash of temper. Clearly, the girl is not quite so vulnerable as she has suggested. Suddenly, Kerry remembers that Susan must be no more than nineteen years old, ten years younger at least than herself. She thinks of when she was nineteen and is filled with a sudden pang of sorrow.

Susan relaxes as they eat the chicken in green almond sauce which Robin has prepared and which even Marco would have had to admit is pretty good and un-student-like. Kerry is surprised that Jill was prepared to eat any as she has all the hallmarks of a vegetarian or someone who is allergic to nuts or possessed of some other food fetish. It is the nose-ring, probably, or the roll-ups.

'This is delicious,' says Susan.

'I learned to make it in Mexico. I did a trip to Central America before coming to college. We went to Mexico, Guatemala, Costa Rica, Nicaragua . . . practically everywhere, really. I went with Jill.'

'Is that where she got the jumper?' Kerry asks.

'What?'

'The jumper she was wearing. Did she get it on your tour?'

'Oh. Yes, I think she got it in Guatemala.'

So Jill is your ex, thinks Kerry. Makes sense really. And now she lives in your house with her boyfriend . . . stop it, Marco, go away, you judgemental bastard. This is good, this is nice. Stop judging, Kerry. Tour of Central America, Guatemalan jumper, colourful indigenous people . . . stop it, stop it now.

They eat and gossip and joke about the assignment. Susan says that she loves *The Wasteland* but has no idea what it is really about. Robin starts to explain some of the references that he has been checking up on over the weekend. Kerry goes up the stairs to the toilet. On the way, she passes an open door and glances inside. She pauses as she realises that it is Robin's room from the books which lie on a desk under a large anglepoise light. Holding on to the door-frame, she peers inside. There is a large double mattress on the floor with a white duvet pulled back. Clothes spill out of half-open drawers and books are piled by the side of the bed. A large paint-smeared cassette player stands on the chest of drawers with a mess of tapes around it, most out of their cases. The room is spacious and an orange street lamp glows through the branches of a large tree outside the sash-window, casting shadows across the room. There is a poster for the film *Bladerunner* on the wall – Sean Young's deep brown eyes gaze from under her piled hair and turned-up fur collar. Kerry looks away and is startled to find a different pair of eyes fixed on her. It is Jill, standing on the staircase watching her.

'I was just looking for the toilet,' Kerry says, unsure how long Jill has been observing her nosing into Robin's room and trying not to blush.

'It's down there.' She points to the end of the corridor.

'Thanks.'

There are more books piled up by the side of the toilet; the *Rough Guide to India*, the *Observer Book of Cats*, *Homage to Catalonia*, a book showing examples from a women's patchwork collective in Honduras. Kerry wonders if Jill will report her to Robin. If Jill were a replicant, what would she have been designed for? Certainly not a basic pleasure-model. An intergalactic social worker? There is another Steve Bell cartoon on the bathroom door showing Jacques Derrida sitting on the toilet. '*Où est le papier?*' asks Jacques desperately, referring not to any conundrum of deconstruction but rather the lack of bog-roll. Kerry smiles. It is quite a funny cartoon.

Downstairs, Robin has opened another bottle of wine and put some music on – an Otis Redding compilation. Susan is wobbly drunk and clearly has a low alcohol threshold. Kerry, whose own alcohol threshold is respectably high after years of practice, accepts another glass of wine.

'We were just talking about you,' Susan giggles indiscreetly. 'Robin thinks you are mysterious.'

He frowns slightly.

'Are you mysterious, Kerry?' Susan asks. 'Do you have, you know, some dark secret?'

'No. Sorry. I'm pretty boring really. Do you have secrets?'

'Oh no. What you see is what you get with me. I grew up on a farm in Fermanagh. I've got six brothers and sisters. There wasn't much room for secrets. Everyone knew everything really. But I came here. That was good.'

'Are you glad you came then? Do you get homesick sometimes?'

'Not homesick exactly. Lonely. London's so big.'

Kerry considers this. She never really thinks of London as big, partly because she never gives much thought to the parts that she doesn't move around in. Even Marco stays principally within a certain patch, avoiding West and South London as much as possible. Marco's map has various certainties. They are like points on a star he moves between: up, down and sideways, but rarely deviating from the fundamental structure. Apart from home and work, there is Soho, Islington, Hoxton and Farringdon. Most nights of the week, Kerry has a fairly good idea where he will be.

'What about you?' Susan asks, slugging down her wine as if it were juice. 'Why did you go to college, Kerry?'

'I wanted to go when I was at school but it didn't work out. So I went and worked for a while, and then I just decided to give it another try.'

'Why?' Robin asks.

'What do you mean, why?'

'Why did you suddenly decide to stop working and go to college again? What did you want to get out of it?'

Kerry remembers a phrase from school. *That* – pointing to nose, *gets you that* – pointing to clenched fist. How would Robin react if she suddenly said that to him? She fights back a smile.

'I was bored. And I knew I had to do something, and it was something I wanted to do, and then . . .'

And then everything had started speeding up. Everything that was going wrong had started to go wrong very fast. Coming home that day and Gary knowing immediately that she had done it, and his face twisted with rage and pain, a glass in bloody shards on the floor that she would later numbly pick up, and the shock of his leaving the flat and her with no idea where he had gone until . . . until . . .

They are watching her; the silence that she has created has almost paralysed them. Kerry looks up and sees them: two strangers who know nothing about her, nothing at all, not even the most minor things. And she doesn't want to know them any more, doesn't want them asking trite questions about secrets, doesn't want to be listening to Otis Redding singing 'Try A Little Tenderness'; she wants to go back to her flat, back to her room, back to Marco who does know, who knows a lot. Wasted time, she thinks. Is there such a thing as wasted time? Lost time perhaps, there is a long period of lost time, of time she cannot give any meaning to, that long time in the sunken flat waiting, waiting for something to happen, time lost and gone for ever. People who lose time like that – perhaps that is what being a loser really means? In which case it is not a term to be used with sneering condescension. Gary was a loser and Kerry lost Gary. Is that why you went to college then, Kerry? Because you had nothing else to lose?

'I should get going,' she says quietly, feeling a massive fatigue coming over her. Robin is staring at her intently and Susan is looking bewildered as if she has suddenly lost the thread of everything. She gets up and goes to the toilet and Robin says to Kerry, 'You can stay over, if you want?' in a calm and neutral voice that could mean nothing or everything. Kerry shakes her head.

'No, I want to get home. Thanks for the food. It's been really nice.'

Robin raises his eyebrows and dials for a cab. Then he stretches his hands in front of him and knits his fingers together.

Kerry winces, thinking that he might be about to click his bones but he doesn't. Instead, he fixes her suddenly with his eyes and says, 'Do you think that holding everything in is going to do you much good? I really like you, Kerry, a lot. And I think that you might like me too if you . . . just let yourself.'

Kerry is more astonished than irritated. Where does he get his incredible self-assurance from? Why does he think he has the right to say things like this to her? He is watching her, waiting with an almost detached curiosity for her reaction. No man has ever tried this approach with her. A few men at college have made clumsy attempts to interest her but then withdrawn in the face of her obvious lack of response. But here is Robin saying that not only is he interested in her but that he thinks she is interested in him. And in that strange euphemism perhaps there is a small truth. Perhaps she is stirred a little to interest by his placid flattery, by the way in which he seems quietly determined to forge a bond between them. But what is she interested in? She genuinely doesn't know. She doesn't find him either attractive or unattractive. He is very good-looking certainly but she has been unmoved by good-looking men before. Perhaps she too is curious. She wants to say 'You don't know me' but knows that there is something too clichéd, too submissively coquettish, in such a response.

She is saved by the sound of Susan thudding down the stairs and the almost simultaneous horn of the taxi outside.

'That's my cab,' she says. 'I'll see you both in college next week.'

Robin walks with her to the front door, opening it to the chill air of the street and the cab with its lights on pulled alongside the parked cars.

'Kerry. . .' he starts, but she cuts him off, shaking her head.

'Don't!' And she almost runs to the cab, slamming the door as she gets in and not turning to see if he is still in his doorway watching her as the car pulls away and the cabbie mumbles, 'Where to, love?'

Chapter 4

'That Brie looks heavenly,' says the woman in Marco's delicatessen. 'Could I have some of that lovely Brie as well?'

Marco slices and wraps the cheese in Cellophane for the woman. He feels shit – his stomach is sore, his eyes twitching. He has had a hangover hunger all day, experimenting with a constant succession of food, none of which has really worked. He has eaten a jam-filled croissant, a double cheeseburger, a Dime bar, and a bag of salt and vinegar crisps, swinging between sweet and savoury in an attempt to make himself feel normal again. It would be so great just to feel normal. The only slight relief came from a can of ice-chilled Coke which lulled him into thinking he was better. Then he had a fag which nearly killed him.

'Anything else?'

'Oh, those olives look extremely tempting . . . what do you think, Stephen . . . would you like some olives?'

The man she is with shrugs indifferently. He has big red-rimmed glasses and looks like Christopher Biggins. Why the fuck, thinks Marco irritably, would anyone buy glasses like that? He is filled with a sudden temptation to throw the man out of the shop. *Go on, piss off, and take your glasses with you.* The woman puts her finger to her lips as if this is one of the most important life-changing decisions she has ever faced. Marco feels his bowels start to twist. Come on, come on, make up your mind.

'Oh, maybe another time. Yes, that's all.' She gives him a nice smile and he forces his face into some kind of response. When the couple have gone, Marco goes out to the back where the owner, Gerald, is slicing pastrami.

'All quiet?' Gerald asks and Marco nods. Gerald is OK. He

is an old hippy who sometimes asks Marco to get him drugs. He has a craggy face and long straw-coloured hair and doesn't usually complain too much when Marco staggers in late. He also – inexplicably in Marco's opinion – has a very pretty girlfriend called Gina who does modelling and is about twenty years younger than he. Gerald is from a wealthy family and went to public school and Oxford where he spent most of his time protesting about the war in Vietnam, shagging like crazy and experimenting with every kind of available drug until he got kicked out of college and renounced by his family. Gerald is hardly the most typical delicatessen owner and Marco has never really found out why he does it. Gerald just says that it had always been his ambition to run a delicatessen.

'How's your head?'

Marco cocks an imaginary pistol and holds it to his temple. Gerald laughs.

'Gina and I had a fairly quiet one this weekend. Just stayed in, had a few friends round.'

'Woodstock reunion, was it?'

'Nah. Most of them were Gina's friends.'

'Babes?'

'One or two. Put the kettle on, Marco, after you've served the customer who's getting rather impatient out there.'

'All right . . . oh, Gerald, can you give us some money today? I'm a bit short.'

'Sure, man. No worries.'

At closing time, Marco cleans up, gets thirty quid off Gerald and takes the bus to Bethnal Green where his dad lives with his step-mother, Anne. Marco's real mother was Italian and died of cancer when he was two years old. John Fisher was a printer, a member of the Communist Party and met Marco's mum at an International Congress in Bulgaria. He is still a Communist but no longer a printer, since when it came to the flight from Fleet Street, he was an early and obvious candidate for redundancy, no longer needed to churn out the capitalist propaganda he despised so heartily. His last great battle was at Wapping where he was arrested several times and smacked over the head with a police truncheon. This had the odd effect for a couple of weeks of making him suddenly start walking backwards. He still follows the fortunes of the Italian Communist Party with a keen interest, and was devastated when they changed their name and replaced the hammer and sickle with an oak tree.

Marco walks back up towards Roman Road when he gets off the bus, past the basketball pitches where he used to go and sniff Zoff plaster remover from the sleeve of his school jumper, and where he first put his tongue in a girl's mouth. Tracy Robbins – he wonders what she is doing now. She had a mad dad who used to kill her if she came in late. Everybody knew that her dad was a bastard. At the time, Marco just thought it was bad luck that somebody had a horrible dad who was always shouting. Now he thinks that the dad was probably abusing her. People always think that they are unlucky not to have been born into wealth or good looks or amazing intelligence. But what about the luck they do have, like not having Tracy Robbins's dad as a parent? Not to mention avoiding the really bad luck of those poor little bastards who know nothing other than abuse and violence and finally death at five years old, ending up the subject of an enquiry into the negligence of the authorities. The thought makes him uncomfortable as he passes the church on Weavers Fields, also surrounded by trees like the one next to their flat.

'All right, son?' John Fisher says as he opens the door to Marco and ushers him into the living room. Everything is as normal in the house. The silver bust of Lenin sits in untroubled immortality on the mantelpiece, the *Morning Star* is folded on the table, the books on the shelf that Marco knows so well: collected works of Karl Marx (red covers, black lettering) and James Connolly (green covers, gold lettering); histories of the Spanish Civil War, the British Trade Union movement and the struggle against apartheid; biographies of Lenin, Rosa Luxumburg, Stalin, Nelson Mandela, and Harry Pollit. There is a separate neatly ordered section for books about Shelley, in whom John Fisher has an obsessional interest, once shared with his young Italian wife. There is also an *Atlas of the World*, several books about Italy, and a guide to the Lake District.

'I brought you some Parma ham.' Marco hands his dad the meat in its white plastic bag.

'Oh, that's good of you.'

'That's all right.'

'Still working in that place then?'

'Yeah, it's OK. Cash in hand, you know. I can still sign on.'

John Fisher pauses, the ham in his hand as if it has suddenly developed a lead-like heaviness. Then he sighs and goes into the kitchen to make some tea. Marco follows him in.

'How's Anne?'

'Not bad. She might be up for a promotion. Head of Department.'

Marco's step-mother works as a Geography teacher in one of the local schools. She married John Fisher when Marco was ten years old. He remembers the wedding: the champagne bubbles going up his nose at the first sip, the speeches from the London District Communist Party. Marco likes Anne. She is quiet and patient but you can't mess her around.

John Fisher chuckles as he spoons tea into the pot. 'You know what happened the other day? She's asking the class questions and she says, "What is a plateau?" So this kid sticks up his hand and says: "It's a type of cake, miss." You know, Black Forest Plateau.'

Marco smiles dutifully as they make their way back into the living room, thinking how good a pint of Guinness would be right now. He is going to run out of things to say to his dad soon.

'How's Angela?' he asks. John Fisher frowns at the mention of Marco's half-sister. It must be painful for him, thinks Marco, his son a no-hoper, and his beloved daughter living with some hard-nosed City yuppie out in Essex who has only the deepest contempt for his politics. Angela's fiancé Tony works in the futures market, still thinks it's cool to own a Porsche, and is a blue-chip, triple-A-rated wanker. He hates Angela's family, his only concession to the principle of equality being to divide his contempt between them without discrimination. Every time there is a stock-market crash or financial crisis, Marco hopes to hear that Tony has thrown himself out of a twentieth-floor window or filled his Porsche with exhaust fumes, but Tony only appears to get even richer. His idea of a good joke is to send Angela's dad a copy of *The Downing Street Years* for Christmas. Last year he gave Marco a pair of gold initialled cuff-links which Marco has been meaning to try and sell for some time. The bastard probably had the initials done so that he couldn't.

Marco hates Angela for colluding with Tony, using her family as a means of securing his patronising affection. *You see how good I am*, she is saying to him, *look how amazing it is that I've turned out the way I am given my weird upbringing. I understand that it's painful, darling, but we only have to see them once or twice a year . . .* None of which stops John Fisher from doting on her and shouting at Marco when he reduces her to furious tears by asking Tony what the price of orange juice and pork-bellies will be next year, or Angela whether she got her Versace dress from British Home Stores.

'They're not coming for Christmas,' his dad says.

'Good. What are they doing?'

'Skiing or something like that. A winter break in the Alps.'

Avalanches, thinks Marco hopefully. He hopes that there is a winter break – a neck or a leg at the very least. He fantasises briefly about rescuing Angela from an avalanche and then finding Tony with his nose still sticking out and carefully kicking snow over it to finish the job. He is also pissed off with Angela for not telling him about this, since it means he definitely has to be home for Christmas now. Still, he doesn't have anywhere else to go really. His stomach twists up again and he grimaces as acid rises to his throat. He glances at the clock, wondering whether to go home or head into town and find out what's happening, have that soothing pint of Guinness. He does not want to go home if Kerry isn't there, so he decides to make for Soho.

His dad picks up the remote control and switches on for

the news. Marco watches him as he tuts and frowns at the politicians discussing whether there will be any scope for tax cuts in the next budget. He looks old and fragile and Marco feels a wave of hatred for the politicians for whom his dad and people like him are at best an irrelevance. And still he will dutifully vote Labour and nag Marco to do the same. But Marco will not vote again – not now. He doesn't want anything to do with any of it any more. Nor does he want to live in a tree-house to stop roads being built, nor lie down in front of lorries to stop veal being deported. Old Communist politics, New Labour politics, New Age politics, Socialist Worker politics – it's all bollocks. Marco remembers the last rally against the Criminal Justice Act, where one of Danny's pissed-up Celtic crowd was wearing a team shirt and went face to face with a young policeman. 'Kiss that, you cunt,' he snarled, holding the badge of the shirt up to his face, and the copper had not moved, but his hand had tightened on his truncheon and his eyes had followed the kid the whole time, and when the line had broken and the police started wading in, he had pursued him like a greyhound after a rabbit, the truncheon cracking down on his head before dragging him for a further kicking into the police van. And that, as far as Marco was concerned, was how it was, and how it always would be – Tory government or New Labour government, Internet or no fucking Internet.

Marco stands up and stretches. 'I'd best be making a move, Dad.'

His dad rubs his eyes. 'All right, son. Come over on Sunday, if you feel like it, for your dinner.'

'Yeah.' Marco grins.

'You won't, will you?'

'Yeah, yeah I might.'

'You'll never be able to get up will you?'

''Course I will. I'll phone you.'

'Yes, well . . . we'll see, won't we?'

'I'll phone you.'

His dad shakes his head, half laughing, half irritated. Marco decides to get out quickly before they start having another argument about his dead-end job and self-centred life-style.

Marco catches a number 8 bus heading for Tottenham Court Road and gets up as he sees Centrepoint coming into view. He walks down the Charing Cross Road to Cambridge Circus and makes for the pub, remembering wistfully the summer when everyone stood outside balancing pints on the parked cars, flyers lying all around – pure colour and temptation in the gutter. It had been a good summer, a hot summer, plenty of parties, one or two nice girls. Soho in the summer – nothing better than that, a sunny world away from this dark, drizzly, November shit.

It is packed in the pub and he wriggles through to the bar and buys a pint of Guinness. There is nobody in here that he much wants to speak to; too many men without hair, too many retard expressions. Moody Dave is talking to a Japanese girl – complete with rucksack like a protective tortoise shell – and acknowledges Marco with raised hand and eyebrows. But Marco can't be bothered to listen to another ficticious project that is supposed to make Dave immensely rich but which will either fail or – more likely – never happen, making him even moodier than before. Marco finishes his pint and heads out of the pub. He wants to go home now but decides to go via Hanway Street just in case. The Guinness hasn't made him feel that much better, he can taste the sourness in his mouth. Walking down Greek Street, he grins as he passes the two black bouncers in dinner suits guarding the entrance to a dodgy-looking club that he and Danny always pretend that they want to go into when they are pissed. Reaching Soho Square, he passes Lorna with a group of friends heading in the other direction. She ignores him. He emerges into Oxford Street and buys a slice of pizza from the Lebanese on the corner, with whom he once had a ferocious drunken argument about the amount of pepperoni on the slice.

'All right, my friend?' grins the Lebanese as he sees Marco. 'Plenty of pepperoni for you, innit?'

'Yeah, but don't give me that little slice there.'

'Ah, you are so hard to please, my friend.' And he hands Marco the slice of pizza.

Marco pauses for a moment, contemplating his next move, stuffing his face with the dry pizza. Then he flips the paper plate away like a Frisbee, and crosses Oxford Street into the crescent of Hanway Street with its piled cardboard boxes, the smell of Spanish *tapas* drifting from doorways and basements, a couple of guys pissing up against the wall. Marco checks out a basement bar but there are only a couple of skinny-legged casualties drinking slush-puppy margaritas so he makes his way into a narrow corridor where, from downstairs in the Spanish *tapas* bar that nobody goes into to eat *tapas*, a guitar is flamencoing, heels clicking across a crowded bar. But Marco climbs the creaking stairs to the tiny Electra club upstairs – like a doll's-house pub – where various other casualties including Danny are crowded around a table. 'Wa-hayyy!' shouts Danny as he sees him, 'Get the drinks in, Marco.' He has his arm around Marina who is drunkenly trying on his cycle helmet.

'No Jeremy tonight then?' Marco asks her snidely as he pulls a chair over. But she just smiles languidly at him, her cat-eyes stretching effortlessly, and pulls closer to Danny who puts his hand inside her thigh on the shiny silver of her long skirt, and Marco feels a bitter stab of envy which dries his throat and makes him turn away, back to the bar.

Later, they end up in a flat near the Grays Inn Road. The flat has no character at all, no effort has been made to stamp any personality on it. There are dusty cobwebs where the walls meet. Marco almost clucks with disapproval as he sees the cack-crusted pans and empty tins in the kitchen. How could you possibly cook in that mess? Yet he is all too familiar with these flats, the routines of their owners hardly lending themselves to home-making. He is familiar with the bare walls, the mess of torn Rizla packets and disembowelled cigarettes around the ash-tray, the red candle-wax dripping down a beer bottle, old club flyers stuck up around the toilet. He is used to waiting for the owner to start putting records on, the cries of 'Tune!'

as they are recognised. Somebody passes him a charlie spliff and he sucks quickly on it, aware of the hand anxiously waiting to receive it, feeling the plastic richness of it as it enters his lungs. 'It's raining,' Marina says and her voice is softly normal, with a melancholy elegance as she passes on this simple fact, and Marco glances at her almost tenderly as he turns to the window and sees the streaks of rain on the night-blackened glass. He thinks of the massive world outside this shabby flat, great dark oceans and the sharks that swim in them, sliding graceful and primitive with their cold eyes. Do sharks exist in the dark oceans at this second if nobody sees them? Elementary philosophy, like the sound – or not – of a tree falling in a clearing when nobody is there. Shark or bundle of sense-data? (A question of secondary concern if one were speeding towards you, jaws agape.) They are out there, thinks Marco, they are there *at this very moment* cruising their territories, hanging off beaches, flicking their tails to change direction, even at this very second, thousands of them, a great hierarchy of sharks: Great Whites (the *Carcharodon carcharias* and indisputable shark supreme, also known as the White Pointer in South Africa, notable for its ferocity and lack of nictitating membrane over the eye), Tigers, assorted Whalers, Greys, Blues, Lemons, Porbeagles, Makos, and Hammerheads. Plus of course the sharks of lesser interest like Basking and Nurse sharks; both names suggesting their relative lack of danger. Marco knows the names of sharks, he likes knowing their names.

And things do happen when you don't see them, like the cocaine they are smoking being transported at this very moment from Bolivia or Colombia or Peru. How? They don't know. Small planes criss-crossing the oceans in which the sharks swim, money changing hands, the so-called invisible economy. How can something so enormous be called invisible? The money doesn't change hands, it changes accounts. It's a jungle out there. Why don't people say, It's an ocean out there? In the ocean the chances of being eaten by something bigger are considerable. Except sharks, who have few predators apart, of course, from Mr Obvious whose dynamite, hooks and beach-protecting nets do a lot to reduce their numbers. Marco is ambivalent on this subject. He does not want sharks to disappear but he also does not like blond-bearded scientists from Californian universities hogging documentaries (which could more usefully be showing images of the Great White in action) to claim that sharks would prefer to eat seals and that they are no danger to humans. Of course they are dangerous – that's what makes them interesting. Anyway, the ocean is more savage, more wild, than the jungle. It is also almost completely unexplored, has no real frontiers apart from where it comes crashing in on beaches. Marco contemplates sharing this reverie and turns to the guy sitting next to him. 'The ocean's mental,' he says but the guy ignores him, as he is talking to somebody else about the Underworld gig.

Later, Danny and Marina enter into some kind of whispered, giggling negotiation which, knowing Danny, involves whether they should sneak into the bathroom or go back to one of their flats. Marco guesses the dilemma must be that Marina is reluctant to have sex in the bathroom, that Danny is reluctant to let her see his hovel of a flat, and that Jeremy would be reluctant to admit Danny for a night of passion in the flat that he shares with Marina. A flat which undoubtedly bears little resemblance to this one, which probably carries the marks of their personalities, their shared lives together, invitations to classy media parties tacked on the noticeboard. Marco starts to feel anger towards Marina again – her little adventure, her bit of rough. Then he has to concede that he wouldn't mind so much if it had been *him* she had chosen in her bid to drive Jeremy mad with jealousy before their inevitable tearful reunion. Finally, Danny and Marina leave together and Marco is left talking on the fag-burned sofa to the guy next to him – a spotty, skinny kid from Middlesbrough – not about sharks but about Juninho.

Marco puts back his head and lets the kid just talk, feeling – not for the first time – that if he had a real loaded gun in his hands now, he would put it straight to his own temple and produce an instant Jackson Pollock of blood and brains; what were once his thoughts and memories spattering the bare walls of this dreary space, a pure fountain of raw matter to drown out all this empty nonsense. It is strange how intense this feeling is, when in the morning it will just seem like even greater melodramatic nonsense. But now the melodrama pleases him, gives him a rush which makes his head throb slightly, and then somebody is handing him another charlie spliff and he takes three or four quick long drags on it and decides that he will walk home, and this thought pleases him even more.

Chapter 5

November nights take hold of the city, sending people hurrying along rain-streaked pavements, street-lights glistening in the soft but persistent rain. Robin invites Kerry and Susan around to work again, although he does not refer to his last conversation with Kerry. And Kerry starts to enjoy going: walking quickly to the warm house with her coat pulled around her, her feet splashing through the pavement puddles, looking forward to the door opening into the comforting light of the hallway. She begins to watch out for Robin and Susan in college and feels disappointed when they are not there. She likes working with other people and the transition from the initial slight awkwardness to the enthusiasm and pleasure of articulating ideas. They get good marks in their assignments, people tease them affectionately for being swots, ask to borrow notes and essays from them. Kerry grows accustomed to Susan's clumsiness, her occasional little flashes of temper, and also to her devotion.

Sharp-eyed Matilda also notices and teases Kerry about it.

'Are you seeing that guy then?'

'No, not at all.'

'I don't know why not. I tried to get him interested once but he just looked at me like I wasn't there. His loss. But I reckon he likes you. And it's not as if that blob in your threesome is any competition.'

Kerry giggles guiltily. 'Don't be a bitch.'

'Come on, Kerry, she's a loser.'

Kerry frowns. 'I don't like that expression.'

'You don't? Well, you shouldn't be in this college then. Look at them all. Students. What do they think they're doing? You think people are like you, Kerry, but they're not . . .' Matilda almost seems to be getting angry as she speaks ' . . . and what

69

are you going to do when you're out of here? Once you've got your precious degree?'

'That's not the point.'

'You think it isn't now. But it will be the point when you finish. What will you do then? How will you be any different from all these other losers who will also have a degree? Nobody will be able to tell you apart.'

'I will though. And that's what matters at the moment. I'm sick of hearing about how there's no point in going to college any more. I'm not stupid. If I'd wanted to get on in life I would have done a Business Studies degree.'

Kerry thinks of one of their lecturers who keeps insisting that the students need to be prepared for the job market, develop transferable skills that will attract potential employers. Instead of working individually on essays, they should work in groups to learn about teamwork. They should video themselves giving presentations, write mock reports instead of essays. *You should always be thinking of your audience,* he says, and Kerry winces. Who is her audience apart from herself?

Matilda is looking sceptically at Kerry so she continues, willing her to understand a little: 'I'm studying English because I like it, and I like studying because it makes me think harder about books. My ex-boyfriend and my flatmate both used to say the same thing as you. In fact everyone I've ever known has said it to me. "What are you studying for? What's the point?" But you could say that about anything. So what if I go back to temping after doing this? I'll still have done it. I'll still be a different person from the one who started this course. I don't know why people find that so hard to understand. I don't think that it's the key to a better life, I don't think that it's just an excuse to live in the bar for three years and get up late. I like English Literature and I want to study it. That's it. It's the people who can't understand that who are losers.'

Matilda laughs and holds up her hands as if surrendering. 'I only asked if you had a thing going with Robin. All right, you've convinced me. But I'm afraid I'm not quite as . . . pure as you are, Kerry. I don't think I'll be doing another year of this crap. I'm out of here.'

After Matilda has gone Kerry sits day-dreaming, half thinking about their conversation. She remembers a sarcastic expression her sister often used when they were growing up: *Got any more little pearls of wisdom, Kerry?* But Kerry always liked the thought of wisdom as pearls – precious stones fashioned into a polished necklace. She supposes that in a way she still thinks like that about it: the long dive through the colour gradations of the ocean to struggle with the shell, triumphantly bursting the surface back into the sun to hold up the treasure. *Dripping with jewels* – she likes that expression as well. She is not doing much, she is a student at a polytechnic that has changed its name to university, but she also knows that it means something. *There is no long-term for young people any more.* Somebody said that on a Sunday morning political programme. Is it a bad thing though? Not entirely. The short-term is good as well. There was a long-term for her mum and dad, a long and unchanging future of job, marriage, children, retirement. And are they happy, or any happier? Would the security, the long-term of the sunken flat, be preferable to her life now? She doesn't care about whether she can call herself a graduate or not, has no particular interest in initials after her name – she is diving deep, she is selecting her pearls.

One evening, after they have been working late in the library, Kerry invites Susan back to the flat.

'You're so lucky,' she says, looking out at the city view, towards the pyramid of Canary Wharf dusted with white light, 'having this all to yourself.'

'Well, it's not just me. Marco lives here as well.'

'But you're not . . .' Susan blushes. 'I mean, he's not . . .'

'My boyfriend? No, he's just my friend. I've known him for years. He might be back later, you'll meet him.'

Susan nods, looking around all the time at the things in the living room, taking the measure of Kerry.

'What does he do?' she asks.

Kerry laughs. 'He goes out, gets drunk, takes lots of drugs, signs on, does a bit of work here and there.'

'Drugs?' Susan looks alarmed, as if she expects to find dirty needles scattered all over the floor. 'I've never taken any drugs.'

'Really?' says Kerry carelessly, looking for some music to put on.

'Well, I had a puff of somebody's joint once at a party. It made me feel sick.' Susan pauses, looking worriedly at Kerry who is now searching for the corkscrew.

'Do you?' Susan asks suddenly.

'Do I what?'

'Do you . . . you know . . . do you take drugs as well?'

'Where is that corkscrew . . . I saw it just a little while ago . . . well, yeah now and again. Not as much as Marco though.'

'What sort of drugs?' Susan asks faintly.

'Whatever I get offered.' Kerry laughs. 'No, I mean, I don't know, it just depends.'

'Have you ever taken heroin?' Susan is staring wide-eyed at Kerry, desperate for her new friend not to be a smack-head.

'No, I've never taken heroin. Nor crack.'

'Has Marco taken heroin?'

'Well . . .' Kerry considers. 'I guess he probably has. But not injected it. You know, just smoked it.'

'A lot of people in college take Ecstasy, don't they?'

'I suppose so. A lot of people take Ecstasy full stop.'

'I'd be really scared. I mean, a pill like that. Once you had taken it, that could be that. You might end up like that girl. You know, the one who died on her birthday.'

Kerry pours them some wine. 'I think you're more likely to end up with lung cancer from smoking. Or getting run over staggering out of the pub pissed. Some people die from eating a single peanut.'

'Is it nice?'

'Mostly. I don't do it as much as I used to.'

'Why not?' Susan asked.

'I'm not sure.' Kerry considers. 'I suppose I get tired of their after-effects sometimes.'

Susan laughs. 'I'm such a coward, really. I'd love to try it though. I mean, it's part of us, isn't it? Part of our generation, part of our culture. It seems so boring not even to have tried it. Look at all those poets we were doing a couple of weeks ago. I bet they would have loved it . . . they all took tons of drugs. Opium and all that.'

'Ah, talk to Marco about that one,' Kerry replies. 'He's got loads of theories about it all.'

There is a pause as they sip at their wine. Susan picks up a paperweight filled with gold, red and blue bubbles and spins it round. The bubbles descend slowly, hypnotically, through their watery entrapment, flashing in the light.

'I haven't done much,' she says quietly. 'I haven't even . . . I haven't ever had a boyfriend.'

'Oh, right.'

'I haven't . . . you know . . . I've never . . . I'm a virgin. You probably think that's really weird?'

'Not really.' Kerry shifts uncomfortably, thinking of Matilda and glad she is not witnessing this conversation. 'I bet loads of people are still virgins at college – they just don't admit it.'

'Have you had lots of boyfriends?'

'No. Not lots. I went out with the same one for quite a long time.'

Kerry thinks about losing her virginity. She was fifteen. It was at a party, the boy was older, they were lying beside a pile of coats. Until then, she had only French kissed, and some boys had clumsily put their hands up her skirt, scrabbled about, and then seemed to run out of ideas. Sometimes, they were so drunk, they did it when there were other people in the room. Kerry winces with embarrassment at the thought. But this boy had seemed to know what he was doing, so she had not objected when he had begun unbuttoning her jeans. She had shivered with pleasure as she had put her hand around his penis and he had groaned and removed her hand quickly. In the next room, she could hear 'Ch-ch-ch-ch-changes' on the record player which she thought was rather appropriate. Unlike the often-reported feeling of disappointment and *is that what all the fuss*

73

was about? Kerry thought that it was brilliant. She had scrunched the sleeve of one of the coats in her hand with the pleasure of it. She was disappointed that the boy did not want to see her again after finding out from his friends that she was only fifteen, and wondered whether he had known that she had never done it before.

'When did you split up?'

Kerry draws in her breath. 'We didn't . . . not really anyway. He died.' Her shoulders tighten and she looks straight at Susan who is blushing furiously.

'Oh, Kerry. Oh, God, I'm so sorry. Me and my big mouth. I always do that. God, I'm sorry . . .'

'He killed himself. Or they think he killed himself. He drove out to Essex and got out of the car and started running up this road towards the traffic and he ran straight into a car and was killed almost instantly. He was depressed anyway, but he was very angry with me because I'd got pregnant. Well, he wasn't angry because of my getting pregnant – he wanted the baby. I think he felt like it was his last chance or something. But I knew it wouldn't work like that and I've never wanted a baby anyway, and it would have been me trapped for ever, and so I had the abortion and he just knew when I came home so he ran out of the flat and that was the last time I saw him . . . the last time . . .'

Lost and gone for ever. All that time, all that lost time, all those years of Kerry's life, all those lost years. Years spent temping, talking, drinking, laughing and fighting. Wage slips, empty wine and beer bottles, a new red coat, the remote control, ashtrays spilling butts, soap operas, running jokes, videos, dull Saturday nights – all the fragments of those years, that other Kerry, the Kerry who would bring things home to the sunken flat with its desperately, ridiculously unhappy inhabitant. All those years just brought to a stop in an instant of dazzling headlights, the frantic blaring of a horn, an appalled face behind the wheel, an appalled face in the road, the whole scene framed by the dark, bare winter trees of the Essex countryside. As if by running, as if in that last desperate sprint, he was outpacing everything, the lost years falling away from him, the freezing air in his tear-stained face, leaving behind for ever the lost and the wasted years.

Susan is looking as if she has just tipped a bottle of red wine over a white carpet. Kerry takes pity on her.

'Don't worry. I'm OK about it now.'

'Are you?'

'Well, yeah. You know, sometimes obviously I get a bit down about it and everything . . .'

'You always seem so calm. So sure of what you're doing. I sometimes think you're so lucky. You know, you're pretty and you're clever and people like you.'

Susan says this slightly wistfully as if she perceives in herself the opposite of all these qualities. Kerry pours them both more wine and studies Susan. The problem is that in many ways her self-assessment is not particularly inaccurate. She is not pretty and not especially popular, although she is certainly not stupid. Kerry likes her but her presence is not essential to her, her entrance to a room does not cause that little unmistakable flicker of excitement that some people just seem to bring naturally with them. If she is honest with herself, it is Robin whom she is really looking out for in college. She is pleased to see Susan but it is not the same. So what? Kerry suddenly thinks irritably. Why should it be the same? The people who have the quality of making people pleased to see them can also bring pain, trouble and stupidity with them.

'So,' she says, trying to lighten the conversation a little, 'are you thinking about getting a boyfriend now that you're young, free and single in the big city?'

Susan giggles. 'There is someone I like, but I can't tell you.' She looks archly over her wine-glass. 'You'd die if you knew.'

'Really?' says Kerry who knows perfectly well who it is.

'I like him a lot. But I think he likes someone else.'

'Oh, yes? Is it Simon Davis?'

'Kerry! Please! Give me some credit. Ugh, he's horrible, he always spits at you when he talks to you. No, ugh, he's disgusting. He said I was stupid!'

'Is it Michael Osborne?'

'Well he's pretty nice, you know. But he's a lecturer. And he's married.'

'And he wears horrible jumpers.'

'I think his jumpers are sweet. No, Kerry, I can't tell you. Anyway, like I said, nothing's going to happen because he likes somebody else. I can tell.'

'Have it your own way,' Kerry says, lighting a cigarette and hearing the sound of the key in the door.

'But this year I have two objectives . . .' Susan continues, oblivious to the opening door ' . . . I'm going to take Ecstasy and lose my virginity.' She giggles, wine-flushed, as Marco comes into the room behind her, carrying a French stick and some stuff from the delicatessen.

'Sounds good to me,' he says, winking at Kerry and sending Susan leaping from her seat with a little shriek. 'I know a few geezers who could sort out both for you in one night.'

Susan turns as red as the wine in her glass. 'Oh my god,' she whispers to Kerry, 'he heard me.'

'It looks like it,' Kerry agrees. 'Don't worry about it though. He's heard a lot worse.'

'Have you eaten?' Marco re-emerges from the kitchen. 'I've got some stuff from the deli – salami, olives and stuff, if you want it?'

Susan is still flushed with embarrassment as Marco sets out food on plates and brings in the tea-cups, milk and sugar. Kerry notes that his eyes are blood-shot, his hair greasy, and that he hasn't changed his clothes for a couple of days.

'So you're a student as well then?' he asks Susan as he pours the tea.

'Yes,' she says, blushing again and looking around as if the walls will provide her with some inspired topic for conversation. 'And are you Italian?'

Kerry smiles at the strange abruptness of the question.

'Half-Italian. My mum was Italian.'

'Oh, does she live here or in Italy?'

Kerry winces as Susan fails to spot the past tense. Not

because Marco is sensitive on the subject, but because Susan is about to get the same answer as she received to her enquiry about Kerry's boyfriend.

'She's dead.'

Susan's mouth drops open a little as if she cannot believe her bad luck. Surely she can ask about someone who won't turn out to be a corpse?

'Yeah,' continues Marco cheerfully, folding some salami in a piece of bread and stuffing it hungrily in his mouth without stopping talking. 'She died when I was only two so I didn't get much experience of my Italian side. My dad remarried. I met my grandparents though – they're from Bologna. Big Communist city.'

'You look quite Italian,' Susan says with a tone of relief at Marco's apparent lack of trauma on the subject.

'And you look quite Irish,' he replies.

'Sure, that's because *both* my parents are Irish,' Susan says, exaggerating her accent and Kerry starts as she realises that Susan is beginning to flirt with Marco.

'You look like . . . oh what's that actor's name? Not one of the really famous ones . . . he was in a film about a psychiatrist who gets involved with a conman . . . he was the conman not the psychiatrist . . . oh, it's on the tip of my tongue . . .'

'Joe Mantegna,' say Kerry and Marco together.

'Yeah, yeah, that's it, Joe Mantegna.'

'Congratulations,' says Marco. 'You win the prize for being the one millionth person to tell me that.'

'I think he's gorgeous,' says Susan dreamily, and then realises the implication of what she's just said and adds hastily, 'but it's quite a superficial resemblance really.'

'Thanks. So you're studying with Kerry then?'

'I am.'

'You must know her boyfriend then?'

'Boyfriend! Kerry, you never said . . .'

'Marco . . .' Kerry tries to interrupt but it is too late.

'Yeah, some posh geezer who phones here every hour of the day pretending he wants to talk about college. What's his name again, Kerry? Lord Rupert? Christopher Robin? He's wedged up anyway, got a massive house that Pater left him when he died. Kerry's always sneaking off there for special revision sessions.' Marco flicks breadcrumbs from his lap on to the floor and grins at Susan.

She looks bewildered. 'Robin?' she asks faintly, looking at Kerry who shakes her head, glaring at Marco.

'Take no notice of him. He's just being stupid. He's only ever spoken to Robin on the phone, and because *his* life is basically empty and shallow, he likes to fantasise about other people's.'

'Oh, yeah? So what was he doing here for breakfast the other morning? What was all that about how he liked his eggs in the morning?'

Red blotches appear on Susan's face as she fights to appear normal and gives a nervous, shrill little laugh. Kerry glares furiously at Marco again.

'Don't worry, he's lying. He never gets bored of a joke.'

'Hey. . .' says Marco in a display of bewildered innocence ' . . . have I said something out of line? Is there some hidden agenda here that I don't know about? I'm sorry if I've put my foot in it.'

'I should be going,' Susan says anxiously, 'I've got to get the train back to Dollis Hill.'

'You idiot!' Kerry snaps at Marco, moving away from the window after watching Susan walk along the pathway until it turns into Old Street, towards the tube station and the long journey home to Dollis Hill.

'What? I was only messing about.'

'Yeah, but she fancies that guy. And she doesn't know you, does she?'

'Well, you made it worse, didn't you, getting all serious about it?' Marco's voice is rising as well. He begins to clear the plates and cups from the table.

'Because I had to let her know it wasn't true, didn't I? You must have seen her face . . .'

'Isn't it?'

'What?'

'Well, Kerry, you seem pretty wound up about what was just a stupid joke. If it isn't true, why are you getting so wound up?'

'Oh, brilliant. I forgot you had a degree in psychology.'

'No, sorry, Kerry, wrong person. I haven't got a degree, remember. I'm not one of your little student friends . . .'

'Yeah, that's right, Marco. 'Cause life's been tough for you, hasn't it? It's the University of Life for you, isn't it, Marco? Remember who you're talking to. Don't try that I'm-from-the-gutter bullshit with me. I've never judged you. I've never given you a hard time about your friends, most of whom are bigger, more self-indulgent wankers than you'll meet in any student bar. You think some of *them* don't have a rich mummy and daddy? I don't care whether you study. I don't care if you spend half your time with your nose glued to a toilet seat. But don't give me a hard time about what I do. Because you've got no right.'

Kerry can feel the rush of fury now; she wants to hurt Marco, she wants him to wilt in front of her. She can feel the blood pounding in her head.

'What? What are you talking about? I don't give you a hard time about studying. I think it's brilliant that you're at college.'

As long as I remain a widow, thinks Kerry bitterly. As long as you can depend on me being around when you roll in after an all-night session. As long as the only time I enjoy myself is under your watchful eye. Like some patronising elder brother you are sometimes, Marco, turning your scorn on anything that excludes you or that you can't control.

'Thanks very much. It's so important to me that I have your approval,' she snaps.

Marco is genuinely bewildered now and his lack of under-standing quickly turns into anger.

'Fuck this shit, Kerry. Stop changing everything around. All right, I'm sorry if your Paddy mate had her feelings hurt. But I wasn't to know, was I? It's obviously more than that anyway.

I don't know why you're making such a big deal about it. If you fancy Little Lord Fauntleroy, just go for it. It's about fucking time you . . .' He stops as he realises what he is about to say.

Kerry stares at him for a second, her eyes dark with anger and contempt, her lip curling slightly.

'Kerry, I . . .'

'Shut up,' she says, and turns quickly and walks into her bedroom.

She lies on her bed staring at the ceiling. The bathroom door clicks behind Marco and she hears the sound of taps running which irritates her even more because she had just been thinking about having a bath.

It's about fuckin' time you . . .

And maybe it is. Because not only has she not slept with anybody since Gary's death, but in the last year that they were together they only had sex twice. And it was one of those times that she got pregnant. They had been drunk and desire had risen suddenly, unusually in both of them at the same time. Because of the rarity of sexual activity between them, Kerry had come off the pill, thinking that there was little point in risking thrombosis or cervical cancer for such small return. The strange and deep pleasure of physical passion between them meant that she could not bring herself even to mention the word 'condom' which would in all probability have upset the delicate balance of energy and caused Gary to roll over, limp and furious. And as Kerry had felt her own orgasm building inside her there was no way that she was going to murmur anything about pulling out and they had cried out together in the darkened room as she felt him come inside her, and at that precise moment, even through her own pleasure, a voice inside her head said 'You're pregnant', and then disappeared again like a match in darkness.

Kerry paid little attention to the lateness of her period so her body devised a less subtle way of alerting her to her condition. Nausea took control of her, invaded her; it felt as if it was practically destroying her. She could not eat, smoke or drink. She threw up in the morning, spent the whole of the tube journey to work trying not to think of the nausea poltergeist inside her and would have to run from the tube station, through the doors of the office block and straight to the toilet where she would retch and retch with such violence that in the absence of food she began to fear that her internal organs might drop out into the toilet in front of her. The pregnancy test wasn't particularly traumatic because she knew by then what the result would be.

She told Jeanette first.

'Don't go to the doctor and don't waste your time with the NHS. That's a total lottery. Go to this place I know. It's private but I'll lend you some money if you ain't got any. It's about two hundred and fifty quid.'

'How do you know I want to get rid of it?'

'I know. And if I were you, I wouldn't tell that idiot Gary.'

But Kerry did tell Gary and then wished she had taken Jeanette's advice. Because it was as if somebody had just been handed the key to happiness. Somebody who had been standing and staring at a locked door for some considerable time. He had hugged her, he had told her to sit down and not overdo things, he had started making jokes about eating for two and naming it after football players, before Kerry managed to blurt out, 'I don't want to have it.'

Gary had stared at her. 'What do you mean?'

'What I say. I'm not ready to have a kid. I don't want one. I don't even like them much. Well, they're all right, I suppose, once they've stopped being babies. In very small doses. I'm filled with sickness, I just want it to stop.'

Gary lit a cigarette, narrowing his eyes at her. 'And I don't get any say in this matter?'

'Oh, it's not like that. Look at us, Gary, we can't even take care of ourselves properly, let alone a kid.'

'Yeah but that could change, Kerry,' he said eagerly, 'that *would* change. I'll sort myself out, I'll get a job. I really will.' He sat on the edge of the chair as if ready to sprint out of the flat and start looking for one immediately. 'It's not like you're really young either. I mean, look at the girls on this estate, they're ten years younger than you and they've got kids. More than one, most of them.'

'What has that got to do with it? Don't start comparing me to them. Age has got nothing to do with it. I've been thinking about going to college.'

'College? What for? Things have changed, Kerry. You're going to come out of college and be lucky if you're even able to go back to what you're doing now. Fuck college. It will be brilliant, Kerry, this is what we need, this is just what we need.'

'It's not what I need. It's not what I want.'

Kerry was beginning to feel desperate. She lit a cigarette and then stubbed it out almost immediately as nausea tightened its transparent ghostly hand around her stomach.

'We could get married, if you want? If that's what you want . . .'

'It's not what I want.'

'Well, what do you want, Kerry? Eh? What the fuck do you want, you selfish cow?'

'Don't start shouting at me.' She turned as if to leave the room but Gary quickly detained her.

'I'm sorry, I'm sorry. Kerry, please, please think about it? Look at me, I'm a mess, I know I'm a mess. I'm crap but I'd be a good dad. I've always known that. I'd be a good dad. I'd try, you know, Kerry, I'd try and make him happy. Or her. I'd want that more than anything. We could do it, we could make it happy.'

'And how would we do that when we can't even make ourselves happy?'

'But this could make us happy as well. Please, just don't make any decisions just now. Please, just promise? Promise me you'll think about it? I'm fucking begging you, Kerry. Look, I'll go down on my knees. On my knees, I'm begging you.'

And Gary did go down on his knees and start sliding across the floor towards her, his hands together in supplication so that he looked like a beggar with no legs, and Kerry had to laugh.

'Get up, you idiot.'

'Please, Kerry. Just promise you'll think about it?'

'I'll think about it.'

'It could be so good. It could be happy. I'll be good, I'll be a good dad.'

'I said I'll think about it.'

But there was nothing to think about so far as whether or not to have the baby was concerned. She just didn't want one. Her thoughts were different. She thought about the nausea-inducing blob inside her as a potential human being, a thing which did not have life but was a possible life. In fact, she spent more time thinking about this issue than she did about whether or not to have the abortion which, in spite of her promise to Gary, was not something on which she was going to change her mind. Of all the unsettling aspects of the process this was perhaps the greatest. If she just did nothing, then in five years' time she would have a four-year-old child. It would be real, alive, thinking, a product of that night, that pleasure, that person she still loved. But that was crazy because what was inside her was not real, alive or thinking. 'It' did not exist except in Kerry's imagination. And possible lives are always with us, unborn phantoms, like unknown planets; the millions, billions of potential lives born or not born, known or unknown, in an insane combination of possibilities. She had no sentiment about what was inside her – any more than she felt sentimental about an egg or a sperm – but rather about what the thing inside her might be, its imaginary life, like Gary's vision of happiness and good fatherhood. She knew with complete clarity, however, that this imagined life was not powerful enough to make her go through with it.

'Well?' Jeanette demanded when she phoned Kerry the next day at work.

'I'm gonna have to take you up on your offer to help out with the money. Not all of it, just about half. And I want to get it sorted as quickly as possible.'

'Did you tell Retard?'

'Don't call him that. Yes, I did and yes, you were right. I shouldn't have.'

'I'll phone and make an appointment for you. You've got to go and have this bollocks counselling first, answer lots of stupid questions. But it's better than the doctor. At least it's a woman – well, actually, I wasn't completely sure of that with my counsellor. Anyway, once you've gone through all that bullshit they make an appointment with the clinic and you just go out there, lie on a bed, they give you a jab and the next thing you wake up and you're all clean and ready to go again. My counsellor told me I might feel guilty and I said to her that I wouldn't, so she said that in that case I might feel guilty about not feeling guilty. Can you believe that? I said to her, well, in that case, what if I start feeling guilty about not feeling guilty about not feeling guilty? Stupid cow! Anyway, forget guilty, Kerry, I've never felt so brilliant in my life. Open the champagne, mate, that's how I felt. The only problem was that idiot Darren was late to pick me up and there's all the other girls getting met and me like a lemon the last one . . .'

'So you'll make the appointment? As soon as possible.'

'Yeah, don't worry, Kerry. I'll call you back. And those receptionists where you work could do with some training. No manners at all. I got some rude cow who sounded like she was doing me some massive favour and not her job. I said to her, "Listen, love, if you was working for me you'd be picking up your P45 by now." And she went, "Well I don't work for you, do I?" so I said . . .'

'Jeanette, listen, I've got somebody coming through on the other line. I'll call you back, right? Or call me when it's sorted.'

'Speak to you later.'

Kerry had few problems persuading the counsellor about her need for an abortion. The date was fixed, she arranged two days off work and didn't tell Gary. Jeanette said that she would take her to and from the clinic and that she could stay the night with her afterwards.

Jeanette paid for a taxi to the clinic from her house. She had been in a club the night before and had not found it easy getting up that morning. Kerry watched her sister with affection as she packed some magazines and a rather incongruous banana into a carrier bag for her. Jeanette was taller than Kerry, with long legs that she managed to show off at every opportunity. She had more shoes than anyone Kerry had ever known and would sometimes give virtually new pairs to Kerry after wearing them once and deciding that she no longer liked them. Marco and Gary always referred to her as the babe-sister and Marco teased her about her preference for handbag house, preening black queers and clubs where you could buy tights and cosmetics in the bogs. 'Better than those slums you go to,' Jeanette would retort, 'with all that headache techno shit and dodgy pills and ugly men.' When they were drunk once, Jeanette told Kerry that she would shag Marco if she were in the right mood and Kerry made a mental note never to pass this information on to him.

The clinic was situated in a dull suburb of North-west London – a rapists' paradise, thought Kerry as she surveyed the long dreary streets of semi-detatched housing from the taxi. She would hate to walk home down these streets at night. The clinic looked like a large house, set back slightly from the road and surrounded by trees. As they descended from the taxi, Kerry noticed what seemed to be a big family milling about by the entrance – a group of adults and some children. They were staring at Kerry and Jeanette and one of the women, wearing a headscarf, broke away from the group, dragging a child behind her, and made straight for them.

'You're not going to go in there, are you?' she demanded.

'What's it to you?' snapped Jeanette, who was irritable anyway after rising early that morning.

'They murder babies in there, they slaughter innocents. Look at this beautiful child here and reconsider your decision. Don't play into their hands, don't murder that beautiful young life. It feels the agony, you know, it screams with pain.'

The woman's eyes were bulging, there was something appallingly gripping about her fanaticism. The kid – who was far from beautiful, resembling instead a small potato with legs – was staring up at Kerry with a blankly weird expression.

'Number one . . .' Jeanette looked almost pleased at this

opportunity for confrontation with the pro-lifers. 'Number one, it's none of your fucking business, you miserable old hag. Number two, you should see an optician if you think *that* . . .' and she flapped contemptuously with her hand at the child who shifted its blank gaze to her ' . . . is beautiful.'

The woman followed them towards the entrance where the group began a strange wailing as they passed.

'Oh, get a life,' snarled Jeanette without a trace of irony as she passed them.

'Come on, Jeanette.' Kerry pulled at her arm.

'We'll pray for you,' called the woman in the headscarf. 'For you and your murdered baby.'

'Pray for yourself, you witch!' Jeanette threw back over her shoulder. 'Honestly, Kerry, it's terrible that they let them stand out there hassling people. Where's the police? They go about shooting doctors, you know. I read this article in *Marie-Claire* about it . . .'

But Kerry could feel nerve-compounded nausea rising inside her again. She was glad that Jeanette had been with her for this confrontation with the pro-life pickets. Despite her contempt for them, despite feeling no moral doubt about what she was doing, they were still unsettling. She imagined some teenager from Ireland, alone and nervous, confronted by these fanatics. They reminded her of characters from a film she had once seen about two couples in a van trying to escape from Satanists. As they fled across Texas, all the ordinary-looking citizens had managed to convey the same unhinged quality that left little doubt that they were directly in the employ of the Prince of Darkness.

Even Jeanette couldn't find any fault with the nurses and doctors in the clinic. She left, promising to come back at the appropriate time and then Kerry was alone. She was taken to change and then to a bed on a ward where several other women were already waiting. The girl next to her smiled cheerfully at Kerry as she got into bed and Kerry smiled weakly back. She felt like shit. Outside the window, a great tree brushed its leaves against the window, letting shafts of rainy light fall through on to the walls and floor of the ward. She remembered her interview at Oxford when she was eighteen years old, the way she had stared at the slip-on shoe of the don or whatever he was called as he had jiggled his crossed leg impatiently at her answers.

Eighteen years old. A shy girl with the wrong accent. Or not even that, not even the wrong accent. Just that she didn't make the right noises, touch the right chords. There was no space in that book-lined study for feeling around tentatively, pauses, doubt, hesitation. Whatever the man was looking for, it was a different type of vitality and energy from that which Kerry possessed; something which would make him stop tapping his foot impatiently and smile at her suddenly. But he didn't, the breakthrough smile never came, he almost flapped her away so that she felt as if an invisible stamp had been placed upon her: rejected. It was a definitive moment; her life could have gone one way but it went another – it went towards a world of offices and filing and an inverted home where you went down instead of up. Down instead of up.

Finally, a nurse came to collect her and take her to the place where the operation was to happen. The doctor talked her through it but Kerry barely listened. 'A minor operation . . . we call it the suction method . . . slight discomfort . . . heavy period . . . phone your GP if . . .' She looked at the plastic wristband they had given her, the nurse and anaesthetist smiling encouragingly with their eyes, the white-tiled walls. And then the needle in her arm and a last tiny flash of consciousness before the shutters of oblivion came firmly down.

When Kerry awoke, she felt like there was a great lump between her legs. She put her hand gingerly down under her nightie and realised that it was a sanitary towel the size of a doorstep. The doctor came to see her and told her that it had all gone very smoothly and that he did not anticipate any problems. She did feel a slight cramp in her stomach but apart from that she was OK. She lay in bed reading a magazine about whether length or width – or a felicitous combination of both – made for the ideal penis. A woman was boasting about her lover having a nine-inch penis and Kerry shuddered. The thought of it made her turn the page quickly to an article on why women put up with abusive men.

The time came for the women to be collected. An assortment of neurotic boyfriends, anxious mums, and various sisters and aunties were waiting in the reception area.

'All right, KitKat?' said Jeanette who had been flirting with one of the boyfriends while she waited. The girl who had been in the bed next to Kerry was being met by her auntie. 'Thank fuck that's all over.' She grinned at Kerry as they left to get taxis. 'Until the next time,' said the auntie sourly, but the girl just laughed and thumped her arm.

The boy Jeanette was talking to winked at her as she left and held an imaginary receiver to his ear while making a dialling motion with his hand.

'That's disgusting,' Kerry said wearily. 'He never gave you his phone number while his girlfriend was inside having an abortion?'

''Fraid so, sweetheart.' Jeanette smiled smugly. 'He was cute. I ain't gonna phone him, though.'

The pro-lifers were not outside the clinic any longer and Kerry felt a huge surge of relief as she slumped in the back of the cab, leaving behind the dreary suburban streets. She wondered where the pro-lifers had gone, to which joyless, humourless houses, and felt a stab of pity for the potato-faced kid who would probably never be normal after spending its formative years hassling young women outside clinics. I will never come back here, she thought, as Jeanette chattered cheerfully about what they should get out on video that evening and how it was lucky that Darren would be playing football and getting pissed with his mates afterwards. Then she turned to Kerry and asked, 'What are you gonna say to Gary tomorrow?'

The cramp in Kerry's stomach seemed to worsen. She did not answer Jeanette because she did not have an answer, just stared out of the window at the sky where low black clouds were rolling like smoke from a gigantic fire and beginning to spit rain over London. Jeanette seemed to sense this because she did not repeat the question but instead began a long story about how she had nearly had to fight a girl in a club because the girl's boyfriend had kept eyeing her up. Kerry thought about the suction method, everything suddenly rushed out, pulled by an irresistible force like a massive intake of breath, leaving nothing behind – a vacuum. She placed the flat of her hand over her stomach and let her head roll on to her shoulder.

What are you gonna say to Gary tomorrow? The question repeated itself over and over in Kerry's head as the cab stopped at some traffic lights and she watched a young couple in a bar toasting each other with glasses of white wine. Their Saturday night was just starting, they appeared so carefree. She would have given anything to be them, to be in their shoes. A sense of melancholy weariness, far more discomforting than the pain in her stomach, spread through her. It was a strange expression – to be in their shoes, as if their footwear was what gave them their defining characteristics of lucky or unlucky, winner or loser. I wouldn't like to be in your shoes. Kerry looked down at her own shoes, small on the floor of the taxi. *What are you gonna say to Gary tomorrow?* I don't know, she thought miserably to herself, I just don't fucking know.

Chapter 6

Marco has never found losing drugs very funny but leaving the best part of a gram of coke in the bogs of a bar represents something of a tragedy. 'You stupid cunt!' Danny is almost hysterical as he paid for most of it. 'Check again, check your pockets. Look again, Marco.'

'It's not here,' he says dully. 'Those lairy geezers who were banging on the door must have found it. Look at the grins on them.'

After his argument with Kerry, Marco went out to find Danny. They have spent half the evening trailing around trying to find Arnold who has the irritating quality common to dealers and policemen of not being there when you want him most. Finally, they tracked him down to a pub in the Caledonian Road where Danny got a gram off him after Arnold had inflicted a half-hour coke-driven monologue on them about why he felt that he could no longer wear Patrick Cox shoes because now all the peasants from Essex were wearing them. Marco did not like the pub, it had recently been done up and the toilets shimmered like the lift in their block of flats, the DJs at the back were rubbish, and it was all being carefully checked out by some of the local geezers who sat hard-eyed at the bar watching everything.

Marco and Danny had slipped gratefully away from Arnold into the bogs to do a line and were followed – probably intentionally, Marco now realises – by three guys who began hammering on the door and screaming at them to hurry up. Danny left Marco to go out and face them down but when he heard the sound of a fight about to break out, he skipped out quickly to back Danny up, and somewhere along the line the wrap disappeared. Danny and Marco managed to get out of the bogs without a fight starting but also without their coke.

Arnold is sympathetic. 'I'll tell you what I'll do, boys. I'll give you half a g, right? On credit. And you know I never normally do that.'

'Cheers, Arnold,' says Danny, calming down a bit. 'Marco will sort you out later. Won't you, Marco?'

Marco feels pissed off that all the blame is being transferred to him but knows that it is not worth arguing about. 'Yeah, sure.'

Arnold begins to comfort Marco with stories about legendary drug losses: the time he wrapped a gram in a fifty-pound note and dropped it; the time he put five pills in a packet of Silk Cut with one fag in it, forgetting this later on in the evening and handing the packet to a tramp; someone he knew who taped some trips inside the freezer compartment of their fridge which then disappeared. 'Every time we was round at his house and pissed we used to have a go chipping the ice out of that freezer compartment to see if we could find them.'

'Yeah,' Marco says, feeling around forlornly in his pocket, 'you never lose hope.'

'That tramp must have had a laugh for a few days,' says Danny.

'Well, I've gotta chip now,' Arnold says, sliding the wrap to Marco. 'Catch you later, boys.'

'Give me that,' Danny snaps at Marco, 'I'm not trusting you with it again.'

As they are finishing their pints and about to leave, one of the boys who was banging on the door sidles over. He puts a finger over one nostril and sniffs loudly and then he giggles. Marco glances quickly at his two mates who are not paying that much attention. The boy at the bar is small and black with closely cropped hair. His two mates are big, white, born-and-interbred-in-Islington geezers. Marco does not respond so the boy turns to him and says, 'You been staring at me a lot like you wanna say something to me. You wanna say something? You wanna talk about lost property maybe?' Marco can hardly believe that someone lucky enough to find a gram also wants to make something of it with the people who lost it. He turns to the guy who has a gold-toothed grin.

'Talk to you?' Marco says quietly. 'No, mate, I don't wanna talk to you about anything.'

The boy laughs. 'That's lucky, man. 'Cause I thought you was lookin' at me a lot. Do you know what I'm sayin'? Maybe I need an eye test. Is that what you're sayin'?' Danny finishes his pint in one gulp and rests it on the bar with his hand still around it.

'I ain't sayin' nothin', mate.'

'You ain't sayin' nothin'? That's good, man, that's good. 'Cause don't fuck with me, right? Don't fuck with me.' The boy is wired and getting ready to kick off. ''Cause I'm warning you right, you fuck with me and you're fuckin' with a nigger in a million. Do you know what I'm sayin'? A nigger in a million.'

'That's funny,' Danny suddenly speaks, ''cause I thought you was just a nigger.'

The boy turns to him but before he can react Danny has caught him full in the face with his head and he goes flying across the bar on to a table, sending glasses scattering and people leaping out of the way. Danny is renowned for his speed in that department, even Gary used to acknowledge it and he never had that much time for Danny. Fortunately, they are close to the door, and Marco and Danny are out before the boy can recover and before his mates can get across the bar to them. They sprint down Caledonian Road, Marco trailing slightly as Danny is much fitter. Marco turns his head to see if they are being followed and sees a bus coming. 'Danny, bus, there's a bus!' The bus-stop is about a hundred yards further down and Danny increases his speed in order to make sure that they catch it. But then Marco sees the beautiful sight of a taxi with its orange light on. He slows down to a jog. 'Come on, hurry up, hurry up.' He still can't see anyone in pursuit of them but as he is hailing the cab, a couple slightly further up also stop and hold out their arms. Desperately, Marco runs back in the other direction, just passing them and getting his arm in first. 'Hey,' the girl protests, 'that's our cab.'

'Buy yourself a travel-card.' Marco gets the door open and flings himself in. He looks behind him and sees the three guys jogging slowly down the road looking around them. Then they must have seen Danny trotting back from the bus-stop because all three break into a sprint.

'Quick, mate,' Marco tells the cabbie. 'We've got to pick my friend up there.'

Danny has now seen his pursuers, and is running towards both them and the cab. The fact that the cab is moving towards him though gives him the advantage. 'Here, here!' Marco almost shrieks at the cabbie, trying to open the door, but the red light stays on. 'Open the fucking door,' Marco yells and the cabbie turns around.

'If you're gonna give me lip, mate, I ain't gonna take you nowhere. There's no need for that.'

Danny is scrabbling with the door, his face panic-stricken, not understanding why it won't open.

'Sorry, mate, really I'm sorry. It's just we're in a hurry. Please open the door? I never meant to be rude.'

The cabbie sighs and shakes his head and the red light goes off. Danny bursts into the cab and they pull away. Marco watches the three blokes slow their pace as they realise that they're not going to catch them.

'Fuck me . . .' Danny is still panting. 'They would have murdered us. I caught him a beauty, though. He wasn't gonna get up after that one.'

'He did get up,' Marco says.

'Yeah, but after we had time to get out of there. Nigger in a million! Mug in a million more like. Walked right into it . . .'

Danny glances at Marco, shakes his head and murmurs, 'Stupid schwartzer.'

Marco sighs inwardly. He has had arguments with Danny before about his use of casual racism. Sometimes Danny does it as a wind-up, sometimes he just does it. Marco thinks that Danny is probably unclear in his own mind any longer as to why he is saying it.

'Don't start with all that again, Danny. It's got nothing to do with it.'

'Hasn't it? It was him who started with all that nigger in a million stuff, remember. Anyway, you should be thanking me not getting all politically correct, mate. I nailed him while you was just sitting there like a lemon waiting for him to start.'

'I never said you didn't do well, I ain't saying he wasn't a nasty little fucker . . . just don't start up with all that schwartzer routine of yours. I don't get shocked by it and I don't think it's funny. Save it for some mug in Soho, Danny.'

Marco feels a sense of weariness. Talking to Danny sometimes is like playing a game with a person who can't really be bothered to learn or observe the rules properly. A goal-hanger. He supposes that, deep down, he does not think that Danny is really a big-time racist. Danny has plenty of black mates, more, probably, than many of the people who use all the correct terminology yet who don't sit down next to a black person on the tube. But Danny has also slid into a mode of speaking that can be skilfully – and sometimes not so skilfully – laced with irony to deflect criticism. It is the sloppy lad-language that Marco – although guilty of it himself sometimes – does not really like. There is a kind of dreary orthodoxy about it, whether used by cockneys, mockneys or self-conscious public school boys snorting charlie at the parties of lad magazines and gleefully talking about totty. Marco knows, however, that it is an increasingly large and fixed part of Danny's vocabulary; that Danny is no longer just tossing these comments out as a self-conscious strategy for mocking the self-righteous hypocrisy of the liberal middle-classes.

They don't say much more on the way back to the flat, both pissed off with the other, both still hyped up from what might have happened if they had been caught. When they have picked their way into the mess of Danny's living room, Danny throws Marco the wrap and goes to the bathroom.

'Chop 'em out while I have a piss.'

Marco pulls out an album cover. It is Anita Baker, sitting holding her knee.

'Do you mind if I do it on a cover with a black woman on it?' he calls to Danny.

Danny comes back in grinning. 'The difference between Anita Baker, Marco, and that little . . . bastard back there is that she's never stolen my drugs, never tried to give me a kicking, and plus she's a brilliant singer. Which I doubt if he is.'

'Exactly.' Marco licks alone the edge of the card and takes the note from Danny. 'But they're both schwartzers in your book, eh, Danny?'

'Ah, shut up, Marco. Change the fucking record. You know I didn't mean it like that. And that's my tenner you're putting back into your pocket by the way.'

Marco cannot be bothered to continue the argument. He knows, however, that Danny will be more careful in future. At least when Marco is around.

'How's Marina?' he asks to change the subject. Danny grins.

'She only went and told her boyfriend about me.'

'I knew it.'

'Yeah, she's a wind-up. Anyway, the idiot finds out my number, right, and starts phoning at night and not saying anything. I'd give him a slap if he wasn't such a loser, so I told him on the phone. I said, "I know it's you, mate, and phoning me up ain't gonna change the fact that I shagged your bird." So he starts crying and babbling down the phone about how he's gonna kill me, kill Marina, kill himself. I nearly said, Stick with the last option, mate. But you know me, Marco, I ain't like that . . .'

''Course not.'

'Exactly. So I tell Marina she'd better have words with him and anyway he decides he's gonna forgive her and they go out for some big meal and now they're talking about getting married. He's a journalist, you know. Writes all these articles about Britain in the nineties – twelve-year-old tarts on crack, single mums in the nick for not paying their telly licence – all that tear-jerking bollocks for people in Hampstead. Anyway, check this, Marco. He tells Marina that there's this new word for people like me that some lefty beardy has dreamt up. You know what he called me? He called me an Underwolf.'

'A what?'

'An Underwolf. You're one as well, I think. It means, right, that you're basically scum but that you bite back and don't give a fuck anymore. Funny, innit? I said to Marina that she was an Overwolf then. Anyway, she don't wanna see me no more and he's taking her to Paris for the weekend.'

'So are you feeling used?'

'Marco, she can use me any time she wants. She was mental in bed, mate. Totally and utterly Radio Rental.'

'What do you mean? Did she do cartwheels or something?'

'No, Marco. For her, right, sleeping with me was like losing her virginity. Do you know what I mean? Up until then she hadn't experienced real sex.'

Marco sniggers. 'She tell you that, did she?'

'Not in so many words. But you can tell. It was dead obvious that she hadn't been getting satisfaction from that sap.'

'Maybe 'cause she'd never had sex with an Underwolf before. Anyway, if it was all so mental, how come she was able to give up this *Wild Orchid* experience and go back to whatsis-name?'

'Come on, Marco. She's a posh bird. She knows what side her bread's buttered on in the long run.'

'She thought that Jeremy the journalist was a better offer than Danny the despatch rider? It's hard to believe.'

Danny starts chopping out another couple of lines on the Anita Baker cover.

'You may mock, Marco, but she'll be back. If not to me then . . .'

' . . . to another Underwolf?'

They start to laugh. 'Underwolf . . .' Marco can hardly speak. 'Somebody really sat around and thought that one up. I'll have to tell my dad, he'll love that one.'

'Still on his Commie tip then, your old man? He hasn't just got fed up with it all?'

'Yeah, well, he gets depressed, you know. But it's not like a fashion statement for him. He still really believes it. The British working class rising like lions after slumber, shaking their chains . . .'

'Like fuck they will! The British working class will do what they're told to do, think what they're meant to think. Like always. It's like that Lady Di . . .' Danny trails off.

'What about her?'

'I dunno. You know, all that Queen of Hearts stuff? It . . . sometimes it makes me feel sick. I mean, literally. I can feel it, you know . . . I watch her and I just wanna be sick. But all the morons still go on about poor old Di. I've always really hated the royal family.'

'Yeah?' Marco is surprised at this sudden outburst from Danny. He feels depressed suddenly thinking about it all: his dad, Lady Di the Queen of Hearts, the silver bust of Lenin on the mantelpiece, underwolves. '*Ye are many – they are few.*' His dad had taught him that poem. '*Ye are many – they are few.*' Doesn't help matters much, though. Poor old Shelley couldn't swim, died when he was as old as Marco. Kerry had been surprised that Marco knew about it when she was studying the Romantic Poets at college and he had picked up the book from her desk and told her that Shelley and Byron were mates and that Byron had got Shelley's sister-in-law pregnant. Kerry's surprise was a bit too obvious and he might have picked her up for being patronising but couldn't be bothered.

The Gulf of Spezia, a summer storm. His dad had gone there with Marco's mum, looked out over a beautifully calm sea to a horizon where more than a hundred and fifty years earlier the rough waves had carelessly tossed, and the fish had nibbled, the body of a great English radical and John Fisher's favourite poet. The disfigured body washed to the Italian coast after the storm had subsided and the sun had come out again, identified by a leather-bound copy of Keats's poetry in the shirt pocket. Marco's dad told him all of this. Poor old Shelley.

But he did a lot in his short life, Shelley, and Marco – what has he done? Fuck all. So poor old Marco. His mum would have been disappointed in him like his dad. And Kerry is disappointed in him now, but they'll make up. She thinks that if she gets her degree it will prove something. But what will she do after that? What is it she's really after? And what about this bloke sniffing around? Marco doesn't know why he has got this thing about Robin. It isn't jealousy, there's just something about him. And Marco thinks, as he leans over to take the note from Danny, anxious for the buzz off the charlie to stop him getting all miserable, that if Kerry gets mixed up with Robin, no good will come of it, no good at all.

Chapter 7

Assignments are being handed back and Kerry has got a first. She is the only one in the class who does and sits feeling a kind of fierce joy running through her. 'Well done,' Susan whispers to her. Robin doesn't say anything but sits reading his returned assignment frowning and straightening it with his fingers. Kerry feels a little bit sorry for him as she knows he spent considerable time and effort on it, with a last two-day-and-night frenzy to finish it off. It is much longer than Kerry's.

It is also Kerry's turn to present the seminar and she feels a confidence-fuelled fluency as she talks, barely looking down to her notes as she stands in front of the class. At one point she stops to glance at them and when she looks up again she catches Robin's eye. He is staring at her so intensely that she almost falters for a moment and feels a slight flush rise to her face. When she finishes, the lecturer beams at her and says. 'Thanks, Kerry, that was thoughtful as usual.' She sees Simon Davis roll his eyes and whisper something to the person next to him and giggle. She couldn't care less, though, she is riding high on adrenaline, could almost turn and say: Do you think I care what you think, you slimy middle-class creep?

After the class, the whole group goes to the refectory for a coffee. They are all moaning about the library and how the books for the assignment are never there and how expensive it is to buy them. 'Some people don't have that problem though, do they?' Simon Davis says, grinning.

'Who doesn't have that problem?' Susan asks. 'We've all got that problem.'

'But you're wrong,' Simon is still grinning. 'I mean, Robin doesn't have that problem 'cause he's rich, isn't he?'

Robin glances at Simon and smiles with half his mouth to show that he can't be bothered replying.

'Then there's Jenny . . .' Simon continues gleefully. Everyone turns and looks at Jenny who blushes slightly and puts both hands around her cup of coffee.

'Yeah,' Simon persists, 'I happen to know that Jenny's on to a nice little earner. Come on, Jenny, it's nothing to be ashamed of. You're just selling your labour-power like everybody else.'

'What do you do?' somebody asks.

There is a small silence and then Jenny stares defiantly at Simon. 'I'm not ashamed at all,' she says quietly. 'I do stripping. Once or twice a month. It pays a lot more than bar work and I get more time to study.'

'Stripping?' Susan stares at her. 'Isn't it horrible, though, all those men . . .'

'No, it's OK most of the time. It's quite controlled where I work. I'm not intending to make it a career for life.'

'But it's not like everyone could do it.' Simon grins insolently at Susan and she flushes deeply at the implicit insult. Kerry feels rage beginning to bubble inside her, she begins to tremble and fights for the calm to transform her crude anger into glittering words.

'Have you got a job?' she asks Simon icily.

'No time, Kerry. Apart from all of this . . .' he waves his hand contemptuously ' . . . there's all the political commitments. The shortage of books isn't a college problem you know. It's a political problem which can only be resolved politically. You should come to our lunchtime meeting. We're going to be putting up a motion for a permanent occupation.'

'Maybe,' Kerry says quietly, 'your organisation should find someone else to publicise their meetings. Because you're not a particularly attractive advertisement for them, Simon.'

He continues to grin, showing a little more of his teeth.

'Because I realise that there's more to college than getting firsts and taking apples to the lecturers?'

'No, not really,' Susan suddenly interrupts. 'Because you're an idiot.'

Jenny laughs abruptly. 'Yeah, I mean, I get to see some sad and sleazy men with the stripping. But you . . .' She shakes her head.

Simon makes a stirring motion with his hand. 'Hubble, bubble, toil and trouble. Water off a duck's back, I'm afraid, girls. Anyway, I've got more important things to be doing than sitting around bitching. See you later. Come to the meeting, right?'

They watch him go, affecting a loping walk, winking at another table as he passes. Kerry sighs. 'He's right. It is water off a duck's back for him.'

'Water off a wanker's back,' says Jenny.

'You shouldn't give him the satisfaction,' Robin says, 'of rising to the bait.'

'Oh, I quite enjoyed that,' Susan replies. 'I don't care whether it bothers him or not.'

Robin sips at his coffee. 'When I was first at college, there was a guy who was exactly like him. It's funny how they never seem to change . . .'

'You were at college before?' Jenny asks. 'Where?'

'I went to Oxford,' Robin replies without a trace of self-consciousness. 'When I was eighteen. It was the wrong time to go and I didn't get on well with the tutors. In the end I hated it so much that I left. I just had to get out of there, it was such a waste of time.'

'You left Oxford?' Susan is astonished. 'And ended up here? Couldn't you have gone back there and started again?'

Robin laughs, playing with a Mars Bar wrapper, twisting it round and round into a tight coil. 'But I didn't want to go back there. I live in London. And, anyway, I don't accept that Oxford has a higher academic standard than here. It certainly didn't when I was there. I met some of the stupidest people I've ever met in my life in the year that I was up there.'

'What did you do,' Kerry asks, 'after you decided to leave?'

'Oh . . .' Robin waves his hand vaguely ' . . . lots of things, you know. I worked for a while with a friend who ran a shop, a sort of cooperative. I travelled for a while in Asia and Central

America. My mum lives up in Yorkshire, so I went and helped her because she was doing up this house in the Dales. Then I decided that I was ready to study again so I came here.'

'Did you go to India?' asks Kerry half-innocently, but Robin is ready for that one.

'You mean, am I just a spoiled rich hippy kid looking for self-discovery? Yes, I went to India. But I was interested, you know. It was a good laugh. Well, it was a good laugh until I got dysentery.'

'I didn't mean that,' she protests, knowing that she did, but Robin just laughs good-naturedly and brushes a curl of hair from his face. Kerry likes the way he does not try and conceal things. He is not embarrassed about anything, he does not tell lies about himself.

Kerry checks her watch. 'I've got to get going.'

'What are you up to now?' he asks.

'I'm meeting my sister, she's taking me shopping.'

'But you're still coming tonight?'

'Yeah, Kerry.' Susan turns to her. 'Remember, we said we were going to that thing in the bar tonight? They do tequila slammers for fifty p.'

'OK,' Kerry nods. 'What time are you going to be there? I'll try and get back about eight or something.'

As she is leaving, however, she sees Matilda sitting at another table. Matilda beckons her over.

'I'm finally leaving this dump,' she announces.

Kerry raises her eyebrows.

'And I'm pregnant,' Matilda adds, lighting a cigarette.

'Oh, dear,' Kerry says without thinking, 'what are you going to do about it?'

'Do? I'm going to have it.'

Kerry is astonished. 'You're going to have it? Why?'

Matilda inhales deeply and releases the smoke in an angry cloud.

''Cause I want to have a baby. I'm twenty-eight, you know, Kerry. It'll be too late soon. And I'm just wasting time with this stupid course.'

Don't Step on the Lines

There is a hard tone in Matilda's voice which Kerry resents. She has heard it before. It is as if Matilda is already part of a special elite, as if the hormonal change already underway also releases a chemical compelling her to patronise childless women. *I'm twenty-eight, you know, Kerry (which is still about three years younger than you). I'm just wasting time with this stupid course (which is exactly what you are doing).*

Kerry's cousins are particularly good at this – they take it in turns to churn out babies on a regular basis, and view women over twenty-five who have not had children in much the same way as they would a woman with no legs or, even worse, as potential lesbians. Kerry's least favourite cousin, Nicola – whom Jeanette used to bully ruthlessly when they were younger – once told her that women who could have babies but didn't were in fact extremely selfish. Especially when there were so many poor women who were desperate to have children but couldn't. Kerry can tell that the existence of these 'poor women' is a source of great satisfaction to Nicola, that she tempers her pity with a deep smug pleasure that she is not one of these unlucky souls and that she is able to reproduce without the aid of science. Great pity is also reserved for Kerry's parents given that both of their daughters have proved to have the selfish streak.

Even the more bearable cousin, Fiona, has said that, while she supposes that abortions should be available to those that want them, and that she feels sorry for the poor women who must carry the guilt and psychological scars for the rest of their lives, she finds it an incomprehensible act, and – gathering the cloak of self-righteousness proudly around her – that when she looks at her little Ben and her little Antonia, it puts the whole question of abortion into context.

At one family event, Nicola unwisely told Kerry that she was sure that Kerry really did want children. One of the more irritating aspects of the baby-fanatics for Kerry is their belief that they have an especially privileged insight into your real state of mind. Women who say that they do not want children really do; women who claim not to feel guilt about abortions are just in denial. Unfortunately for Nicola, her comment was made within earshot of Jeanette, who represents a Myra Hindley figure for the cousins since she has made no secret of the fact that not only has she had an abortion, but that she does not feel a shred of remorse about it.

'How the fuck would you know what she really wants?' demanded Jeanette.

'No, Jeanette, I'm just saying that I think Kerry is the type who'll really regret it if she turns her back on children now.'

The look with which Jeanette met this statement must have reminded Nicola of pulled hair, stolen sweets and chinese burns because her face became suddenly white and pinched and she moved back into her chair as if attempting to reverse away from Jeanette.

'Regret not being more like you? I don't think so.'

Now, Kerry looks at Matilda who is going to give up her course because it is boring, in exchange for pregnancy. She can't think of anything to say, she can't be bothered to say 'Congratulations' because she doesn't see anything to congratulate. It is such a sloppy way out and she feels irritation that she is so often on the defensive, while the magic words 'I'm having a baby' seem to free others from all obligation to justify what they are doing in life. She is especially irritated because this is Matilda, whom she likes, although on reflection it does not surprise her much. Matilda's cultivated sensuous laziness, her unashamedly sexual behaviour, her contempt for college procedure, have all lent themselves to this decision. Now she will surprise everybody by having a baby, not like the boring swot Kerry who spends too much time in the library.

Kerry begins to choke out platitudes about how long, whether the father will take any responsibility, thought of a name yet, prefer boy or girl, but it is obvious that her heart isn't really in it. Fortunately for Kerry a couple of students that she hardly knows come over to talk to Matilda and she is able to slip away.

'Clever girl,' says Jeanette when Kerry tells her about her assignment. 'What does that mean?'

'Well, if I get a certain number of firsts on these assignments and do OK in the exams, then I'll get a first overall.'

Jeanette nods and sips her beer. They are sitting in a pub in Soho, carrier bags at their feet, after a trip around some of Jeanette's favourite shops where she has argued cheerfully with shop assistants, made them take things back which weren't exactly right, demanded to see all the available colours. The streets of the West End were swollen with Christmas shoppers, Kerry saw the lights in Regent Street and had to accept with a weary fatalism that this most hated time of the year was nearly upon them again. It was strange, she thought, how something that as a child had so thrilled and excited her, could have become transformed into this long and tedious countdown to a couple of days of dreary duty and planned excess. But most of all she dislikes it for its unwanted interruption to the carefully constructed patterns of her life – the forced leisure, everything closed down.

As a peace-offering to Marco, with whom she has not really talked since their argument, Kerry has bought a book called *Shark Menace!* which promises a definitive account of the behaviour of Great Whites in Australian waters. Jeanette has urged Kerry to buy things for herself; a new skirt, some tops, a pair of shades, some Nike trainers. Jeanette has also paid for most of it with her joint account cheque book. 'It's not as if Darren will notice, he's wedged up at the moment. I've got to spend all his money before I leave him. Anyway . . .' she glances slant-eyed at Kerry, ' . . . how's *your* love-life? Haven't you managed to find yourself a nice college boy yet?'

Jeanette once tried to set Kerry up with one of her friends, promising her that he was just her type – brainy and serious *and* good-looking. The guy turned out to be a nightmare – solemn, self-important, pretentious. He had kept on and on at Kerry, assaulting her with his theories, most of which were tired, second-hand or incomprehensible. Even his good looks had something over-stated and tiring about them. In the end, Kerry had begun to feel as if a large fly had decided to set up camp next to her, keeping a constant tinnitus of opinions buzzing and whining in her ear. She kept going to the loo and hoping when she came back that she could find somewhere else to sit, but he always kept an eye out for her return, grinning and pushing her chair back for her. Finally, she had mumbled something incoherent and gone home and he had looked disappointedly at Jeanette as if she had broken a promise.

'Well . . .' Kerry hesitates ' . . . I'm not sure.'

'What do you mean, you're not sure? That's the most positive thing I've heard you say in ages. Excellent! Tell me then? What's he like?'

'That's part of the problem. I can't really make up my mind. I mean, he's interested in me but I don't really know why. No, not that I don't know why . . .' Kerry corrects herself as she catches Jeanette's expression ' . . . I'm not being modest, I mean that I'm not really sure where he's coming from, what he's thinking. And I can't make up my mind about him. Sometimes I think he's really good and different, sometimes I think he's a bit sort of . . . self-obsessed. Do you know what I mean?'

'Er, no. Sorry, Kerry. Look, let's start from the basics. Do you fancy this guy?'

'Well . . . yeah, in a way I suppose I do, he's got something.'

Jeanette spreads her hands palms up in front of her like a scientist demonstrating some elementary principle to a particularly dumb student.

'Right, OK. Now sorry I've got to ask you this, Kerry, but I do, I'm your sister and I know you, right? OK, look he's not a nutter, is he? Let's be honest, one Gary in a lifetime is enough for anyone . . .' The mixture of boldness and anxiety on Jeanette's face as she says this forces Kerry to burst out laughing. Jeanette looks relieved at her reaction. 'Well?'

'He's about as far from Gary as it's possible to get.'

'Good. I mean you know I liked Gary. Well, at least before . . .'

Kerry flaps her hand and Jeanette changes tack. 'OK, so you fancy him, he's not a nutter . . .'

'He's rich,' Kerry adds, grinning, and Jeanette throws up her hands.

'Kerry, drop the ice-maiden. Have a laugh. Get him to spend

some money on you. Nobody's saying it has to be the romance of the century. Keep it simple.'

At this point, two boys who have been glancing at them from the bar, make their way over towards them holding their pints, one slightly pushing the other. Jeanette breaks off from the conversation, waiting for the interruption, studying her hand. She is wearing Rouge Noir nail varnish, like drops of dark dried blood on the ends of her fingers.

'Been shopping, girls?'

Jeanette leans back in her chair and glances at them condescendingly without replying. The boy looks down at her legs which are crossed in front of her.

'All alone, are you?' he tries again.

'Do we look alone?' Jeanette calmly lights a cigarette. Kerry grins inwardly as she knows what's coming. Jeanette exhales smoke towards him and sighs slightly. 'I mean, you've been watching us from the bar for long enough. Did we look bored, like we had nothing to say to each other? Did we look . . .' she turns her face towards him and smiles ' . . . did we look that sad and desperate that we were just waiting for two equally sad and desperate people to come and interrupt us?'

'I thought you might want a drink,' the boy mumbles as his mate edges away.

'Do you want a drink from this guy, Kerry?' Jeanette demands and Kerry shakes her head solemnly.

'And I don't want one either. Nor do we want a bag of dry-roasted peanuts. Nor do we want any company. 'Bye.'

He hesitates for a moment, his lips working slightly as if he can't leave without at least retaliating in some way. Jeanette turns back to him and says sharply: 'Have you got a problem, mate? Are you hard of hearing?'

'You're not that fucking gorgeous,' he says, moving away, 'to have that much attitude.'

'Well, if that's the criterion for having attitude,' Kerry looks up, 'then *you* shouldn't have any at all.'

The boy scowls at her and walks away to join his mate at the bar and Jeanette turns back unperturbed to Kerry as if such a trivial interruption is not even worth commenting on.

'Yeah,' she continues, 'so when are you seeing him again?'

'Tonight actually. But don't get your hopes up. I'm still not sure about it.'

'Kerry, you don't have to feel sure. Look, remember when you broke your leg, right? You had that big plaster on and you were going demented 'cause of the itching and you couldn't scratch it. Well, now you can. Just look at it like that – scratching an itch.'

Kerry laughs. 'That's such an erotic idea, Jeanette! Anyway, I might not be itching.'

Jeanette raises her eyes over her glass of golden beer.

'You're itching, honey.'

'I don't know,' Kerry sighs. 'Everything's OK at the moment. You know, it's calm. I'm getting on with things, sorting things out. I'm enjoying my work. I don't know if I need that sort of complication.'

'Who said it had to be complicated? It's only complicated if you make it complicated. Like I said, I'm not suggesting you marry the guy. Just, you know . . .'

'Even that would be complicated for me at the minute.'

'It's got to happen sometime.'

And suddenly, at that moment, a record comes on the juke-box, a tune anchored to the past, strings of memory binding it to her consciousness, bound to another time like sudden unsettling, aching smells with their mysterious, powerful nostalgia. An old summery song and Kerry is suddenly lost. It takes her back to a hot summer, sitting in the park at lunchtime eating her sandwiches from a white paper bag – fragments of cress on greased paper, sun-drunk summer-fattened pigeons hopping around her feet, workers flat out on their backs exposing their bare chests to the sky. She would hear the song on radios, in the office, from cars, from open windows. They would sit outside their flat on the walkway on the storm-bringing hot evenings, drinking beers, letting the sun warm their bare legs, laughing at the kids who would try and sneak round the corner and chuck water bombs at them. Kerry suddenly feels glad that she has bought Marco a present, he was there as well. She could say to him: Do you remember, Marco? That summer sitting out on the walkway, Marco tilting the bottle of beer to his mouth, Gary suddenly jumping up and pretending to chase the kids. You remember that, Marco? And Kerry suddenly wonders whether in the future anything will have the capacity to jolt her like that and remind her of this time now. What strings of memory is she spinning at the moment?

'Well . . .' Jeanette says gathering up the handles of plastic bags ' . . . let's make a move, Kat. My feet are really sore. It's these shoes, I don't really like them any more. You can have them, if you want?'

Chapter 8

Marco is slumped on the sofa, methodically working his way through a box of bread sticks, chomping one without using his hands as if it were a long cigar disappearing into his mouth. He nods at Kerry warily as she walks in. 'All right?'

She walks up to him, kisses him on the forehead and says, 'Close your eyes.'

'What's this?'

'Go on, close your eyes.'

He shuts his eyes and she puts the book in his hand. He blinks when he looks at it. 'I didn't think you could get hold of this any more. I got it from the library once.' He turns it round and flicks through to the photos. 'It's got a blinding story about this girl who jumped out of a boat and this shark got her and they were trying to rescue her. She had really long black hair and they grabbed her by the hair but when they pulled her by her hair they could only get hold of her top half. She had been bitten in two.' Marco flicks the pages gleefully.

'Yeah, that's a really nice story, Marco.'

'Mental though, innit?'

'I suppose it is.'

'Her name was Zita Steadman. I always remember that. Cool name.' Marco flicks through the book to another set of pictures. 'Yeah, nice Tiger that one. See the white covering its eye, Kerry? That means it's gonna attack. Great Whites don't have that membrane, they just kind of roll the eye back into the socket and . . .'

'Marco?'

'Yeah?'

'I'm glad you like it and everything but I'm not that interested in sharks really. And don't leave the book by the toilet.'

'OK. Let me guess . . .' he waves at the shopping bags ' . . . you've been out with the label victim babe-sister?'

'Correct.'

'Going out tonight?'

'Yeah. There's this thing at college. It's quite good sometimes. Cheap tequila. Come up if you want?'

'Nah, thanks anyway. I need to just chill out tonight. My stomach's gone mad.'

'You want to take it easy for a bit.'

'Yeah, maybe. Anyway, I'm gonna just read my book, leave the answerphone on.'

Kerry goes into her room. She searches through her record collection until she finds the record from the pub and puts it on while she gets dressed. Now, rather than stirring memories, it cheers her up. She takes the clothes from the bags and places them carefully on the bed. Then she puts on the skirt, one of the tops and the new trainers. She turns round to look at her profile, feeling the pleasing newness of the clothes, the shape of the skirt clinging to her body. Then she turns back and smiles at herself in the mirror. She remembers studying *Far From the Madding Crowd* for her 'O' levels with Sylvia Gordon. They were reading the part where Bathsheba is spotted smiling at herself in the mirror. Somebody had said that this showed that she was vain and Sylvia Gordon had snapped, 'What's vain about being young and aware of your sexuality and pleased about the way you look?' And the fifteen-year-old girls had stared at her and giggled because Sylvia Gordon was always going on about sex in books and she was old so what would she know about it anyway? And that was fifteen years ago and Sylvia Gordon has gone from middle-aged to old and Kerry herself has doubled in years.

She goes back into the living room where Marco is lying on the sofa, the shark book on his chest, his eyes closed. Kerry calls herself a cab. She stands looking out of the window as she waits for it, smoking a cigarette, enjoying its taste after the toothpaste with which she has just brushed her teeth. Behind her, Marco is making little murmuring noises almost like low moans as he sleeps. The telephone rings and she lets the answerphone take it. It is Susan checking whether she is going to come down. Kerry does not pick up the phone. There are stars in the sky and there are planes which look at first like stars but then their descending lights become more yellow, more atomised, losing the white constancy of the distant stars. Where Jeanette lives, you cannot see the stars, the night never blackens but remains an unnatural orange, a kind of chemical colour choking out the sky. A car turns slowly into the street below, it pauses and Kerry waits for the horn. It sounds, once, then twice in quick succession and Kerry turns away from the window. Marco opens his eyes as she passes him: 'Enjoy yourself.'

The bar is crowded when Kerry arrives and at first she cannot spot either Susan or Robin. Simon Davis is at the bar, a pile of papers under his arm, chatting up one of the German girls who is over for a term on a study visit. Kerry skirts past him and looks around the densely packed tables. The Spanish and Latin American society are running the evening in conjunction with the Gay and Lesbian society – crop-haired dykes and skinny camp couples are messing about on the dance floor to a lambada tune, deliberately bumping into the pool-players who are stubbornly refusing to relinquish their traditional evening activity. Mad Martin from Irish Studies is hunched over the bar, clutching his pint and muttering angrily at somebody. Later in the night he will kick off and have to be dragged out by the stewards who are already beginning to keep an eye on him. Finally, Kerry spots Susan and Robin sitting with a few other English students by the stall where the tequilas are being sold. She pushes her way through to them and they squeeze along on their seats to allow her to sit down.

'I thought you were blowing us out?' Robin says to her.

'I said I was coming.'

He takes a tenner out of his pocket and buys a round of tequilas for everybody. Kerry slams hers quickly, downing it in one, shaking her head and laughing afterwards as the tears prick her eyes. They carry on buying and slamming tequilas until Kerry is dizzy and sick of the sweet lemonade, craving a beer instead. There is a loud tequila buzz around the table, conversations crescendoing, people interrupting each other, raucous laughter, arguments. Somebody knocks over a bottle of lemonade and it froths out in colourless foam across the floor. The music is also getting louder, more people are dancing, a lesbian is yelling at one of the pool players, Simon Davis has his arm around the German girl who, astonishingly, doesn't seem to mind. Mad Martin is dragged out struggling by the stewards after trying to headbutt a philosophy student who has foolishly tried to argue an ethical case against terrorism.

Susan is in a bad way, knocking drinks over as she gets up to go to the toilet, rambling incoherently and being loudly rude to people for no particular reason. She is becoming aggressively self-pitying and people try and shift away from her, turning towards their neighbours on the other side. When she has gone to the toilet and not returned for some time, Kerry reluctantly feels that she had better go and look for her. As she enters the toilets, it is obvious which cubicle Susan is in from the mixture of moaning, retching and weeping noises coming from behind the door. Kerry taps gently on the door. 'Susan?'

'Wha' is it?'

'Susan, it's Kerry. Are you OK? Open the door for a second.'

There is a long pause and then a scuffling as Susan attempts to negotiate the bolt. Finally, she manages to open the door before starting to throw up again. Kerry waits until she is finished and then hands her a tissue. 'You'll be better now you've thrown up,' she observes. Susan looks up at her mournfully, strands of hair plastered to her pale cheeks.

'Better? I'm never gonna be better,' she announces melodramatically. 'I'm a loser, I couldn't earn a living as a stripper 'cause I'm so ugly, I'm pus ugly.' And she starts to cry again.

Kerry feels at a loss. She pats Susan awkwardly on the head. 'Stop being stupid. You're not ugly at all.'

'Why does nobody like me then? Why does the one person I like not like me? It's not fair.'

Kerry begins to grow impatient. She hates public self-pity,

finds it almost vulgar. It is as if the person bewailing their unattractiveness, unhappiness, lack of fulfilment, is actually conspiring with themselves to perpetuate this condition.

'You're just drunk,' she says calmly. 'Come on, come back in and have a soft drink or some water or something. You'll feel better then.'

'I wanna go home. Come outside with me, Kerry, to get a taxi. I can't make it on the tube.'

'Are you sure? OK, come on then. Wipe your mouth. Look, here's another tissue.'

Kerry leads Susan down the white-walled corridor, propelling her gently with her hand. At least Susan has stopped crying, concentrating instead on walking in something approximating a straight line, using her other hand to bounce herself gently off the wall. They step outside into the street, the night air brittle-cold, with a sudden dry clarity which sobers Susan up a little.

'Oh God,' she says, 'what am I like?'

'You're OK. Everyone's had that happen to them sometimes. It's horrible. You just feel like it's the end of the world all of a sudden.'

'But it isn't, is it? It's not the end of the world.' She sniffs and wipes at her nose. 'There's a family we know back home, Kerry. About two years ago, all the men were in the pub watching the football or something. Anyway, these Loyalists burst in and spray the bar with bullets. This woman – her father, her brother-in-law, her husband, they were all killed. I mean that's the end of the world for her, isn't it? That's a bit more important than having too many tequilas and realising that the person you like will never like you.'

Kerry considers this, shivering slightly from the cold dry air. 'Yeah, but it's not a valid comparison, is it? That's like saying that she won't know what suffering is until she's been shot as well. There are people who kill themselves because they think that they're worthless and that their lives are meaningless. And we could say that's just so melodramatic, especially when you think – oh, I don't know – about what people have been through in Bosnia or whatever. But they killed themselves so they must have been desperate enough, it must have seemed real enough to them.'

Susan looks at her through big tearful eyes. 'You know what, Kerry? You're a really great person. I mean, I can talk to you. So many people you can't really talk to, but I can always talk to you. You always have something to say.'

With a guilty gratitude, Kerry sees the bright orange light of a taxi turning into the street.

'Here's your cab now, take care of yourself. Ring me tomorrow or something.'

Susan waves feebly. 'Dollis Hill, please,' she says to the cabbie and Kerry has to fight a sudden impulse to laugh at the name. If you were really worried about your life, the first thing to do would be to get out of Dollis Hill.

She turns back into the college and as she is walking down the corridor sees Robin coming towards her.

'I thought you'd gone.'

'I've just put Susan in a cab. She wasn't feeling too good.'

'Yes,' he says simply, standing in front of her, looking down at her.

'It's really cold out there, freezing. You know, you think the cold's gone away but then it comes back . . .'

He looks at her and she stops gabbling. It is going to happen now. He puts his hands on her shoulders and draws her towards him and she feels him stoop slightly to kiss her. He opens her mouth with his lips. Over his shoulder, Kerry can see the stairway and is certain that somebody is going to come up. She can taste tequila on his tongue, feel a curl of hair brushing her face. Voices are coming up the stairs and she pulls away but Robin steers her gently into one of the side rooms.

It is the table-tennis room. The bats lie on the green table, one of them propped up by the white, hollow ball. The room is also cold and white-bricked. Robin is pushing against her with more urgency, his hands sliding. He is whispering to her, hands moving under her t-shirt. She puts her hand on his neck, pulling his head towards her. His neck is cold. She doesn't want him to touch her now in the table-tennis room; she just wants this sensation, this pleasure of kissing somebody for the first time. Now she can close her eyes without looking for people on the stairs. One of Robin's hands is sliding down to her hip. 'Let's go somewhere else,' she says. He holds her head in his hands.

'I was watching you today in the seminar when you were talking, and I wanted you so badly. I wanted to touch you so badly.'

Kerry feels a rush of awakened desire. She lets her hands slip down from his back. 'Let's go,' she says. 'Let's go somewhere.'

He takes her by the hand and leads her out again on to the white-walled corridor with its harsh light and collage of posters.

'We'll go back to my house.'

She nods and they walk towards the exit. He is still holding her hand. But as they get to the door a figure comes through towards them. It is Marco.

'Marco . . .' Kerry drops Robin's hand. 'I thought you weren't coming. We were just leaving.'

She knows that Marco has turned up to surprise her. He sometimes does this, refusing invitations to her college and then appearing later. He knows that she likes it when she sees him pushing through the bar towards her, grinning, flirting with the girls from her course, claiming that Stalin was the greatest ever world leader in order to wind up the Trotskyist students.

Marco stares at them. 'I thought I'd just drop in for a little bit. Don't worry, I was just going to have a quick drink. Changed my mind about staying in. I'm off somewhere else anyway.'

He looks at Robin. There is a split second of unspoken hostility between them. Robin smiles calmly, riding out the moment of confusing, awkward silence; it is almost like a hissing in Kerry's ears. She cannot break it, though, cannot reach out in any way to Marco, just stands dumbly in the clumsy, stupid silence.

'Is it very cold outside?' Robin asks suddenly.

Marco hesitates for a moment as if unwilling to enter into any communication with him.

'What's that, mate?' he replies without really looking at him.

'Is it cold outside?'

Marco shrugs. 'Yeah, I suppose so.'

'In that case Kerry, let's get a cab. It's too cold to walk to the tube.'

She looks at Marco. 'Can we drop you anywhere?'

He shakes his head. 'I'm going into town.'

'Oh, sorry,' says Robin pleasantly, 'we're going to Hackney.'

Marco glances at him for a second, as if taking a rapid mental photograph.

'We could stay for a quick one,' says Kerry desperately. 'Just another drink. Since you've come.'

Robin says nothing, but breathes out with barely perceptible impatience.

'You're all right,' Marco replies. 'I was just coming in on the off-chance. I should be off into town anyway.'

''Bye then,' says Robin and leads Kerry out on to the street. He hails a cab quickly and holds the door open for her. Kerry turns to nod goodbye to Marco and gets in. He watches the fat black rear of the cab reach the end of the street, its indicator flashing before it turns the corner, away from him.

Marco sits on the south-bound Charing Cross branch of the Northern line, rattling towards Soho, watching the purple and black-grimed cables of the tunnel walls. He is willing the train not to stop in the tunnel because he gets panic attacks when they do. Marco's panic attacks have been increasing recently; terrible feelings of imminent death, his veins twitching, his breathing forced, his heart racing, his brain sending out stupid incoherent messages about his own unreality – anything could happen, anything. The only good thing about these attacks is that when they stop, the residual adrenaline gives him a buzz and he wonders whether his mind and body actually conspire to produce them in some crazy masochistic addiction. The knowledge that it will stop is one of the things that just about prevents him from sending a demented fear-sodden wailing through the stalled carriage. This and the knowledge that sometimes his anxiety is perfectly rational – being trapped hundreds of feet underground in a small tunnel, with London Transport attending to your safety, is, after all, something to be scared about.

A genuine nutter gets on at Camden Town, making wild flapping gestures in his filthy old suit, muttering violent threats to the people around him. The woman opposite Marco sits tightly, clutching at her bag, nervous, wanting to get off and change carriages, not wanting actually to do it though, willing the man to go away instead. He lurches down the carriage towards them, grasping at the hanging handles, filling the speechless, frightened carriage with his crazed ramblings. He is not pissed, just violently mad, a medication-free loose cannon who might have a six-inch knife in his pocket. Marco stares at him. If he touches him, or speaks to the woman, he is going to kick his arse for him.

The man starts to harass a studenty-looking guy wearing tight black jeans and black DMs, who is reading a book. The geek is obviously terrified but doesn't look up from his book. He looks like he would like to climb into the book and shut the cover over himself to get away from this apparition of stinking demented fury in front of him. Bastards, thinks Marco. The government, nutters, students, London Transport, everybody responsible for this moment on this shitty, rattling, swaying tube train with its stupid posters warning people not to encourage buskers by giving them money, this stupid line with its stupid loops and branches, its three Claphams, its southern intersections with the useless, brown Bakerloo line. The nutter gets up and stands by the door.

Marco knows that he'll probably get off at Euston. He doesn't feel sorry for him. He hates him. If he had a gun in his pocket he would shoot him. So would the woman. So would the student. They all hate him. They might blame the government but that doesn't alter their fear and hatred in the here and now of this subterranean, mobile asylum. They would rather he were dead than here with them. Or at the very least locked away somewhere, immobile and stuffed full of drugs, stunned by chemicals into dumb bovine passivity. Out of the way. The train rolls into Euston. The man gets off. People exhale, begin to talk again.

It is a cold night in Soho and once again Marco feels a deep longing for the sun, for a long lazy hot evening and people on the pavements laughing outside the pubs. Maybe he is starting to suffer from missing-the-sun syndrome, maybe he needs some ultra-violet rays in his life. He takes a few flyers half-heartedly as he walks down Charing Cross Road, stuffing them into his jacket pocket without reading them.

The pub is packed but he spots Danny and a few others over by the far door and makes his way towards them. People are talking about video production, about graphic design, about club magazines, about the struggle to get into the first night of a recently reopened event on Saturday night, about the relative merits of amyl nitrate, about the terrifying charlie drought that has suddenly descended on London. The babble rises into the air like the smoke from the Silk Cuts and Marlboro Lights, hanging above them, over their heads.

'Check this, Marco,' Danny says as he arrives, 'this guy's been driving a truck in Bosnia.'

He gestures to a young Asian guy who can be no more than nineteen years old. He is sitting with his brother who is older and drinking a pint. The younger boy is sipping orange juice. He has big, dark serious eyes and looks at Marco carefully. He is more smartly dressed than his elder brother, wearing a short waistcoat over a polo-neck jumper, and has a slight, well-groomed beard.

'How's that then?' Marco asks, putting his pint down on the table.

'We was driving supplies out there. It was an international Muslim support mission. Taking food and stuff to villages.'

Danny glances at Marco to see how he is going to react to this, whether he is going to give the signal and allow a mocking tone into his voice. The elder brother watches Danny. The other continues to regard Marco steadily. His eyes are deep and dark.

'What made you decide to do that?' Marco asks.

'Well firstly it is my duty as a Muslim. Secondly, you see what is happening over there and nobody is doing anything about it, right? Nothing. I mean the things that are happening over there . . . one day, you see, our generation is going to be judged on how we responded, how we reacted to those crimes, just like people in Germany are judged on how they reacted to the Nazis. And I knew I had to do something.'

'But it ain't the same, is it?' Danny replies. ''Cause why should we be judged? It's a civil war. It's got fuck all to do with me whether the Serbs are bombing the Muslims, or the Croats are messing with the Serbs.'

'No, that is not right. This is an international issue now, an issue of humanity.'

'Like in Spain,' says Marco, thinking of his dad. 'Like people going to Spain to fight. You can't imagine that happening any more. But there were two sides in Spain, it was understandable . . .'

'This is understandable,' the boy replies, 'if you want to understand it. But you are right about Spain. It is no longer about those types of ideologies. The world doesn't need them any more. They are finished. Dead. Especially Communism.'

'Well, I wouldn't celebrate too much. 'Cause none of this ethnic cleansing stuff was going on until Communism fell apart.'

'It suppressed it.' The boy sips his orange juice, clinking the ice against the side of the glass. 'It never got rid of it though. Anyway, it is not a question of celebration. Communism died because it had no spiritual relevance, no eternal truth.'

'Where are you off to next then?' Danny asks, growing impatient. 'Chechneeaar? Or off to Algeria to cut some bird's throat for not wearing a veil?'

Marco watches the way the elder brother flashes a look at Danny. *Don't*, says the look. Danny had better be careful because while orange-juice drinker might be a bit of an idealist, his brother looks like he could be more of a handful. Plus, he will clearly tolerate no piss-taking of what he regards as an act of heroism. The younger boy doesn't seem to care very much and glances at his brother as if to say, I can handle this.

'I don't wanna cut anyone's throat. I just wanna help people who haven't got any food or supplies, and who spend the whole time wondering whether a shell is gonna drop on their house.'

Marco is fascinated by him, so dark-eyed, so young and serious, calmly sipping his orange juice while his elder brother leans over him protectively. He has something at his core, some belief like a spine running through him, some ethical code that does not relate simply to his immediate wants and desires. It both fascinates and saddens Marco because he has no access, does not want any access, to his certainties, his guiding code. There is just no possibility of it for Marco, son of John Fisher – unemployed printer, lifelong Communist, devoted fan of an atheist, radical poet. *The storm came up and the boat went down and then just a body tossed on the waves.*

'See why I don't like Commies,' says the brother. ''Cause when there was any shit where we was growing up, they'd all be down with their banners and their papers and their "black and white unite and fight" bollocks. Do you know what I mean? They'd come down for the day, have a laugh, then they'd fuck off again with their yellow lollipops under their arms. Remember, eh?' He nudges his brother.

'Not all of them,' says Marco quietly. 'That's like him saying that all Muslims go around cutting the throats of girls who don't wear veils. Anyway...' he doesn't want an argument especially with Danny around ' ... what's your names then? I'm Marco.'

'I'm Arif,' says the younger brother. 'This is my brother Mushtaq. He thinks he's looking after me, but really I am looking after him.'

Danny turns away, bored with the conversation now that there is no chance of its turning into a slagging contest. Marco continues to talk to Arif. He tells Marco about the massacres, about trying to get through to villages that were cut off, about the fear and the suffering of the people, especially in winter. His brother says little, just sits and nods occasionally and mutters encouraging noises for him to continue his narrative. And Marco is genuinely enthralled, not just by the stories but by his calm certainty and by his youth and how it is so beguiling and yet so distant from him. Not because of any religous impulse, some hidden spiritual envy, not that at all; it is in fact the secularity of Arif's conviction that has him so entranced, hanging on his words. He listens and he forgets about Kerry and the guy from her college, until last orders is rung and the two brothers get up to go. They shake hands with Marco but ignore Danny. Normally, when he has chatted to strangers in pubs, Marco drunkenly asks for their numbers and then loses them. This time he doesn't bother though – he knows that it is pointless.

Danny, Marco and a couple of others head up towards Hanway Street. Marco chats amiably to a girl called Nicole about how she has been working as an extra on a TV police series. When they get up to Oxford Street, he decides to return home. Walking down the long tree-lined path to the block of flats, beside the abandoned church, he looks up hopefully in case Kerry has also returned home but there is no light from their floor, the windows are dark like a blacked-out limousine.

In the flat, Marco wanders from room to room and finally ends up in Kerry's bedroom. He picks up the record sleeve left on the bed and smiles – a summer tune from years back, before Gary got bad. He looks around at her make-up, the clothes hanging on a rail, the wooden desk with an angle-poise light, piled books, notes in her neat round handwriting. Marco sits down on the bed, crossing one leg over the other, enjoying the strangeness, the transgression, of relaxing in Kerry's room, the difference of a strange bed, a dim illumination provided by the lamp in the hall.

On the bedside table, beside the alarm clock, there are some rings and an old photo. He turns it over and it is Gary. Marco stares at his old friend, the taut angular face, hair tied back in a pony-tail. Why did you have to die? Marco thinks. Why aren't you here now? If Gary were here now, things would be different. They could go out again, they could mess about in bars, they could laugh at everything. They could get kicked out of pubs like they used to, swinging their arms, spinning round, as they laughed their way down the street, respecting nothing and nobody. Everything went wrong. Why? It was as if Gary had just wound down, as if he had developed a fracture that had sent all his energy and humour leaking gradually out of him. Why though? Perhaps he had realised something, perhaps something had suddenly struck him, apart from the knowledge that he was not very likely to get any more acting jobs.

And Marco suddenly thinks that however depressed and tired he might get with the repetition of his life, he is still glad to be alive. He is still glad to mess around with Gerald at the deli, to have awkward conversations with his dad, to read about savage attacks on surfers by the mighty *Carcharodon carcharias*, to get off his face and have a laugh with Danny, to drag Kerry out to the pub to get pissed, to watch football with the volume turned down while she sits with her legs tucked under her, reading on the sofa. It's not that easy sometimes, but he is neither a victim nor one of the living dead like Angela's Tony with all his money and his objects, nor any boring bastard whose whole life revolves around their job. And as he looks at the pile of books on the table, he understands again that for Kerry her education is an end in itself, there is no other motive, it is something she has to do, her individuality blossoming.

Then Marco realises almost with a surge of relief, with the pleasure of inspiration, the foundation of his hostility towards Robin. It is not jealousy – or not simply jealousy. He does not know how or why he knows it, nor how or why Robin will attempt to do it, but he knows that Robin will interfere with this. He suddenly understands, and understands on the flimsiest of contact with Robin, the attraction which Kerry holds for him: it is one of the oldest attractions in the world. Robin too has caught the scent of her individuality, her liberty blossoming. Instead of watching and admiring it, however, he wants to pluck it, he wants to own it, he wants to control it. He will win her with his flattery, his quiet attention, the difference his money gives him. Then he will try to reshape her somehow. How does Marco know this? He does not know how he knows it but he does.

He saw that languor, that detached pleasantness tonight and he knew, it confirmed what he had always suspected: Robin is trouble, he is danger. But what is the best way – is there any way – of fighting him?

Chapter 9

The mattress is close to the floor, and Kerry wakes to see her bare arm trailing from under a large white duvet which smells fresh and cottony, soft against her skin. Her hand is cupped upwards as if she is waiting for a tip. A fragile sun is breaking through a gap in the curtains. On the floor near the mattress, her clothes lie intermingled with Robin's where they were dropped the night before as they undressed each other. She rubs her eyes, looking at her empty clothes and trying to assemble a response to what has just happened.

In the taxi they had sat apart without saying much and when they had arrived at Robin's house he had opened a bottle of wine and they had sat in the kitchen for a little, both waiting, unsure of how to build up again, both wanting to, the air becoming hot and tense with their expectancy. Finally, Kerry had made a joke about being kissed in the table-tennis room and this allusion to what had gone before had meant that the laughter had been followed by a thick, significant silence, and then they were leaning towards each other, their mouths meeting again. And after that it had become frantic, there was simply no time for Kerry to wonder at the significance of this action, she was completely overwhelmed by her own desire, her need for mouth on mouth, skin on skin, to touch and be touched, to gasp with pleasure and surprise again. As they made love, Robin had whispered to her, talked to her, confessed his desire for her, told her how he had been waiting for this moment when they would be in bed together like this; and somehow these references to the waiting, the inevitability of their falling together, increased her desire and pleasure even more – she remembered his eyes burning on her in the seminar that morning.

Now he lies asleep, his back towards her, breathing with calm regularity. She looks at the curved pattern of his spine, the taut bone, the tiny marks and freckles on his back, the newness of him. Kerry props her head on her hand, regarding the sleeping man who the night before had half carried her up the stairs to this room. How has this happened? She had been unsure of Robin, both pleased and displeased by his self-centredness, his detachment. But she knows that the attraction was always there because Robin had an awareness of himself as an individual, it was unshakable, he was what he was, he was an end in itself. Finally, she knew – perhaps had known for some time – that his unembarrassed interest in her had awakened something in her. It was that sense of inevitability he projected towards her, the clear, bright awareness that two individuals such as they just had to come together, that had started first confusion and then desire stirring in her. She had responded. He had known that she would. Because he knew that she too was striving towards something, some concept of herself that she could understand, something more than just her name, her past.

There had been the foot-tapping don and she had been just a girl at the moment that her life could have gone one way but went another. And now what is she? A young woman, no longer a girl, a mature student clinging to her education as if it were a piece of flotsam after a shipwreck, still looking back at that shy eighteen year old with her brittle, fragile intelligence, and wanting almost to compensate her, to pay her back. She can't turn back the clock, she can't stop the arrogant impatient don from shattering that fragility, she can't avoid the lost years. They are all part of her, just as that eighteen-year-old girl whose intelligence had been so delicately awakened, so carefully nourished by Sylvia Gordon, is still a part of her. She is still a part of her, that girl, carried inside her like a . . . like a . . .

Kerry gets up carefully and puts on a t-shirt and knickers. She leaves the room softly and makes her way downstairs to the kitchen to get some water. Her throat is dry from the quantity of drink consumed the night before. The bottle of wine and the glasses are still on the large, solid table. She shakes the wine out of one of the glasses and fills it with water. It is simple and satisfying as only water can be. She feels its coldness spreading through her, nourishing her like a plant, her cells greedily absorbing it. She drinks another glass and puts it down by the sink. As she makes her way back up the stairs, she meets Jill coming down the other flight from her room on the top floor. They stare at each other for a second. Jill is dressed and Kerry feels vulnerable and exposed in her t-shirt.

'Hi,' Jill says flatly. She pauses for a moment and Kerry feels a reluctance to open the door to Robin's room and slip back inside. But Jill is waiting, willing her to do it and eventually Kerry smiles at her and opens the door, closing it quietly again behind her. Robin is awake, leaning on his hand in the same position that Kerry was as she watched him sleeping. He smiles at her and brushes his hair from his face. He looks beautiful, his body easy and relaxed, his smile confident and assured. 'Come back to bed,' he says, holding the covers up for her. Kerry gets back into bed and he pulls her to him again, his hands moving quickly to take off the t-shirt.

Chapter 10

It is perilous for the lone surfer, suddenly separated from the rest of the group, when a rogue Great White is in the area. Especially when the sea is murky after recent rainfall, and the sky is overcast . . .

Marco, lying on the sofa reading again, cannot understand how this latter could make any significant difference to the shark unless they also get moody when there is no sun. The telephone rings and he puts the book down. It is his dad with good news.

'Good news, son,' he says. 'Angela and Tony aren't going away after all, so the whole family can be together at Christmas.'

'Great news,' murmurs Marco insincerely. 'Can't Tony go away on his own?'

'Listen, Marco, it's that I wanted to talk to you about. I just want things to be peaceful, all right? And that means you behaving yourself as well. 'Cause Tony might be a prat but he's Angela's boyfriend. And you know who'll really get the hump if you start stirring, don't you?'

'You,' Marco replies bitterly. His dad is an idiot. He hates and despises Tony, but his blind, stupid love for his daughter will mean that it is Marco who will get blamed if anything goes wrong.

'That's right, Marco. Me. So I'm just marking your card for you. Do you understand me?'

'I think I do. Yeah, I think I see where you're coming from, Dad.'

'Don't get sarky, Marco. I'm just sayin', that's all. I want this to go well. For everybody's sake. Anne's as well. She puts a lot of effort into Christmas and I don't want it spoiled for her.'

'Yeah, well, don't worry, Dad. I'll be on my best behaviour. By the way, a word of advice. Let's avoid gift duplication. I've already bought Tony a copy of *Mein Kampf* for Christmas.'

In spite of himself, John Fisher chuckles. 'Now that's what I'm talking about, son. That kind of lippiness. You can do it with me, I know he's a prat. But Angela gets upset. So leave it out at Christmas, yeah?'

Fuck Angela, Marco wants to say but doesn't dare. His dad would burst a blood vessel. Then he would probably come round and burst a few of Marco's.

'How is it they're not going away?' he asks.

'Oh, change of plans. Tony's too busy to get away at Christmas so they might have an Easter holiday instead.'

Doesn't want to miss the office party more like, thinks Marco. He's probably shagging his secretary.

'Lovely,' he says. 'Yeah, I was thinking of an Easter break as well this year. Can't decide, though, if it's going to be Mustique or the little island of Phuket, where I'm told the beaches are simply wonderful.'

John Fisher laughs. 'You couldn't even make it to Brighton, you dozy sod.'

Marco imagines Tony surfing with a group of friends. Tony attaches little significance to the fact that the surf is slightly discoloured after recent rain. They all catch a wave but he misses it. As he is awaiting the next wave, inspecting his tan, a massive nine-foot Great White streaks in and – BAM!

Tony is flung into the air, tossed cruelly around and snapped in two. Angela stands on the beach, beneath an overcast sky, watching a broken surf-board floating on a blood-reddened sea.

' . . . did you hear me, Marco?'

'What? Oh, sorry, I thought I heard the door.' He holds the receiver between ear and shoulder and lights a cigarette. It is good not to have a hangover.

'I asked how your job was going?'

'Yeah fine. I've got some stuff for you – a nice bit of Dolcelatte, some more Parma ham, a few other bits and pieces.'

'Oh, that's good of you, son. When are you gonna pop round?'

'Boxing Day.'

'. . .'

'All right, I'm only joking. I dunno, next Sunday all right?'

'Yeah, come on Sunday. Simon's coming up for his dinner as well.'

Marco groans inwardly. Simon is an old Communist friend of his dad, an elderly East End Jew who runs the local branch which is increasingly beginning to resemble a geriatric social club for unrepentant Stalinists. John Fisher is one of its most youthful members. Even Marco's dad had looked embarrassed when Simon had suggested that Marco – despite having nothing whatsoever to do with the Party – should join a youth delegation to North Korea. It was quite obvious that youth were rather thin on the ground in the Party at the time, since the other members of the youth delegation included a weird train-spotter type of indeterminate age who spent all of his spare time collecting and scrutinising the newspapers of British Trotskyist organisations, and a scruffy, troll-like figure who worked for the council as a social worker and who could not possibly be a day under forty. Marco knows that his dad faces implicit and sometimes explicit criticism for the fact that his son is not prepared to swell the dwindling ranks of the organisation. As if children are simply there to follow dutifully in their parents' footsteps. To give John Fisher his due, he knows this is a lost cause. Sometimes he asks Marco to help out at events and when he cannot find a decent excuse he does help out, escaping afterwards with an urgent need to find Danny and get completely off his face.

'These are difficult times,' Simon always says in the face of Marco's ill-concealed scepticism. 'That's why it's so important to keep the flame alive, now of all times.' Marco does not particularly disagree with this, but he is simply not prepared to waste his life being one of the guardians of the flame. 'I'll . . . erm . . . leave that task to people who are more ideologically prepared than I am,' he once told Simon who simply clucked disapprovingly and returned to his conversation with John Fisher about whether any kind of reconciliation with a minuscule ultra-orthodox faction of the old party would be possible. Simon, unsurprisingly, thought that it would.

'I might come up a bit later on. You know, early-evening like,' Marco says cautiously to his dad.

'Well, whatever, whatever. And remember what I said to you about Christmas. I'm counting on you.'

'Sure,' Marco replies, knowing that the chances of Christmas passing off peacefully are about as likely as Santa suddenly appearing down the chimney singing the *Internationale* with the reindeers on backing vocals. If they had a chimney. Whatever happens, Tony will be an arrogant prick because he has been genetically programmed that way and there is no other possible mode of behaviour for him. He will insist on watching the Queen just to start an argument. And Angela will take offence at even the most muted criticism of him, and people will start shouting, and Anne will sigh wearily and go and do the washing up, and Marco will go and help her in order to get out of the way of his dad's reproachful glare. That is how it will be. And Marco will get the blame.

He lies on the sofa staring at the phone after he has replaced the receiver. He had thought Kerry might phone. She has not been home for two nights and now it is late into the next day. He picks up the book again and half-heartedly starts reading a story about a young couple frolicking in the surf which ends up with the girl getting her arm bitten off. What do people go in the sea for in Australia when there are sharks around? They must be mad. Wild horses wouldn't drag Marco off the shore if he ever went to Australia. He would rather go on a youth delegation to North Korea. Even though he knows the risks are tiny, even though he understands that most sharks don't attack humans, that doesn't mean that he would be prepared to end up as an exception, documented with a case number in the International Shark Attack File.

Marco wanders into the kitchen, thoroughly bored and yet agitated about Kerry's absence. Boredom and agitation – not the most desirable cocktail but one which is becoming increasingly familiar to Marco. He hopes he is not going to get a sudden panic attack and distracts himself by opening a can of tomato soup, enjoying its bright orange artificiality. He heats the soup and eats it, dunking buttered bread into it. He turns on the radio and listens to the charts. Finally, when he is contemplating ringing Danny, the key turns in the lock and Kerry enters.

Marco's initial pleasure at seeing her is diminished considerably by the tall figure that follows her in. They are laughing, Kerry is flushed and happy, still wearing the clothes that Marco saw her in when he met her leaving college.

'What are you sitting in the dark for?' she exclaims, switching on a light, and Marco notices in surprise that while he has been absent-mindedly making the soup, the twilight hour has descended swiftly, the light has been sucked from the room, darkness has crept in.

'I'm just going to change out of these clothes,' Kerry says. 'Make some tea or coffee if you want it, Robin. Marco will show you where everything is.'

Robin smiles easily at Marco who shows him his teeth in return.

'Would you like a cup of tea?' Robin asks and Marco pretends not to hear. Robin whistles in the kitchen, opening cupboards until he finds the tea-bags, lining up three mugs, and putting the kettle on.

When he comes back into the room, he picks up Marco's book. 'Sharks?' he says. 'I saw a shark once when I was skin-diving in Indonesia.'

'Yeah?' Marco replies nonchalantly, fighting not to show his mounting interest.

'Yes. I was pretty scared. But the guy we were with wasn't that bothered. Said it was only small, a Lemon shark or something, no hassle really. It just swam off in the end.'

'Oh, well . . .' Marco says condescendingly. 'Lemon sharks aren't anything to be frightened of. They're not even sharks really.' Marco knows that had he been told that a Lemon shark had been spotted in the last century within fifty miles of the place, he wouldn't even have dabbled a toe in the water.

'It certainly looked like a shark,' Robin muses, putting down the book.

'You're not going on about sharks again, Marco?' Kerry comes back into the room in different clothes.

'He started it,' says Marco babyishly. 'He was telling me about how he frightened off a Lemon shark in Indonesia.'

'I didn't say that exactly. . .' Robin begins, but Marco jerks his head towards the kitchen.

'Kettle's boiling.'

'What have you done this weekend?' Kerry asks him, perched on the edge of a seat.

'Oh . . . not much. We went to this do last night. Some photo exhibition thing in Soho where there was tons of free vodka. Then we got kicked out 'cause Danny got caught stealing a bottle to take home with us.'

Marco grins. It had been a good laugh really. You weren't supposed to smoke in the gallery so they had shared sneaky fags in the corner – like being back at school. Marco kept getting caught by the same woman because every time Danny spotted her coming through the crowd he had passed Marco the fag. When she had caught Marco four times, she told him it was his last warning, her anger increased by Danny's inane giggling. But then Danny had rendered the whole matter academic by getting caught sneaking a bottle into his bag. After they had been thrown out, they had no money so they had wandered around a bit trying to find someone to blag drinks off. They had managed to get a free pint in a pub where they knew the barman. After that, Marco had come home to a flat which was empty for the second night running.

'There were a few messages for you,' he tells Kerry. 'Your handbag sister called a couple of times. And that mate of yours, Susan.'

Kerry twitches uncomfortably at the mention of Susan's name and Marco remembers their argument when he had pretended that Kerry was seeing Robin. Well, she *is* seeing him now and Marco can tell that she is worrying about how to break the news. Tough luck, he thinks unsympathetically. This is what you get when you descend into the real world, Kerry, when you dip your toe into the water again; things get messy. Then, looking at her still slightly worried expression, he feels a wave of love and protectiveness towards her. He can't start thinking like that, wanting Kerry punished just because she has lowered her defences slightly.

Robin comes back into the room with the tea. He sits on the chair beside Kerry and she rests her arm on his shoulder. Marco looks at his tea trying to find something wrong with it – too milky, too strong. But it is fine. He gets up anyway and adds some more milk to it. Robin watches him but does not say anything. Marco tells Kerry about his conversation with his dad about Christmas and she laughs. Robin wisely decides not to join in the conversation and after he has finished his tea, announces that he had better go home.

'You can stay if you want?' Kerry says but he shakes his head.

'I've got a few things to sort out. I'll see you in college tomorrow.'

She takes him to the front door. As he leaves, he turns round and smiles lopsidedly at Marco. 'Goodbye, Marco. Really nice to meet you properly this time. I'm sure I'll see you again soon.'

Marco nods vaguely, not meeting his eyes. I'm sure you will, he thinks. And you had better get used to me as well because however much you hate me, I will always be around. And he knows that Robin has already begun to hate him and will fight back in his own way. He can hear Robin and Kerry by the door, giggling. Then a long silence. Then the door slamming. Kerry comes back into the living room and waves at Marco. 'I'm going to crash out for a bit.' And she disappears into her bedroom. Marco goes into the kitchen and starts to tidy up half-heartedly.

Chapter 11

Kerry does not like deception, and decides to tell Susan immediately what has happened with Robin. Carrying the knowledge around with her will just make her uncomfortable although she feels awkward and half irritated by the task. It is made slightly easier by the fact that Susan has never actually told her directly that it is Robin of whom she is so enamoured.

Susan is already in the library, head bent over a book, when Kerry arrives early in college. Kerry sits down and grins at her.

'What are you reading?' she whispers.

'D.H. Lawrence. It's doing my head in actually. Do you want to get a coffee before you start work?'

'OK.'

The cafeteria is nearly empty and they buy coffee and Kerry takes out her first cigarette, ignoring a recent resolution not to smoke in the mornings.

'I phoned you over the weekend,' Susan stirs her coffee. 'I left messages because you were out the whole time. I had a terrible hangover after Friday night, one of the worst ever. I called to see if you wanted to come to the cinema on Saturday.'

'Yeah, I had a bit of a strange weekend.'

'But it was OK 'cause I doubt whether I could even have managed it to the cinema. I was still feeling terrible in the evening. Worse, in fact.'

Kerry feels as if she is back at school. This is a ridiculous situation, feeling guilty because she has messed things up for her friend by sleeping with the guy she fancies.

'Actually, Susan, there's something I had better tell you. I mean, you'll probably find out soon enough, what with the gossip in this college and anything.' Kerry sucks hard on her cigarette. She is almost shaking.

'Oh, yes? Great. I love a good bit of gossip. Did something happen on Friday night? Apart from me making a complete fool of myself, that is.'

'Well, yes, it did actually. Erm . . . well . . . it's embarrassing. Basically, I was pretty drunk and Robin was pretty drunk and we ended up going back to his house and . . .' she tails off.

Two tiny red blotches begin to appear on Susan's face like small cherry tomatoes. Apart from that, however, she remains quite calm.

'You and Robin?'

'Yes.'

'I knew he liked you. But I didn't know whether you felt the same way about him.'

'I didn't either. I just . . . it's been so strange, you know. Since my boyfriend died . . . well, I haven't seen anyone else since then. It was the first time.'

'And was it, like, a one-night stand? Or do you think you're going to carry on seeing each other?'

Kerry shifts awkwardly. 'I don't know. I think . . . yeah, I think it might be a bit more than that.'

The cafeteria is beginning to fill up. Simon Davis and a group of hangers-on clutching papers sit down at a table near them. A couple of other students join the queue for coffee, waving at them. They will probably come over.

'Well, that's great. You've got loads in common. And you're the same age and everything. I'll have to be careful now, though. I don't want to start being a gooseberry.'

Kerry winces again at the awful schoolgirlishness of it. She is thirty years old, for God's sake. The word 'gooseberry' grates on her unpleasantly and she suddenly feels something like cold anger towards this bright-cheeked nineteen year old. Why should she be sitting explaining to Susan, listening to words like that?

'Don't be stupid,' she says almost harshly. 'It's not like that at all. I'm just telling you so, you know, you don't get freaked out by it . . .'

'Why should I get freaked out?' There is also an edge creeping into Susan's voice now. 'It's not such a big deal after all. It's not like the world's suddenly different because of you and Robin . . .'

'No,' says Kerry coldly. 'Absolutely not.'

Jenny the stripper and Matilda come over and sit with them. They are joking about whether it would be worth sleeping with one of the lecturers in order to get a first.

'I'd sleep with him anyway,' announces Matilda loudly. 'And I wouldn't be the first,' she adds knowingly.

'I've got to go,' Susan says, extracting her bag from under the table. 'I'll see you back in the library, Kerry.'

She nods and sips her coffee.

'She's a nutter that one,' Matilda observes watching her departing back. 'I know she's your friend and everything, Kerry, but did you see her on Friday night? Talk about losing the plot. She was ranting on at me about how I was really beautiful and popular and she was just a loser and everybody hated her . . .'

'That's funny,' Jenny replies, 'she was saying exactly the same thing to me.'

'She was just pissed,' Kerry says, lighting another cigarette.

'Well . . . can I scrounge a fag, Kerry . . . I know she was pissed . . . cheers . . . she was completely wasted, but she also had a mad glint in her eye. You know? When somebody starts ranting at you about all their paranoias and hang-ups. I mean, it might sound a bit harsh and everything but I was just like . . . take it somewhere else, love, I'm not in the mood. Have you got a light as well?'

Kerry begins to feel an almost physical sense of discomfort. The coffee and the fag have made her heart race, the idle bitching is beginning to depress her. She feels a terrible need to calm herself down with some work, to immerse herself in her books for a couple of hours. She just wants stillness and silence, to bring her mind back into equilibrium. She tries to grin normally.

'Well, I've got to get going now . . .'

'Oh, sit down, Kerry. You're gonna get another first anyway.

Have another coffee. All you have to do is print your name on
the essay and they'll give you an A.'

'That's crap and you know it. Anyway, I have got to get
going 'cause I'm also doing a lot of part-time work this week
to try and sort out my overdraft. See you later.'

She wonders if they'll start bitching about her after she's
gone but doesn't care particularly. Susan is not back in the
library when she returns so she sinks gratefully into her seat
as far away as possible from anybody else, takes out a copy of
The Rainbow, sniffs at the pages which are pleasingly discoloured
by age, and starts to read.

After a couple of hours' reading, she is feeling whole again,
relaxed. The nervous coffee and fag speediness has left her.
She rests her head on her arms for a little, closing her eyes and
letting her thoughts drift off.

Kerry knows that she should feel as if some significant bridge
has been crossed – the first time since Gary that she has slept
with a man. In fact, she does not feel like that at all. During
the weekend, it never surfaced as an issue in her mind, much
less threatened her with any kind of trauma. For this, she knows
she owes something to Robin – the fact that he is so different
from her and from most of the people she knows. Certainly
different from Gary.

You bitch, you fucking murdering bitch!

Kerry had spent the evening after the abortion being pam-
pered by Jeanette, lying on the sofa watching videos, her hand
over her stomach. At night she had dreamt that she was telling
Gary and that he was pleased, relieved almost. In Kerry's dream
he had told her not to worry and that he was going to go to
the Cup Final with her instead, because he had been selected
to present the cup for that year instead of the Duchess of Kent.
Kerry had woken the next day half smiling and then a ghastly
feeling gripped her as she revisited her dream and she knew
it had been just that – an electric storm of wishful thinking in
her brain.

Kerry had stayed most of the next day with Jeanette as well,
and then the nervous energy started to make her feel nauseous

again and it was more than she could stand. She asked Darren and Jeanette to drive her home. Darren had not known why his girlfriend's sister was staying at his house – he had learned with Jeanette not to ask questions about anything he did not actually need to know. He had picked up on the troubled vibe in the car though and worn a slightly puzzled frown all the way back up the Essex Road.

They had dropped her in the street and although Jeanette offered to accompany her, Kerry once again preferred to make the walk alone. Fatigue, nerves and the still-present cramp in her stomach had assailed her as she approached their flat down the long walkway.

Gary had known immediately, he had known anyway. He was bug-eyed mad when she entered. She cannot remember now what words passed between them, they were just noise anyway. His rage and hurt sent him spinning around the room, crashing into things, bouncing up against walls. It was as if all the energy he had conserved during his long seclusion had suddenly become condensed down into this one moment. He had lost all control. At one point he was screaming at Kerry with his face pushed right up to hers. But he was no longer seeing her and she no longer recognised anything in his bulging eyes. What Kerry had done had nothing to do with it any more. It was not the life that she had briefly imagined that he was mourning – deep down he must have known that the idea of a baby was as ridiculous as she did; he was simply raging at the might-have-been. He did not know what to do with his fury, spinning into walls, breaking things like a child possessed by a universal sense of injustice, and she had thought that he might hurt her. When he had picked up the glass and held it up, she had waited but Gary had never been able to hurt Kerry however much he might have wanted to. Instead, he had smashed the glass to the floor and almost danced on the broken shards, a fire-walker trapped on orange-smoking coals, lacerating his feet, spiralling around in the blood and broken glass; howling, shrieking with pain and rage and humiliation. Then he had screamed – 'You bitch, you fucking murdering bitch! You've

killed me now, Kerry, you bitch.' And he had forced his torn
and bleeding feet into a pair of trainers, hopping towards
the stairs as he squeezed his damaged feet into them, half
stumbling, nearly falling, and Kerry knew that she too was
making a noise, she was uttering something, some crazed
lament that lost itself in the madness of the moment. And
Gary, who had not felt fresh air for some months, was scrabbling with the door and she was screaming his name over
and over, now she was pleading with him, but the slamming
door had shaken the walls in the sunken flat. He continued
yelling and shouting down the walkway, but this was not a
particularly unusual occurrence on their estate. Then he was
gone.

How long did she sit in the silence, staring at the walls, the
blood spirograph, the purple-smeared glass on the floor? It
was dark and quiet and empty in the flat. Finally, she had picked
up bits of broken glass and dropped them into newspaper and
put them in the bin, along with a butt-stuffed ash-tray. She
had dropped the whole ash-tray in. Then she had phoned
Marco. It was only when he had arrived that she had fallen on
to his shoulder and wept, while he waited, confused, for some
kind of explanation.

They had gone out of the flat to look for the car which had
gone. Gary had driven off so there was little point in going
out to look for him. Kerry had no idea where he might go. He
had lived with his grandad before the old man had died, he
had not seen his parents for years. He had a sister but she
lived in Kent and Kerry doubted whether he would go anywhere near her. He no longer had any friends apart from Marco
who had left a message at his place to tell Gary where he was,
with instructions to phone him immediately at Kerry's if Gary
appeared. But they both knew he wouldn't.

So where had he gone? Kerry had wanted to call the police
immediately.

'He's lost it completely,' she told Marco. 'He's going to do
something, he'll hurt himself, he shouldn't even be driving.'

But Marco said that it would be pointless. The police

wouldn't do anything about a person who had been missing for half an hour, after storming out of the house following a row with his girlfriend. So they had remained in the house watching TV and drinking tea. The phone had rung but it was only Jeanette to find out if Kerry was OK.

'Best thing really,' Jeanette said when she heard. 'You don't want him around giving you a hard time. He'll turn up. They always do.'

But Gary had not turned up. Kerry sat up all night while Marco dozed on the sofa. She heard the birds in the morning, felt the grey light creeping back into the flat. Then, almost desperate with impatience, she had gone to the police station to explain what had happened to an insolently sceptical officer.

'He'll turn up.' The officer yawned after taking the details from her. 'He'll just need a couple of days to calm down. He's probably gone fishing with a few mates. You know, clear his head a bit.'

It would take more than a fishing trip to clear Gary's head, Kerry thought bitterly as she left the police station.

'Weird.' Marco shook his head as they stood waiting for a cab.

'What is?'

'I think that's the first time I've been in a nick when I haven't been in a cell.'

All that was left was waiting. Kerry had phoned the temp agency to say that she was ill. Marco went to the shops and cooked, but Kerry could hardly eat. She drank tea and ate toast, nervously nibbling at it before leaving it half-eaten on the plate. A phrase kept running through her head, a line from a kids' poem they had recited at junior school. '*Waiting, waiting, waiting for the party to begin.*' She stared at the drops of blood which trailed up the stairs towards the door.

The next day the same officer had come round, accompanied by a woman officer. Kerry and Marco had been sitting half watching a debate with a studio audience about capital punishment. It was making Kerry almost mad, it was so desperate, the host running round with his microphone interrupting the audience, and Gary out there somewhere, out of his mind and blood on his feet. There was a knock on the door and she went upstairs to find the two officers outside like something from a police series. She knew immediately from the changed tone what was going to happen. And there was that instant before their mouths opened when she still had not had it confirmed, when she was a different Kerry, and then they had asked to come in and taken off their hats and looked uncomfortable and then a throat was cleared and one of them began to speak. They told her that a car answering the description she had given had been found and that a young male believed to be the driver of the car had been found near it and that he was dead after being struck by another vehicle. They would like her to make an identification of the body which would involve going to Essex as that was where the body and car had been found. And Kerry felt that everything had just been pulled out of her, she was hollow, a vacuum, she had to concentrate on breathing or she might just fall over. The only thing she said to them flatly, as she saw Marco's pale face at the bottom of the stairs, was that she could not understand why Gary would have gone to Essex.

Kerry jumps as somebody puts their hands on her shoulders.
    'Hello, dreamer.' Robin is standing behind her, smiling.
    'Hi.' Kerry feels shy but Robin seems quite unperturbed.
    'How long have you been working?'
    'A couple of hours.' She turns the book around to show him.
    'Yes, I've been reading it as well.'
    'What do you think?'
He doesn't answer her. Kerry has noticed that if Robin does not want to answer a question he simply acts as if it has never been made. A girl working across from Kerry looks up at the interruption and then back at her books.
    'You want to have a break?' Robin glances at the girl who is sending silent waves of disapproval at them for talking in the library. People always do though and Kerry actually likes it when she hears a sudden giggle breaking through the silence.

'OK. But I don't want to go to the refectory. We could go to a caff.'

'Come on then.'

They walk out on to the street, not saying anything to each other. Then as they get to the end of the street, Robin takes Kerry's hand.

'Have you got any plans for tonight?' he asks her.

She smiles. 'I thought I might see you tonight actually.'

'OK. Your place or mine?'

Kerry pauses. She thinks of Marco and his unmistakable hostility towards Robin. She thinks of Robin's comfortable house with the kitchen table, the half-drunk bottles of wine with their corks sticking out, the door from the kitchen into the garden. Then she thinks of Jill, prowling silently like a slant-eyed cat, watching her movements.

'What would you like?' Kerry asks.

'I haven't slept in your bed yet.'

'Come to mine then.'

'I'll bring some food.'

'OK.'

Robin arrives at Kerry's flat that night with a couple of bottles of wine and a bag of shopping. She kisses him on the lips as he walks in through the door and he puts the shopping down to kiss her properly. Kerry feels happy and relaxed, touching his face which is still cold from the hard winter air. She leads him into her bedroom. 'You can cook later,' she says.

Afterwards, she sits watching him preparing a fish stew, sipping at her glass of wine. This is good, she feels comfortable, she has a boyfriend again, although she hesitates to call him that. It is a strange feeling and she revels in it, in his newness, in the pleasure of sex. Her feeling of relaxation is interrupted briefly when the front door opening signals Marco's arrival. Guiltily, she wishes that he was not taking it easy and would disappear on another three-day extravaganza.

Marco has been at work and is also carrying a bag of shopping.

'Good, you're here,' he observes cheerfully, 'I've got some

pasta and some fresh swordfish that Lee got for me from his restaurant . . .' He tails off as he senses another presence. Kerry can tell that he is outraged at the occupation by a stranger of what he considers with some justification to be his kitchen.

'Robin's cooking already,' Kerry says. 'Do you want a glass of wine?'

Robin emerges with the bottle of wine in his hand. 'Hello, Marco. Been at work?'

Marco stares at the imposter. 'I suppose this will keep,' he mutters, squeezing past Robin and opening the fridge door. He picks up a packet of ready-cooked prawns, looks at it scornfully and then holds his glass out for Robin to pour him some wine.

'There's plenty of food here,' Robin says lightly. 'Shall I put rice on for you?'

'I suppose so,' Marco replies gracelessly. 'There's not much point me cooking for myself. I'll just get in your way.'

'Good.' Robin begins to chop up some fresh basil. The sweet pungent smell fills the air.

Marco sits down with Kerry. She notices that his eyes are no longer blood-shot and that his clothes are clean.

The door buzzer rings and Marco goes to answer it.

'It's Danny,' he says when he returns.

'Oh,' Kerry replies flatly.

'I said I might go down the pub for a quiet drink with him.'

Kerry nods. The name Danny and the words 'quiet drink' do not often share the same sentence.

'Hi, Kerry,' Danny says cheerfully swinging his I LOVE SATAN cycle helmet. 'Wicked smell, Marco. What are you cooking? There's definitely something fishy going on in the kitchen.'

'There definitely is,' Marco agrees. Kerry scowls at him. Robin emerges holding a large knife.

Danny laughs. 'Heeere's Johnny!'

Robin looks confused. 'I'm Robin,' he says wiping his hand on the back of his jeans and putting down the knife.

'Danny, mate. Nice to meet you. So, Marco let you into the

kitchen-shrine? He must really trust you. He won't even let me boil a kettle. Smells great though.'

'Well, there's plenty,' Robin says to Kerry's horror.

'Oh, nice one. Cheers, mate.'

'I thought you were off out to the pub,' Kerry remarks desperately, lighting a cigarette.

'Oh, yeah, we are. But I wouldn't mind putting something in here first.' Danny cradles his stomach and shakes it up and down. 'I had one of those mental pizzas for lunch. You know, the ones where they inject the crust with cheese and pepperoni? Well tasty it was. But you know me, never say no to more food. The only thing I can't eat, I simply cannot abide it, is cabbage. No cabbage in that, I hope, Robin? How's the old studies coming along, Kerry? Here . . .' he throws a bag and some Rizlas to Marco ' . . . skin up while I have a piss.'

Danny leaves the door to the toilet open so that everybody can hear his piss crashing against the bowl.

'You're a despatch rider then?' Robin gestures at Danny's helmet when he comes back into the room.

'Ten out of ten, Sherlock.'

'My flatmate's a despatch rider,' Robin says. 'You might know him.'

'What's his name?'

'Olly.'

'Not lanky Olly? Big geezer with cropped hair, yeah? Nice one. He's a top laugh old Olly. Major stoner that kid. If he was here now he would have got through that little lot . . .' Danny gestures to where Marco is skinning up ' . . . on his own.'

Robin laughs. 'Yes, he's pretty partial to a smoke.'

'Pretty partial? I dunno how he gets on that bike sometimes. That's mental. Totally Felicity Kendal. You live with Olly. Nice one.' Danny holds out his hand and Robin dutifully slaps it.

Kerry notices that Marco is glaring at Danny over the joint he is rolling. She laughs inwardly. Danny is too stupid to pick up on the fact that he is not meant to be being friendly to Robin.

'Robin's a student,' Marco says. 'He's what our taxes are going on.'

'Shut up, Marco. You ain't paid a penny in tax in your whole life. Look at you, you moany bastard. That's what not having been out in a few days does to you. Just hurry up with that joint. Here, Robin mate, splash a bit more of the old vino in here.' Danny laughs and holds out his glass and Robin grins at him as he fills his glass to the top. Kerry is beginning to warm to Danny for the first time in her life.

'Blinding,' Danny exclaims as he takes his first mouthful of the food when it is ready. 'Master-chef of the evening is Robin in the red kitchen. Commiserations to Marco who put up a frankly lazy effort in the green kitchen ... ha ha ha ... he's a prat, ain't he? Eh? That Lloyd whatsisname. You ain't never gonna cook any of that stuff either, are you? Medallions of smoked reindeer with a coriander and samphire glaze ... eh?'

'Well *you* certainly ain't,' Marco snaps. 'You can't even boil an egg. It took you a couple of years to master the art of taking the lid off a Pot Noodle.'

'True enough,' Danny observes cheerfully. 'I'd love to be able to cook. But I can't. Even ready-made meals, somehow I just manage to fuck 'em up. Remember that Marina, Marco? I tried to make her a meal once. I bought one of them Indian things from Sainsbury's. Chicken something with nan bread. Anyway, I went to take it out of the oven and I thought the dish it was in would be strong but it was all floppy. So when I took it out it just bent in two and dropped all over the floor.'

Marco laughs. 'Then there was that French bread pizza. Remember? When you put it in the oven without taking it off the plastic tray and all the plastic melted into the pizza. We thought it was bones in the pizza at first, but it was solid bits of plastic.'

'Well, there's other things besides cooking, you know.'

'That's true,' Robin agrees pouring more wine.

'That all depends on whether you can cook or not.' Marco scowls down at the fish stew that he is ostentatiously pushing around on his plate with his fork.

'So what pub are you thinking of going to?' Kerry asks when the last of the food has been eaten.

'The Duke of Edinburgh. Shit, I said I'd meet that mad German bird in there. Come on, Marco. D'ya fancy coming down, Kerry?'

'Oh, er, no. It's OK, thanks, Danny.'

'Got to get on with a bit of revision, eh?' Danny smirks. 'Well, fair enough. Come on, Marco. See you later, Robin. Nice to meet you, mate, thanks for the food. Tell Olly I was asking for him.'

Kerry breathes a sigh of relief as the front door slams behind them.

'Sorry about that,' she says to Robin, not sure why she is apologising really.

'What are you sorry for?'

'Well, they can be a bit much sometimes.'

'It was fine. I can look after myself anyway. Your friend Marco doesn't like me very much, does he?'

'Oh, I don't know if it's that he doesn't like you. He's just a bit . . . a bit . . .'

'Of an inverted snob? Jealous?' Robin arches an eyebrow.

'No, not jealous. Well, not in that way anyway.'

'It doesn't bother me at all. It's just a bit silly, his hostility, that's all. He's got to let you be an individual, live your own life.'

Kerry sips some more wine. She feels uneasy at the criticism of Marco, however muted. Marco is part of her, part of her life. He always has been. But Marco is irritating her also with his churlishness towards Robin. Yet if anyone is going to criticise him it is going to be her. Robin does not even know him.

'Marco's a brilliant person,' she says simply. 'He's one of the most loyal people I know.'

'Loyal?' Robin frowns slightly. 'If you want loyalty you should get a dog. Do you value loyalty above everything else?'

'Well, what do you value?'

'Interesting people. For me, the most important thing is that somebody is interesting, not just existing. I don't mean necessarily doing crazy things, I mean that they are able to hold your interest. Once they stop being able to do that, then

153

there's really not much point in knowing them. There was a point in my life when I was bored, really bored. And I thought about it and realised that part of it was to do with the people around me. They were boring, not doing anything. So . . .' Robin reaches for the bottle of wine and studies it for a moment before pouring some into his glass ' . . . I thought I would give college another try and make it an objective not to get dragged down by boring people.'

'That could sound a bit arrogant . . . you know . . . a bit egotistical.'

Robin laughs easily. 'Who cares? I am arrogant, I suppose. I want my life to be interesting.'

Kerry ponders this. It is quite an attractive idea. Who else does she know who talks to her like this? She remembers the conversation in the refectory that morning, the dizziness she suddenly felt at its hollowness. Perhaps Robin is right after all. He is strange, he is different, there is something unsettling about him. But she is enjoying being unsettled, she is enjoying being talked to about things that don't just relate to assignments or hangovers or cheese-crust pizzas.

'Take Susan, for example,' Robin continues.

'What about her?' Kerry shifts uncomfortably.

'Well, there you have a person who is almost totally lacking in self-esteem. Right? But she is interesting – where she's come from, what she's doing. It's a massive step that she's taken. Who knows how it will turn out? But I'd rather talk to her than, say, Simon Davis who is utterly and totally predictable with his parrot-like revolutionary politics and who you know will leave in the end to do something utterly and totally predictable in the City or something. He is full of self-esteem but only because he is stupid.'

'But it's easy for you. I mean, I don't want to be rude but it's easy to take your sort of stance when you're rich, when you've got a great house you don't have to pay anything for, when you're a man.'

Robin frowns as if he is slightly disappointed by Kerry. He plays with the stem of his wine-glass. Kerry realises that he is reverting to his trick of not answering comments or questions that he cannot be bothered with.

'You don't agree then,' she says a little sarcastically, 'but it's not a personal attack on you. It doesn't bother me about you as a person. I'm just saying that it does make things easier for you. For one.'

'But we're talking about two completely separate things. Of course I realise that it's easier for me than for some kid in Moss Side. But that's not what I'm talking about. Money can also make you boring and conformist. It doesn't always come down to money.'

'I know it isn't just money. It's lots of things. But I don't think you can underestimate it either, that's all. And I don't necessarily agree that the best people are just those who are non-conformist in your terms, that that's the only way to measure them. It's difficult . . .'

Kerry thinks about Jeanette, about Marco, about Sylvia Gordon. She loves them all. She thinks about Gary whom she did love, right up to the bitter end. And here is Robin, so different, to whom she is attracted because . . . because what? He excites her, he flatters her, he is good in bed, he talks about things that other people would laugh at as being too deep, too pretentious. And he talks about them without being on an alcohol or drug rush of enthusiastic honesty. *If you want loyalty you should get a dog.* Perhaps she likes that as well, the edge of dismissive cruelty about him. *Who cares? I am arrogant.* She likes arrogance as well. Gary had an arrogance about him before he got ill, there was arrogance in his humour, his mimicry. She looks at Robin's long legs, his easy posture, the buttons of his jeans, his soft brown hair, and feels the knot of desire tightening again. She wants to feel him again, take him back to bed, his hands and mouth on her breasts, between her legs, her hands on his buttocks pulling him into her. As if he knows what she is thinking, Robin slides across to her, smiling.

Chapter 12

Marco glances impatiently at the clock as he sits waiting in the flat for Kerry on Christmas Eve. She is late and he wants to get to the pub. Marco knows that large amounts of alcohol are going to be needed to get him through the torture of the next few days and it won't do any harm to start tonight. He has also secured two pills and some grass from Danny, hoping that this might also increase the likelihood of its all passing off without a serious bust-up in the Fisher household. It is all right for Kerry, her family is more or less normal. He has met her mum a few times – a quiet, neat, distant woman with Kerry's eyes and smile, who works as an occupational therapist in a hospital. She likes Marco, though, especially after all the business of Gary's death.

At least once Christmas is out of the way, he consoles himself, there is the New Year to look forward to. Although that is not exactly without its stress factors: trying to decide where to go, stupid prices, queuing for cloakrooms at midnight – all the usual New Year nonsense – but at least without his family anywhere near him. Kerry is going away for the New Year with Robin to the Yorkshire Dales, meeting Robin's mum for the first time. Marco curls his lip slightly at the thought. Going to the country for New Year? Going to the country at any time is bad enough, but at New Year! 'What are you gonna do at midnight to celebrate?' he asked Kerry when she reluctantly told him. 'Go out and worry some sheep?' Marco's hatred of Robin has not diminished in the slightest with the passing of time. The good thing is that he is leaving today to go to his mum's for Christmas so at least he won't be around tonight.

Marco looks down at his carrier bag of presents which he has already impatiently wrapped. He hates wrapping presents and his inability is manifested in the untidy packages with twisted Sellotape and clumsy flaps of paper sticking out. He is pleased with the presents, though. Gerald gave him an unduly generous Christmas bonus so he has been able to make up for last year when he didn't have any money to buy presents. Nobody had mentioned it apart from the creep Tony who kept asking snidely, 'Is that one from Marco?' every time somebody unwrapped something. He has bought good presents this year though: a history of radical and underground printers of the eighteenth century for his dad; a video of *Casablanca* for Anne; a fish steamer for Angela; a £5 book token for Tony. Marco is particularly satisfied with the last present since it had been something of a challenge to find a gift which managed to be insultingly impersonal, cheap, and as inappropriate to the recipient as a pair of gold initialled cuff-links. Marco has also bought from the deli a whole side of smoked salmon, antipasti, and some Roquefort cheese. He realises that he is going to have to cart this lot around with him all night since he is going straight from the pub to Bethnal Green.

The telephone rings. It is his step-mother.

'Hello, Marco love, I just wanted to check everything was OK with you for tonight?'

'Oh yeah. I told you I was going out for a drink with Kerry tonight first. Say goodbye to her.'

'Yes, I remember. Well, we won't be going to bed early or anything. The other thing I wanted to check was whether you're still OK to help out with the food and everything tomorrow?'

''Course. No problem. I'll do the stuffing. I've brought some things from the deli as well.'

'Good. Thanks, Marco. Tony and Angela should be here soon. They're driving off tomorrow evening to see Tony's parents.'

'That's a shame, having to spend Christmas evening in a laboratory.'

Anne laughs. 'I gather your dad had words with you.'

'Yeah, he dropped a gentle hint that he'd break my neck if there were any arguments.'

'He's really looking forward to seeing you for a bit,

Marco, you know. He wants everything to go well.'

'Well, I'm sure it will,' he lies. 'I mean, it's not like he's invited a raving Nazi bastard for Christmas or anything.'

Anne giggles. 'I just wanted you to know, Marco, that I had words with Angela as well. I know it's not always your fault. She has to stop throwing tantrums if anyone says anything to Tony. And he can be very provocative.'

'Well, honestly, Anne, I'll try my best.'

As soon as Marco replaces the receiver it rings again.

'Hi, Marco darling, it's Jeanette.'

'Hello gorgeous.'

'Is Kerry back yet?'

'No, she went to put whatsisname on his train.'

'Oh. Well, listen, I said I might meet up with you two in the pub tonight.'

'I didn't think you went to pubs. I thought you only went to bars where the beautiful people hang out. I'll get them to charge you on the door so that you feel at home.'

'Yeah, very funny, Marco. Just give me the name of the pub.'

'Well, get your passport out, 'cause it's not in Soho. We're going to the Duke of Edinburgh. In Farringdon.'

'I know it actually. Is that idiot friend of yours going to be there?'

'Who would that be?'

'Oh, is there more than one? You know, quite nice-looking but stupid as fuck and the manners of a pig.'

'Ah, that does narrow it down a little. Yeah, I think it's quite probable Danny might put in an appearance.'

'Well, make sure you tell him the answer's the same as it was last time so not to bother me.'

'You're unavailable tonight then?'

'Well, not to the right man.'

'Sorry, Jeanette, I always go to midnight mass on Christmas Eve.'

'I said man, Marco.'

'But I'm dressing up 'specially. Just for you. It's a D and G night for you, Jeanette.'

She laughs. 'OK, sweetheart. I'll put you on my B-list.'

'What about blagging me in somewhere nice on New Year's Eve then?'

'I've got my reputation to think about, you know. Anyway, I'll see you later. About nine. Have a Jack Daniel's waiting for me.'

'Your sister phoned,' Marco tells Kerry when she comes in hauling carrier bags with bright starry wrapping paper sticking out of the top. 'She's gagging for it, you know. I'm well in there.'

'Is that right?' Kerry laughs. 'I'll have to ask her about that tonight.'

'Er . . . no, don't do that, Kerry. I think she wants to keep it under her hat just now. We're taking one step at a time at the moment.'

'It'll be a pretty long walk then. Anyway, what time did you tell her to meet us?'

'She's gonna be down there about nine. But I thought we could go a bit earlier.'

Kerry nods. 'OK. You can help me wrap this lot up and then we'll go.'

This is more like it, Marco thinks as he sits on the floor obligingly holding his finger on the wrapping paper while Kerry Sellotapes. No Robin prowling around with his lop-sided grin and creepy, hypocritical good manners. Kerry pulls out a beautiful soft wool jumper and holds it up.

'What do you think?'

'Who's it for?'

'Robin.'

'Nice,' Marco concedes grudgingly. 'But it hasn't got any llamas on it.' This is a reference to one of Robin's Central American souvenirs that he unwisely wore round to the house one evening when Marco was there. Kerry laughs.

'I've hidden that one. He's given up looking for it now.'

Pity you won't throw him out with the jumper, thinks Marco. But he's not going to squabble with Kerry tonight.

When they have finished wrapping the presents, they exchange their own presents. Marco has bought Kerry a leather rucksack for college. From Kerry, he unwraps a plastic battery-powered shark which swims in the bath, and a bottle of melon vodka.

'Brilliant!' Marco is ecstatic with the shark. 'Let's try it out. It's dead realistic.'

Kerry fills the bath a little while Marco puts the batteries in. He turns it on and it begins to make a whirring noise and wiggle its tail. Marco grins triumphantly like a little kid.

They sit on the edge of the bath watching the grey plastic shark jerking its way around the bathtub. Kerry reaches in and spins it round every time it bumps its nose against the side of the bath and it tracks off again, jerking its tail to and fro.

'It sits just right in the water,' Marco exclaims. 'Look, the fin's at the right height and everything. Where did you get it?'

'Hamley's. It was like hell in there. I thought it was pretty funny, though. There's everyone queuing with their screaming kids and everything, and there's me buying a plastic shark for a thirty-one-year-old man.'

'Why should kids have all the good things?'

'Oh, well, don't ask me to understand your obsession with sharks.'

'It's just a thing. I just like them, that's all. They're ten times more interesting than dolphins, balancing balls on their nose and jumping through hoops. The way they look, the way they don't give a fuck, those mad eyes. A shark ain't gonna let any hippy go swimming on its fin. And they're scary. You can't see them, can't run away from them. They just open those big evil jaws and . . .'

'Marco!'

'OK, OK.'

'Maybe you should become an expert on sharks? You know, study them properly or something . . .'

Marco looks at her sharply. 'You don't *have* to study something to enjoy it. It's just an interest. Anyway, shall we have a little shot of vodka before we head out?'

'Don't you wanna save it for round at your family's? In case you get desperate.'

'Nah. My old man'll have tons of booze.'

'Come on then.'

'Switch Jaws off there. He's looking a bit knackered.'

Kerry lifts out the shark which is head-butting the side of the bath, lets the water drip off it and places it on the side of the tub where it sits oddly with her cosmetics and body lotions. They fill two glasses of melon vodka and sit in the living room.

'When are you back from Yorkshire?' Marco asks, wrinkling his nose as he tastes the melon vodka which is disgustingly sticky.

'A couple of days after the New Year, I think.'

Marco nods. He is going to miss Kerry. Over the last few weeks she has spent a lot of time at Robin's. Marco is torn between his hatred of having Robin in the house and the feeling of emptiness when Kerry is not around. His hatred of Robin also needs fuelling, and he is sometimes quite relieved to see him loping in behind Kerry so that he can concentrate on hating him again. He has given Danny a good dressing down for being nice to him, along with strict instructions not to do it again, but Danny just laughed and said that Marco was a silly cunt and that if Kerry was happy then what business was it of his? 'Don't try and be the voice of reason,' Marco retorted. 'It doesn't suit you. We hate the guy, right? He must be hated. End of story.'

'It's a bit sweet.' Kerry looks doubtfully at her melon vodka. 'But it sounded good and it looks quite cool in the bottle.'

Marco grins. 'It'll be all right in the desperation cupboard, though. It's been running low since Danny and I drank that bottle of Sambuca the other night.'

Kerry glances at the hole in the sofa where Danny set fire to it by attempting to do the Amaretto paper trick with bits of tissue paper. Marco knocks back his melon vodka in one and winces.

Kerry and Marco walk together down Old Street towards the Clerkenwell Road, entering the pub which is filling up with despatch riders in tight Lycra shorts, other people sitting at large wooden tables tucking into plates of Thai food. Danny is already at a table, stuffing his face inelegantly with a plate of noodles. He grins and raises his hand as he sees them, a noodle trailing from the side of his mouth like the disappearing tail of a small rodent.

Danny tells them about how he got a kicking in a club the night before, after he managed to flood it by swinging on the sprinkler-system pipes and breaking them.

'We was really havin' it, you know? Me and Lee was totally off our faces. Anyway, we were just messin' about at first. We was being the monkeys from *Jungle Book*. Then I tried to swing upside down from the pipes by my legs and the whole thing came crashing down. It was like fucking *Towering Inferno*. Water everywhere, all over the decks, the DJ's records . . . it was too much, man. They had to call the Fire Brigade and stuff. Lee managed to do a runner but they caught me and battered the fuck out of me. I feel like I've got a hard-boiled egg on my head, they was just ramming it against the wall. Then you know how they all come in afterwards for FLUID? Starts at four. Well, they couldn't, could they, 'cause we'd turned the whole place into a lake. A bit too fluid, know what I mean? I was more frightened of those massive geezers waiting outside when they heard it was off than the bouncers. Still, they cheered up when the firemen arrived.'

'So you won't be going back there again,' Kerry observes, sipping a rum and Coke.

'You're jokin', ain't you? Twelve grands' worth of damage, I was told.'

'Yeah, but they can't hold you responsible for that,' Marco says, picking a noodle off Danny's plate and dropping it carefully into his mouth. 'It's not your fault if their pipes are unstable. In fact, you should threaten to sue them. Anyway, the whole point about that club is that it's *meant* to be mental. That's what they've built it on. They can't complain if some idiot like you takes them at their word and starts hanging from pipes pretending to be a monkey.'

But Danny isn't listening. He is staring across at the pub

entrance where Jeanette has just come in. She comes over and kisses Kerry, ruffles Marco's hair and pulls a sideways face at Danny.

'I've just had a massive argument with a cabbie,' she announces indignantly. 'He kept getting lost. Then we got to that bit where they've closed the road and he couldn't find his way round, but the meter kept running. I said to him that he was meant to have done the knowledge not the ignorance. He kept asking me the way so I said that I was gonna knock a pound off every time he asked me. The point of getting in a cab is that you're meant to relax while the cabbie takes you to your destination.'

'Maybe he got a bit distracted?' Danny suggests.

'What by?' Jeanette rounds on him.

Danny smirks and leers at her. Jeanette sighs.

'Oh, go and buy yourself a copy of *Loaded* if you're that frustrated, Danny. Anyway. . .' she flops down next to her sister and takes out her Marlboro Lights ' . . . Marco, do me a massive favour and get me a Jack Daniel's and Coke. I'm knackered and that bar's heaving with sweaty cyclists. Here, get a round.' She hands him a tenner.

'Look after my bags,' Marco says to Kerry.

'So you put Prince Charming on his train then?' Jeanette asks as Marco relays the drinks to the table. 'Dabbing a tear from your eye and waving a hankie.'

'Not exactly,'

'Well, I think he's very nice. Good-mannered, handsome, a certain *je ne sais quoi*. More than can be said for some people . . .'

'Yeah,' Danny says wickedly. 'Top geezer, eh, Marco?'

Marco sits down and does not reply. Jeanette looks at him shrewdly.

'Don't you like him then, Marco?'

'Oh, Marco loves him, don't you . . .'

'Shut up, you idiot,' Jeanette snaps. 'I'm talking to Marco. Well?'

Marco glances at Kerry. Her face is still, unmoving. She is watching him, holding her glass.

'He's all right,' Marco says finally. Danny sniggers. Marco gives him a look which is enough to make him straighten his face pretty quickly.

Jeanette furrows her eyebrows at Marco, puzzled, and Marco glances at Kerry again. She is expressionless. Jeanette leans over to Marco and takes his hand, pressing a wrap into it.

'Go and do a line. Leave some for me and Kerry.'

Marco looks at Danny who is now like a small child with a burst balloon. He is angry with him but it is still impossible to exclude him. It is not right. Jeanette catches his hesitation and smiles. 'OK then, take him with you. It's Christmas after all. Goodwill to all . . .' she hesitates as she regards Danny. 'Well, goodwill anyway.'

The awkwardness caused by the last conversation disappears after several more drinks and a couple of lines each. People entering the pub come up and ask Danny if it is true that he flooded PANIC STATIONS the previous night. And Danny has to tell the story again and even Jeanette is reduced to helpless giggles at the thought of the mayhem and Danny's terror at the prospect of retribution from thousands of disappointed, muscle-bound queers.

'A few of my mates were going down to FLUID last night,' she says. 'And I've got your name, Daniel. So let's see a bit of grovelling from you or I'll be handing it out with your phone number and address.'

'You're havin' a laaaarrf, darlin'.'

Marco knows that it is time to go. He reaches under the table for his bags. They all stand up. Kerry gives him a hug.

'Look after yourself, Marco. Count to ten a few times.'

'Enjoy Yorkshire,' he says as sincerely as possible. 'See you when you get back.'

Jeanette kisses him goodbye. 'Listen, Marco, give me a ring in between Christmas and New Year. I always get really bored. You've got the number?'

'Your mum's?'

'Yeah.'

Marco shakes hands with Danny and leaves them in the

street. It is cold and people are going home after office parties. There'll be a few nervous calls to the family-planning clinic after Boxing Day, Marco thinks. Some drunken City workers sing their way up the street, holding on to each other, women screeching with laughter. He walks towards the tube station but then feels the bags tugging at his arms and decides to get a cab.

'Roman Road, Bethnal Green,' he instructs the cabbie, slumping back in his seat and watching another group of red and silver tinsel-draped office workers staggering past the window. He just hasn't got the Christmas spirit.

The next morning, Marco looks out of the window to another grey Christmas. A few kids are already out playing with their new bikes. One kid has a new pair of roller-blades. Every time he gets up, he falls over again. Then he sits down on his step and stares angst-ridden at his wheeled feet. Otherwise, the streets are filled with the Bank Holiday deadness that always makes Marco nervous. He yawns and makes his way to the kitchen to get some coffee, stiffening as he sees Tony emerge from his and Angela's bedroom. Tony has grown long sideburns which curve round into a point. He is wearing a t-shirt with a gold chain and Calvin Klein underwear.

'Marco,' Tony says as he enters the kitchen and opens the fridge.

'Tony,' Marco replies, refusing to make eye-contact.

There is a long pause while Marco watches the kettle boil and Tony gets cups for himself and Angela.

'There enough water in there for us?'

Marco lifts the kettle and weighs it in his hand.

'Yeah.'

After this spontaneous outburst of seasonal goodwill they say no more to each other, making their coffee as quickly as possible and returning to their respective rooms.

The mood over Christmas lunch is one of studied politeness. Before the meal, they drink the champagne which Tony has brought and eat the smoked salmon on quarters of brown bread with slices of lemon which Marco has prepared. At the table, Angela talks about where they might go for Easter, Anne tells funny stories about things her kids have said to her and how she is coping with being Head of Department, Tony tells a joke about a skeleton that goes into a bar and orders a pint of lager and a mop. He then typically explains the point of the joke and even Angela touches his arm and says, 'I think everybody understood it, darling.' They pull crackers. Marco pulls one with his dad and his dad ends up with the main body of the cracker. He gets a plastic game with tiny tin balls which are meant to drop into the eyes and mouth of a clown, a strange motto instead of a joke which says '*Beware of the silent man and the dog that does not bark*', and a purple paper crown. Marco watches his dad holding the game, shaking the little balls about, while he also struggles to fit the hat onto his large head and then sits smiling stupidly as it sits half on and half off his head with the paper slightly torn. Marco is overcome with a wave of emotion which almost makes tears prick his eyes. His dad is getting old, he is becoming an old man; an Aged P in a paper crown.

After lunch, John Fisher gets cigars out for himself, Tony and Marco even though Marco would infinitely prefer to slip into his room and skin up. Anne and Angela clear the table and then they sit down to open their presents. It is at this point that the surprisingly long truce collapses with the inevitability of all such brokered deals. Anne is opening her present from Marco and laughs with pleasure when she sees her favourite film.

'Brilliant,' she says, 'we can watch it later on.'

Tony perks up from his food and alcohol stupor when he also identifies it.

'*Casablanca*? But that's on telly tomorrow! I'm sure of it. You just could have videoed it off the telly, Anne. Honestly, I'm sure I'm right . . . yeah, look in the TV guide, it's on at 3.40 on Boxing Day. Bit of a waste of money that, Marco. It's on telly. Look, it's there, Boxing Day . . . I mean it's always on at Christmas.'

Anne regards him quietly. 'Well, it's not the same, is it? This is great, Marco . . .'

'How do you mean, it's not the same. I mean a video's a video isn't it . . .'

'She *means* it's not the bloody same!' John Fisher suddenly roars, and then catching sight of his daughter's wobbling lip, he lapses back into silence.

There is an awkward pause and then they all start opening presents again. Marco receives an expensive leather wallet from Angela and Tony, a Le Creuset casserole and set of Sabatier knives from Anne, an Italian cookery book and £50 from his dad.

'Great,' he says enthusiastically, taking out the largest of the knives. 'You could almost remove somebody's head with this,' He lets his glance linger for a moment on Tony, and receives a warning look from his dad.

'Pukkah,' Tony says sarcastically as he opens his book token. 'I didn't know you could still buy books for under a fiver.'

'You can't.' Angela glares at Marco. Unlike Tony, she is just clever enough to realise that that was the whole point. Her frown deepens, however, when she realises that none of the presents that she has opened is from Tony, apart from a bottle of Chanel perfume. He is watching her, trying not to laugh at her bewilderment.

'Lovely, Tony, thank you very much,' Angela whispers faintly, dabbing a bit of the perfume on her wrist.

'Didn't have much time for presents this year.' He grins. 'Make it up to you on your birthday.'

'No, this is lovely,' Angela squeaks disappointedly. 'You know it's my favourite.'

Tony pauses, thoroughly enjoying her crestfallen expression, and then reaches into his pocket. 'Oh, but . . . hang on. I did get you a little extra something, now I remember. Just, you know, a token.'

He takes out a small parcel and hands it to her. When Angela opens it, a set of keys drops out into her lap.

Marco groans inwardly. He suddenly realises what is coming.

Don't Step on the Lines

'But, Tony . . .' Angela's eyes are flashing excitedly ' . . . what are they for?'

Given that they're car keys, you silly cow, Marco thinks, you can probably safely assume that the fucking show-off has got a car outside for you.

'Come to the window.' Tony grins again.

Angela almost bunny-hops to the window. Anne rolls her eyes.

'You see that little turquoise Peugeot down there?'

'Oh . . . oh, Tony, is it for me?' Angela squeals. 'Is it? Is it for me?'

'Well, who else would it be for? I thought you needed a little run-around.'

Well, who else would it be for? Marco grips the handle of his knife and contemplates plunging it two-handed between Tony's shoulder blades.

'Mum, Dad, come and look . . . did you know, Dad? Oh, you are rotten. Have you seen it, Marco? You must all have known, you rotten sods! Oh, that's brilliant.'

Angela insists that everybody go down and look at the car. They all obey except Marco – probably the only one who didn't know about it – who watches from the window as they huddle around Angela's new toy. He skins up quickly, opening the window slightly to let the smoke out, wafting vigorously with his hand as it starts to blow back in. Fortunately, they have to spend the best part of half an hour exclaiming over the car, until Anne begins shivering ostentatiously and clapping her arms around herself. Marco grins. He can almost hear her exaggerated 'Brrrrs'. He knew Anne would be the first to escape. When she comes back in she wrinkles her nose.

'You'd better not let your dad catch you,' she says to Marco. 'What? I haven't . . .'

'I'm a teacher, Marco. Just don't let him catch you, that's all. Do you want another beer?'

When the rest of the car inspection party have returned, they finish opening the rest of the presents. Tony is still grinning triumphantly and laying into a bottle of Scotch. Angela is sipping a glass of Bailey's. Marco is drinking brandy and Coke.

'Oh, I nearly forgot. Your grandparents sent you something,' John Fisher suddenly exclaims, going into his bedroom and returning with a package which he hands to his son. Marco's grandparents from Bologna always send him something on birthdays and at Christmas. When Marco opens it, it is a framed photo of his mother holding a baby in her arms, standing by a beach with the wind blowing back her hair. She is laughing. The mother he cannot remember, the mother who gave him her dark features. What else did she give him? How much of the smiling woman is in Marco?

'What is it, son?' his dad asks. Marco silently hands him the photo.

'Yeah,' John says after a few seconds of quietly looking at the photo. 'I remember when that was taken. That's you in the picture with her.'

Marco nods. There is a baby in the photo. That baby is Marco. The woman is his mother. She is dead. The baby in her arms is not looking at the camera any more, but at himself and his dead mother. He is sitting in Bethnal Green. Photographs are weird. They are scary. Marco shakes his head and wraps the photo carefully again in its paper.

'Make sure you write and thank them.'

Marco nods again and pours another brandy and Coke, more brandy than Coke.

Tony is sprawled on the sofa, his eyes unfocused. Drink does not agree with him at all. It is as if it acts as a lance to all the pus-like nastiness inside him. Marco looks at him with disgust. Tony begins expounding on his admiration for Michael Portillo, his belief that underperforming teachers should be sacked, his contempt for losers (anyone not as rich as he is), his conviction that, with hard work, anyone can make it in British society.

'Look at me.' He jabs his own chest. 'I wasn't born with a silver spoon in my mouth.'

'You're out of date, Tony,' says John Fisher, 'it's not the 1980s any more, son. Your lot are better off with the Labour Party now.'

'I don't know about that. Tony Blair – he's OK though.'

Marco laughs. 'That's it. The final endorsement. Even beats Murdoch. If there was any doubt ...'

'Coffee, anyone?' Anne interrupts. 'And then we're all going to watch *Casablanca*. That's my one demand today.'

'I've seen *Casablanca*,' Tony yawns.

Everybody, even Angela, looks at him with the same expression.

'No! Have you?' Marco exclaims. 'What's it about then?'

Anne snorts and then coughs, heading into the kitchen quickly to put the kettle on. Tony reaches for the bottle of Scotch. 'Then we'll have to go,' Angela says. 'Looks like I'm driving.'

Marco sits watching the familiar images of the film, letting them wash over him. He is still pretty stoned. Looking around him, he is filled with an insane urge to giggle. He is trapped here for the night, he can't go home, wouldn't want to go home to the empty flat. He has to be here with his family. The thought fills him with an anxiety which mirrors that of the lemur-eyed Peter Lorre charging around Rick's Bar in a futile attempt to escape the wrath of the SS. Still, at least Tony and Angela will be leaving fairly soon. Tony is playing with Angela's hair and refilling his whisky glass. John Fisher has started to snore gently, his paper crown still on his head. On the mantelpiece, Lenin gazes out sternly.

In Rick's Bar some German officers are banging the table as they belt out a Nazi drinking song. Marco can feel the comment bubbling inside him. He tries to hold it back, he is going to giggle out loud, he knows it will cause trouble, he can't, he just can't stop himself.

'Look, Tony, there's some of your relatives!'

Tony jumps and then focuses blearily on Marco.

'You can be a right lippy little bastard sometimes, can't you, Marco?'

The phoney war has ended.

'I don't know. Can I?'

Tony sits up unsteadily in his chair.

'Yeah, you can. An' I'll tell you what. The only reason I don't give you a slap sometimes is because you're not worth it. Look at you! Look at the state of you. You're nothing. You're a miserable little nobody who's just a burden to everybody.'

'And a very merry Christmas to you as well, Anthony.'

'Shhhh.' Anne scowls at them. 'I'm trying to watch the film.'

'Why bother? It's on the telly tomorrow anyway. You're only doing it to be polite to Marco.'

'Oh, Tony, that's not a very nice thing to say,' Angela whispers.

He turns to her bleary-eyed. 'Don't you start as well. You're meant to be on my side.'

'For God's sake,' Anne says, 'it's not a question of sides.'

Tony gets up and staggers slightly. 'Anyway, that's it, I've had enough. Get your things, Angela. I want to go and see my family now. Don't wanna waste what's left of Christmas.'

'*Achtung*, Angela. Get your things,' Marco sneers. '*Schnell, schnell.*'

'Shut up!' Angela shrieks with tears in her eyes. 'This is all your fault, Marco.'

At these magic words, John Fisher shifts in his seat and opens his eyes.

'Wha'? What's goin' on.'

'It's Marco.' Angela bursts into tears. 'He started winding Tony up, taking the piss as usual, and now we're going.'

'Nobody needs to go. Tony, Marco was only joking . . .' Anne butts in.

'Well, I'm sick of his jokes. It's always the same.'

'Sit down and have a drink.'

'Stuff your drink.'

'Oi oi, sunshine, that's enough. Now I don't know what's going on here but you don't speak to Anne like that. Understood? Now, Marco, what did you say?' He pushes his paper crown impatiently away from his eyes.

'I was only messin' about!'

'WHAT DID YOU SAY?'

'I just wondered out loud whether the German officers on TV might be a distant branch of the Hammond family, that's all.'

Marco can't help sniggering again. He puts his hand to his mouth.

'You arrogant little prick!' Tony is shouting again. 'You think you can say things about *my* family?'

'Now stop shouting,' John Fisher yells. 'It's Christmas. Come on, Tony, sit down and have a drink. I'm sure Marco didn't mean any harm. And if he's offended you, I'm sure he'll apologise. Won't you, Marco?'

'. . .'

'Marco?'

Tony stares at Marco, red-eyed, waiting.

'I'm sorry if I implied that you or your family might in any way be connected with the Third Reich, Tony.'

'See! See! He's still takin' the piss. Come on, Angela. That's it. I don't know why I bother, I really don't. You can come and pick up your car in the morning if you want. I've tried, I've done my best, but you never let up, do you, Marco? Come on, Angela, my mum and dad will be expecting us.'

Angela starts to sob. 'Look what you've done,' she wails at Marco. 'I hope you're happy now.'

'Oh, stop whingeing, Angela,' Anne suddenly snaps. 'You're not making it any better.'

'Come on, Tony,' Angela hiccups, and then turns dramatically back to the living room. 'And don't expect us next Christmas. Because WE WON'T BE COMING!'

Tony lurches drunkenly across the living room, stepping on something on the way. There is the sound of glass crunching under his feet. Everybody looks at the spot where he has just stepped. Then they look at Tony.

'Well, it was a stupid place to leave it . . .' he starts defensively and marches out of the room. Angela hurries after him. Marco crosses the floor on his knees and picks up the parcel from Italy that he had wrapped back up and placed by his chair. He opens it gingerly and fragments of glass fall through his fingers. Tony's foot has also bent the photo. He tries to straighten it and then throws it down. His mother smiles ironically up at him from the floor, amid the broken glass. Marco turns and

173

looks at Anne and John Fisher. His dad is still wearing his party hat.

'Don't worry, Marco, we'll be able to fix it,' Anne says.

'They didn't take their presents,' John Fisher mutters as if to himself. He does not even have the energy to blame Marco for the traditional denoument to Christmas Day.

'Marco love, give me a hand with the washing up,' Anne says.

They stand in the kitchen washing dishes. In the living room, Marco can hear *Bridge on the River Kwai* starting. As they wash up, Anne tells Marco that John Fisher hasn't been too well recently and that he is going into hospital next week to have some tests done.

Chapter 13

The Inter-City train to Leeds – delayed twenty-five minutes due to track problems in Stevenage – has finally managed to pick up some speed and is making wavelets appear on the coffee cups as people reach out with steadying hands. Kerry sits reading about the little Ursula Brangwen leaving footprints on her father's seed-beds. She sighs and puts the book down, rolling her head on to her shoulder to stare out of the window at the English countryside – something totally unknown, totally alien to her. Not only does Kerry not know the names of flowers, she does not know what type of tree that is, nor who owns the frosted fields that curve and slope like the small of a back up to a copse where large birds – she does not know what they are either – flap almost menacingly in the cold winter air. Nor does she know where you can walk and where you cannot. *Somebody* owns all of this, there is power here, there is somebody powerful that Kerry does not know, will never know, somebody who can move effortlessly between country and city, belonging to neither, leaving no footprint.

Kerry sees cars heading down narrow lanes, isolated pubs adorned with necklaces of coloured fairy lights, scatterings of houses, willow-lined rivers that curve into lakes, black hills sulking on the horizon. She realises that she cannot remember the last time she left London, and feels like one of the war-time evacuees who had never seen a real cow before, complete with mittens and gas-mask, heading into the great mysterious unknown of rural England. She wishes that she did know the names of things, or rather that she could match the seductive names she knows – silver birch, honeysuckle, lark – to actual trees, actual flowers, actual birds. They pass great farmhouses with orchards of spiky, leafless trees (Kerry guesses they must

175

be apple trees), paddocks with horses and practice jumps, big wealthy houses with sloping gardens and white benches, forlornly cold and empty now, but Kerry can imagine it all in summer – the air languid and honey-scented. She fantasises briefly about sitting on a bench in a cool vanilla-white summer skirt, the air thick and hot and full of the descant of birdsong (the feathered authors of which she would be able to identify with ease). Somebody would bring her tea in a china cup, children would be playing by a stream, she would be lazy and elegant, perhaps a student from Oxford home for the vacations. Then Kerry laughs and shakes her head. The refreshments trolley is moving through her carriage and she buys an over-priced KitKat and a cup of tea.

Drops of rain with their transparent tails begin to race like frantic sperm across the window of the train. Kerry notices that the girl sitting opposite her is fabulously cross-eyed. Men are sitting with lap-top computers staring at pie-charts, even in this week unprepared to relax from the task of monitoring company sales revenue. At all-too-frequent intervals, one of the orchestra of mobile phones begins to chirrup and a loud voice drones through the carriage in a strange monologue about unsigned contracts or, even more mundanely, a report on the current position of the train to a bored spouse. And Kerry has her bag on the seat next to her, and is going to see her boyfriend.

Robin gave her the money to get her ticket up to Yorkshire. At first, she had not wanted to accept it – especially after the luxury of the lap-top computer he had bought her for Christmas. He had noted her moans about being unable to get on the college computers and gone out and got it for her. Kerry had glowed with pleasure, not only because of the way that this would make her life easier but because he had thought about his gift and she has always liked people who do that. But she was completely broke after Christmas and he had insisted on paying for the ticket too, growing irritated in the face of her initial refusal. 'It's what I want to spend my money on. I want you to come up.' And in the end, Kerry had thought, Oh, why not? The idea of leaving London, of getting on a train, after so long was suddenly extremely attractive. She did not have the money, Robin did. No big deal. He was right.

As they pull into Leeds station, Kerry realises that she has forgotten to bring the telephone number of his mother's house. If Robin is not there, what will she do? Make her way to the appropriate Dale somehow and go around asking people? This after all is supposed to be what the countryside is all about; friendly, open and helpful people uncontaminated by the selfish individualism of the city. 'Aye, lass, that'll be Mrs Thomas you want that lives in't big house by top field.' Kerry is somewhat doubtful about this scenario and fears that she is more likely to end up the victim of one of the countryside's numerous hazards: shotgun-wielding farmers, spiteful pecking geese, charging bulls, man-traps, anti-witch fanatics who will decide that she has the mark of Jezebel upon her and is responsible for the milk turning sour or cousin Jeannie's measles. 'You're not from these parts . . .'

When they arrive at Leeds station, Kerry is released from the anxious contemplation of these possibilities by the sight of Robin waiting for her. She suddenly feels a wave of shyness as she sees him again, standing in his usual relaxed posture, half grinning at her. He is wearing a new sky-blue Puffa jacket, obviously a Christmas present.

'Hello,' she says awkwardly, standing in front of him.

He bends down and kisses her and says simply, 'I've missed you.'

They walk to the car where Robin throws maps and a tin of travel sweets off the front seat and fiddles around with the tape. Kerry likes watching him drive, he does it with his usual casual grace. She feels comfortable in the car, looked after.

They drive out of Leeds and start climbing up towards the moors. It is beginning to spit threatening needles of rain onto the car windows and Robin turns on the windscreen wipers. He tells her the names of places as they drive – names like Blubberhouses which fill Kerry with a sense of unease; it is like being in a foreign land, she feels like Gulliver. The moors are misty-bleak and rain-swept, devoid of all life apart from a few sodden sheep which gaze at them with black pear-faced solemnity as they pass. They see a tiny fenced-off graveyard, dripping crosses, high and isolated on the top of the moor. In the distance, the dim, dark shapes of hills are streaked with snow.

'How was your Christmas?' Robin asks, reaching down to turn the tape over.

'OK. Same as usual really. Yours?'

'My mother has been getting on my nerves.'

'Why's that?'

Robin does not answer this question but points instead to some caves which are a big tourist attraction in the summer. He explains what Dales are, about tops and bottoms, fells and becks. He tells her that the Dales were cut out by glaciers, that they are riddled with underground rivers and caverns, that the Vikings camped out there, that the stone walls are limestone. Kerry carefully adds this knowledge to her impoverished names database. She knows now what limestone looks like. Not exactly a pearl, but a useful bead of wisdom.

They enter the small Dale in which Robin's mother lives. Becks, thinks Kerry as she watches the rain-swollen streams cascading down the sides of the valley. They drive alongside a swollen river which Robin informs her dries up in the summer, preferring to go underground. Kerry has to admit that it is impressive and imagines it in summertime with the grass on the fells all green, dotted with blossom-legged lambs, and the limestone shining white in the sun in contrast to its present rain-dulled condition. She exclaims out loud at a waterfall which is tumbling out of the side of the valley. Robin tells her that it is called a foss and that they have arrived.

Kerry feels anxious and awkward as she gets out of the car. She hates meeting people's parents. As she steps out of the car, a black and white shape streaks round the side of the house, bounces effortlessly over the low front wall and almost leaps into Robin's arms. It is so excited that it begins to perform all kinds of weird bouncing gyrations, leaping about on all four feet, frenziedly chasing its tail, before dropping on to its belly and beginning to stalk keenly around Kerry, herding her towards the gate. It abandons this task to herd a tennis ball and then an old shoe left in the front garden. The border collie is completely insane. Robin swings Kerry's bag out of the car. 'That's Max,' he says. 'He's a bit mad because he's not a working dog but he's still got all those instincts, still thinks he's a sheepdog. It's given him an identity crisis.' Max begins to jump hyperactively back and forth over the wall. Kerry smiles weakly.

Robin's mother Celia lives alone in a converted farmhouse, tastefully decorated, with big open fireplaces, book-lined walls, a wide staircase, and huge comfortable chairs. She comes out of the kitchen, wiping her hands, a tall white-haired woman with black pebble eyes behind half-moon glasses, and Robin's features.

'I heard the car but I was just in the middle of peeling some potatoes. You must be Kerry. Let me have a good look at you . . .' She holds Kerry at arm's length and studies her solemnly. 'Yes,' she says at last, 'I thought so.'

Kerry is highly embarrassed by her scrutiny. 'Thought what?' she asks, laughing nervously. Mrs Thomas does not answer this question.

'Robin, you take Kerry's stuff up to the bedroom. Kerry, you sit down there and keep me amused while I finish peeling these potatoes. I assume you won't mind sleeping in the same room as Robin? We didn't really discuss that – I suppose I just thought that you would. Hurry up, Robin, because I need you to slip out and check with Michael about taking a look at the sheep.'

Robin rolls his eyes at Kerry and disappears up the wide, wooden stairs towards the top of the house. Kerry wishes that she could go with him. His mother resumes her task of peeling potatoes.

'Shall I help you?' Kerry asks.

'No, it's OK. Are you a vegetarian?'

Kerry shakes her head.

'Good. So many people are nowadays, aren't they? Well now, so you study with Robin then?'

'Yes, we're in the same year. Sometimes we do different modules though . . .'

'Modules?'

'Courses.'

'All this new jargon.' Robin's mother shakes her head. 'In my day we had tutorials and lectures and that was it. Anyway, is Robin actually working at this poly of his?'

She drops a potato into the pan like a small depth charge. Kerry feels awkward, she senses a trap in the question. Neither does she like the slightly dismissive way that Mrs Thomas's tongue curves around the word 'poly' as if it were something vaguely embarrassing, as if she thinks that her son is slumming it down in London.

'Yeah, he works really hard.'

'Really?' Celia Thomas turns and scrutinises Kerry over the top of her glasses as if she suspects her of lying. Then she turns back to the pan and tosses another potato into it. 'Well, that's something I suppose,' she mutters meaningfully.

Kerry can think of nothing to say to this and there is an awkward silence, punctuated only by potatoes plopping into the pan.

Just as Kerry is racking her brains for something else to say, she is saved by a loud knocking on the door, followed by a huge figure striding into the kitchen.

Kerry half expects this giant straw-haired man to sweep her, helpless, over his shoulder and march off down the Dale, he is so Vikingesque. All that is lacking is a two-horned helmet.

'Ah, Michael,' Celia Thomas exclaims. 'You've saved me sending Robin down to talk to you . . .'

'Never mind that. I've just come up to say, Mrs Thomas, that if your bloody dog gets in among my sheep again, I'll shoot the bugger.'

Kerry turns expectantly to Robin's mother to see how she will respond to this piece of Yorkshire frank-talking.

Celia Thomas tinkles with laughter.

'Oh, Michael, you're not accusing poor Max again? He's been here all day under my eye . . .'

'It weren't today, it were yesterday. It's the last time I'll warn you, Mrs Thomas. If that dog gets in among my sheep again, I'll shoot the daft bugger.'

Don't Step on the Lines

Max chooses this moment to come sliding into the kitchen on his belly, herding an imaginary sheep. Michael regards him without emotion. Presumably, his antipathy to the dog is only activated when Max is in sheep-worrying mode. To confirm this, he bends down and pats the dog on the head, although pat is too gentle a word for the slaps he administers with his huge hands, rather as if the dog were a basket-ball. Max looks up adoringly through melted-chocolate eyes at the man who has just threatened to put an end to his schizoid identity with a twelve-bore shot-gun.

Having delivered his ultimatum, Michael becomes slightly more amenable.

'Your water freeze over again this morning, Mrs Thomas?'

'Yes,' she sighs. 'It came back about lunchtime. By the way, Michael, I'd like you to meet Kerry. She's Robin's . . . partner.'

Michael blushes and extends a giant hand to her. ''Ow do, Kerry? First time up here, is it?'

'Yes,' she murmurs politely, trying not to stare at his tremendous thighs, presumably hardened by a lifetime of climbing fells in his role as guardian of sheep safety. 'I'm from London.'

Michael nods. 'I've not bin to London,' he announces as if this is a point strongly in his favour. 'Well, you won't find as much going on up here as in London, I daresay.'

Kerry agrees that this is highly probable.

'It's nice to get away though sometimes,' she remarks brightly, smiling at him. Michael blushes again and looks at his feet.

'Will you have a cup of tea, Michael?' Robin's mum asks, putting down her potato peeler.

'I'll not, thank you, Mrs Thomas. I'm not stopping. I just wanted to let you know that the next time that dog gets in among my sheep . . .'

. . . I'll shoot the bugger, Kerry is tempted to finish his sentence for him.

'Well, I appreciate that, Michael. But I do think you might find that it isn't always Max . . .'

'Well, we'll soon find out when I shoot him next time round.

We'll know then for sure.' And he bends down to perform his Magic Johnson routine on the dog's head. A potato drops on the floor and Max instantly begins to herd it.

'Daft bugger,' Michael says.

When he has gone, Celia Thomas resumes her task of peeling potatoes. She tells Kerry that there is a certain hostility among the locals in the Dale towards people who have moved in from outside.

'I came here ten years ago and they still consider me an outsider. I can understand them resenting those dreadful people who come up at weekends in their four-wheel drives and green wellingtons, though.'

'You live here all the time then?'

'Oh, yes. Although when my husband died he also left a cottage in Provence and we sometimes spend the summer there. Most of the time I rent it out, though it can be a very relaxing place to get on with my writing.'

'Ah, you're a writer then?' Kerry says, trying to sound breezily enthusiastic and impressed.

'Yes. I'm working on a book on women reformers of the nineteenth century at the moment. Amazingly strong women.' She shakes her head. 'We owe so much to them.'

Kerry nods. Robin comes back into the kitchen and stands with his back to the Aga. He seems tense, knitting his hands together, glancing at his mother as if nervous about what she might have been saying about him.

Kerry gazes out of the kitchen window. The garden outside is full of trees. Beyond there is a small limestone-enclosed field in which a couple of coal-faced sheep stand stupidly. Beyond that, there is a great rise of fell up to a sharply defined ridge at the top of the valley. Kerry wonders what is behind it. Another valley, she supposes, as if some giant hand has gouged these grooves in the land, a finger for each Dale.

'It must be nice to have your own apples,' she says.

'What, dear?'

'Apples. You must get lots of apples in . . . in . . .' Kerry does not know when apples emerge. Spring? Summer? Autumn?

'Oh, no,' Celia replies, lifting a lid of the pale blue Aga and placing the potatoes on to boil. 'They're damsons. And that's a plum tree.'

'Do you want to see where we're sleeping?' Robin asks, and Kerry leaps up a little too eagerly.

He leads her up the stairs and opens a thick dark-pannelled door into a large room, through whose window Kerry can see the water from the foss tumbling down the side of the valley. The bed is huge and comfortable-looking and she jumps on to it and bounces up and down.

'You'll have to be careful with my mum,' Robin observes as he sits on the end of the bed.

'Why?' Kerry is enthralled by the water tumbling down the side of the valley.

Robin sighs. 'She's very manipulative. She's always trying to get at me through my friends, especially my girlfriends. Jill comes up with Mac now to see my mum and they talk about me, analyse me . . . it's fucking awful. And she'll try and do it with you. She plays games.'

'Oh, well,' Kerry replies, 'I don't think that there's much chance of that happening in my case. I'm not sure if I'm her sort of girl.'

Robin turns and looks at her sombrely. 'No,' he agrees, 'I don't suppose you are.'

Over the next few days, Kerry and Robin read or drive over to Skipton or Settle for lunch. Kerry likes driving across the tops, the thrill of wondering what would happen if you broke down in some of the bleaker spots, the pleasure of the car's continued motion like being inside in the warm when it is pouring with rain. They sit in pubs and drink soup and eat jacket potatoes and talk about the books that they are reading and Kerry feels little bright stabs of happiness.

Back in the house, especially when Celia has despatched Robin on some task, Kerry can also feel small naggings of homesickness stirring inside her. Out of politeness, she sits in the kitchen and chats to Celia but she is made uncomfortable by her hostess's attempts to draw Kerry into a kind of conspiratorial bond.

'He's very like his father,' Celia says of Robin and Kerry understands that this is not intended as a compliment

'What did he do?' Kerry asks. She cannot imagine Robin's father.

Celia Thomas does not answer the question and Kerry is beginning to find this family habit sufficiently irritating to repeat it slightly louder, implying that Celia has not heard her.

'What did he do?'

'Oh, he worked for the government.'

'What, like a civil servant?'

'Erm . . . yes, sort of. Could you pass me that tea-towel, please, Kerry darling?'

Later that evening in the pub, she asks Robin about his father but he also brushes the question aside as if it is of no interest.

'I'm not being funny or anything,' Kerry says, lighting a cigarette, 'but how much did he leave you? I'm not asking because . . .'

'Well, he left me the house so I don't have to pay any rent. And then there was another house in Wales which he left to me and Mum, so we sold that and divided the proceeds. I got about seventy thousand pounds.'

Kerry nods. 'And are you investing it or anything? That's quite a lot of money just to have in a bank account.'

Robin shakes his head and laughs. 'I'm spending it. I'm no good at things like investments and stuff. Anyway, what's the point? I just use it so that I can do what I want to do. There's no other way I can deal with it. I'll just spend it until it's gone.'

'He was quite rich your dad, all those houses.'

'Yeah, I suppose he was. I lived with my mum after they divorced. Do you want another drink?'

And Kerry knows that the subject is closed.

The slight tension between Robin and his mother never really goes away, especially as Celia Thomas appears to have a knack of hiding darts of criticism within seemingly innocuous comments. Every now and again, this produces a fierce reaction from Robin and when they argue, Kerry is filled with an urge to slide Max-like out of the kitchen to avoid them. A faint image becomes apparent, like a photo blurring backwards, when Robin argues with his mother. It is Robin as a child, his voice rising, his knuckles clenched white; most unlike the calm, ironic figure from college. Occasionally, Kerry does manage to slip away and go upstairs to the huge bed where she reads D.H. Lawrence and sometimes, wistfully, the Leeds–London timetable. She buries her nose in her clean clothes, reassured by the smell, by their uniqueness to her.

On New Year's Eve, they eat roast lamb, delicately flavoured with rosemary, drink champagne and listen to the bells on the radio. Kerry wonders what Marco is up to. She had suggested that they go to the pub but Celia did not want to do this and they could not leave her on her own. Kerry has always found something rather sad about a subdued New Year's Eve. She is also longing for a proper bath as the water keeps freezing over. She is beginning to look forward to their return.

On the last night, Robin and Kerry do go to the pub. Kerry likes it. It does not respect any licensing laws as both crime and law-enforcement are rather thin on the ground in the Dales, although Kerry notices that this does not stop the non-locals from installing sophisticated alarm systems and lights that flash on suddenly when you walk past their houses. She likes the Vikings propping up the bar, taking the piss out of the walkers from Leeds and Manchester, and deliberately sending them on the wrong routes. She likes the pub food – plaice and chips with bright green peas and tartar sauce. Most of all though she likes the pitch black of the walk back from the pub at night and the star-encrusted, vertigo-inducing sky.

As they approach the house from the pub on this last night, the sky has put on one of its most astonishing displays as if it is saying farewell, and Kerry is dizzy and sore-necked from walking with her face upturned to the dazzling constellations. Her brain is also spinning from the mind-twisting speculations which the galaxies produce. *'Tyger tyger burning bright . . .'*

They reach the house and Robin detains her with his hand

and pushes her up against the wall. She puts her arms around his waist inside his coat. They kiss and then he whispers to her, 'I think I might be in love with you.' Kerry looks up and over his shoulder to the bright novelty of the star-spattered sky, beyond the pale foss, and thinks that this is easily the most romantic place anybody has ever said that to her. They stay up late that night talking and Kerry tells Robin many things she has not spoken out loud for some time. She tells him about Gary, not the whole story but most of it, and at some point in the telling he leans over and wipes a tear from her cheek which is strange because she really had not noticed at all that she was weeping. Then his hand moves from her face to her breast, and she is caught up again in hungry desire. She pulls him on to her, sliding his boxer shorts down his legs and wrapping her own around his body, pulling him inside her, wanting him to come deep inside her, their tongues intertwining so fiercely that it hurts. And as Kerry feels her orgasm building and hopes that he will not shift or change rythm, she breaks from the kiss and over his shoulder sees a window that is packed with bright, hard stars.

On the morning of their departure they are loading up the car. Celia Thomas is worried because Max has disappeared. The mystery of his vanishing is explained just as they have hugged goodbye and Robin is turning the ignition key. A tall thick-thighed figure comes striding up the road carrying a floppy bundle in his hands. Michael the Viking holds it out to Celia like an offering, and Max's lifeless head flops out from a rough blood-stained piece of sacking. His potato- and tennis ball-herding days have been prematurely ended by a blast from Michael's shot-gun. Kerry squeals and covers her eyes.

'I think this is your dog, Mrs Thomas,' Michael the dog murderer announces without a trace of regret. 'I'm sorry but I did warn you and it was in with my sheep. They shouldn't be pets these dogs,' he adds, as if by taking aim and squeezing the trigger he has not only single-handedly resolved the good-natured Max's identity crisis but performed the ultimate act of mercy. Robin groans and switches off the car engine.

Celia Thomas does not react well to the death of Max. She sits in the living room gazing mournfully at the fireplace with Kerry while Robin digs a grave for the dog by the orchard. Kerry tries to think of consoling things to say but they are hard to come by. *I suppose you can always get another one* or *I doubt if he knew anything about it* seem inappropriate somehow.

When Robin returns from the burial he is unusually tender and solicitous with his mother. They stay and have lunch with her while Celia explains that she does not blame Michael as an individual for Max's murder because he is simply obeying an ancient instinct as natural as Max's own frustrated herding. 'Dog among sheep = blast dog to smithereens' is an equation programmed into Michael's DNA structure, according to Celia. She begins to cheer up as she expounds on this topic. 'There's little room for sentiment in the countryside,' she tells Kerry as they finish the bacon and avocado salad and warm pitta bread which Robin has quickly prepared. Kerry agrees that this appears to be the case as she guiltily wonders what will represent a decent amount of time to console Celia and starts to search for excuses as to why she must be back in London tonight. She can see that Celia is still upset about the dog but Kerry is craving buses, buildings, kebab shops, off licences, cinemas, the view from her flat window. Most of all she wants a decent bath. Her desire to escape intensifies as Celia launches into a metaphysical speculation on the nature of death and the different attitudes that primitive, tribal people (among whom she appears to include her neighbours) have towards it. Robin glances at his watch.

They finally get away a few hours later. As they leave, Celia Thomas takes Kerry by the shoulders and then hugs her. She smells faintly of lavender.

'It's been so lovely having you here, Kerry. Do try and make sure Robin sticks to his work. He's terribly bad at finishing things, you know, always abandoning them halfway through.'

Kerry is not quite sure how she is supposed to accomplish this task but she nods and smiles weakly, glancing at Robin who rolls his eyes but thankfully manages to avoid a confrontation with his mother.

As they pull off down the road, they wave goodbye to Celia who is standing waving frantically. They carry on waving as she gets smaller and smaller and then she is just a tiny lonely figure standing by the side of the road still waving rather pathetically. Kerry sinks back into her seat and sighs.

The journey back by car is nothing like the train. It is just miles of motorway, occasional stops at service-stations for tea and tasteless food among depressing families. Still Kerry likes it, likes Robin for it; the newness, the difference of travel. She will forget about the frozen water, the boredom of sitting in the kitchen with Celia, the dog's head lolling lifelessly from its sacking. She will remember driving across the moors, the smell of the sheets on the huge soft bed and the bright stars through the window, the sound of water tumbling down the side of the valley. Night falls and Kerry becomes hypnotised by the dark road and the white lights approaching, the red lights in front, the great lorries rumbling through the night. They are somewhere in the middle of England, the middle of nowhere. She tries to chat to Robin to keep him company but finds that all she really wants to do is sleep. At some point she does sleep because she awakes to find they are nearly in London.

'Sleepy-head,' Robin laughs. 'Great travelling companion you are.'

'I'm sorry.'

'Where do you want to go?' Robin asks as they finally leave the motorway. 'My house or yours?'

And Kerry likes having the choice.

'Yours,' she says drowsily.

Chapter 14

It is dead time, the week between Christmas and New Year. Marco is alone in the flat with plenty of time to re-enact the scenes of Christmas Day. On the whole, he got off lightly. Anne insisted to John Fisher that Tony had over-reacted, and had anyway been drunk and obnoxious himself. So Marco kept quiet, allowing his defence counsel to do his work for him, and not pointing out that obnoxious is Tony's middle name. In the end, they had settled down to carry on drinking and in the absence of Tony and Angela, things relaxed, and they ended up watching *Gremlins*.

But now Marco is back home in the empty flat and there is no Kerry because she is up in Yorkshire in Robin's country retreat and there's pretty much fuck-all else happening either. Marco goes to work and comes home in the evening, smokes the rest of the grass, stares out of the window, watches soaps and gets depressed. Work is no good either because Gerald and Gina had a disastrous Christmas, and Gerald suspects that Gina is having an affair with a younger (naturally) model whom she met on a shoot in the Canary Islands. He spends most of his time on the phone checking on her whereabouts, putting the phone down when she answers. He even snaps at Marco for not cleaning the surfaces properly and for not telling him that they were running low on chorizo and taramasalata. Business is not very good either, and Marco wonders why Gerald even bothered to open up.

Marco's isolation increases his paranoia and tendency towards panic attacks. Staring out of the window one afternoon, he sees three van-loads of police with bullet-proof vests park outside their block. Some of the police are even armed with sub-machine guns and Marco begins to sweat, convinced that they have come for him. It is no good him telling himself that there would be no reason to send fifty armed police to arrest somebody whose biggest crime has been to sell a couple of Es a few times and take one trip to Birmingham – about a year ago – to deliver some coke for Arnold. He begins to contemplate phoning somebody to warn them that armed police are about to break down his door and will probably 'accidentally' shoot him in the process, when his would-be assasins climb back into their vans and drive back up Old Street.

Marco thinks that while his paranoia may have been laughable, it is still a reflection of the ever-narrowing concept of what it is to be an honest and decent citizen. In one of the many news-bulletins he watches during the week, there is a feature on police road-blocks in the city and they are interviewing a Tony look-alike who explains enthusiastically that he is delighted to have been stopped and searched because it makes him feel safer. And Marco thinks that he would rather be dead than be that smug, hypocritical bastard in his company car. This is Tony's big mistake: he genuinely thinks that Marco envies him simply because of his wealth. If Marco were rich – an unlikely prospect at present – he would at least know how to have a laugh with the money. And he would never thank the police for stopping and searching him.

Marco is interrupted in these gloomy reveries by the telephone ringing. He doesn't get too optimistic. It will probably be a wrong number or a market researcher or, at the very best, Danny. The only person who has rung so far this week has been Kerry's lumpy Irish mate who wanted to know if Kerry was back from Yorkshire. That's one threesome that Marco cannot understand. He can see why Robin and Kerry have got a thing going, however much he hates it. But where this Susan girl fits in, he has no idea. She's not Kerry's type at all, but then what is Kerry's type?

When Marco picks up the phone he is surprised to find that it is Jeanette.

'Kerry's not back yet,' he tells her.

'I know that, stupid. It's you I want to talk to.'

'Oh, right, you must be the only person on this planet who does at the moment.'

'Sounds like a case of the post-Chistmas blues to me. Anyway, I'm here to change all that. I want you to come out for a drink.'

'With you?'

'No, with Cindy Crawford. Yeah, with me. Don't sound so surprised. I just want to talk to you about something, ask your opinion.'

'My opinion?'

'Marco, you're starting to get on my nerves now. Can you come out for a drink tonight, yes or no?'

'Hold on, I'll just look through my . . .'

'Yes or no?'

'Yes.'

'Good. You know the Pomegranate Bar off Wardour Street?'

'Yeah, I know it. It's, like, that completely unpretentious place where everybody's really ugly and badly dressed.'

'That's the one. We'll inject some much needed glamour. Meet me there at eight. If you have any problems on the door, tell them to find Rick and tell him you're with me.'

Marco giggles, remembering Christmas Day. 'Is it Rick's Bar then? Tell him not to sell Sam to the Blue Parrot.'

'He's the bar manage— oh, right, yeah, very funny, Marco.'

He feels considerably more cheerful now that he has something to do tonight. He wonders whether he would have the bottle to try and get off with Jeanette and knows that he wouldn't. The reasons for this are: a) Jeanette's boyfriend, who is quiet but a definite geezer, b) Kerry, and c) his fear of Jeanette's rejection and ridicule – not necessarily in that order. It's a beguiling thought though; Jeanette has long occupied a prominent role in many of his sexual fantasies and he spends a cheerful five minutes revisiting his favourite which starts with them in a spacious and clean cubicle together doing a fat line of top-quality cocaine.

Marco is disappointed to find that he has no problems at all getting into the Pomegranate. The holiday period must have lowered the door requirement. He had been looking forward to demanding Rick's presence.

Jeanette is not in the bar which is no great surprise. Marco buys a bottle of beer, raising his eyebrows in ostentatious incredulity at the price, a gesture which cuts little ice with the po-faced bar-youth. He sits on a stool which appears to have been specifically designed for maximum discomfort and surveys the people in the bar: delicate, swan-like girls with skinny arms, long legs, and faces stuck in expressions which cover the whole emotional range from ill-concealed boredom to polite boredom to sycophantic attention, depending on the relative importance of the person to whom they are talking. Marco feels slightly annoyed with Jeanette. If she had wanted to talk about something serious, then surely she could have chosen a better place.

He is beginning to feel awkward and self-conscious sitting on his own. The place is a pick-up joint and he doesn't particularly want the tag of loner on the pull. Not now anyway. So he is relieved to see Jeanette gliding through the bar, nodding occasionally to a few of the clones with whom she is acquainted. He buys her a drink.

Jeanette makes a brief and dismissive surveillance of the bar. Marco notices that when she frowns she looks just like Kerry, a slight furrowing at the centre of her eyebrows which suggests puzzlement as much as disapproval. Then she smiles at him.

'Not really your sort of place, is it, Marco?'

'Not really,' he admits. 'Why did you bring me here then?'

'Oh, I don't know. Maybe it's my idea of a joke. We can go somewhere else, if you want?'

'We're here now.'

'That's right.' She sips an ice-packed margarita. 'We're here now.'

'How was your Christmas?'

'Fucking boring. Poor old Kerry kept sneaking off and reading on the toilet. She's well out of it in Yorkshire. And then I had to go to Darren's parents on Boxing Day.'

Don't Step on the Lines

Jeanette shudders at the memory.

'I wonder how Kerry's getting on up in Yorkshire,' she says, suddenly putting her glass down.

'I dunno. She hasn't phoned.'

'That's what I wanted to talk to you about, Marco.'

'How Kerry's getting on in Yorkshire? I expect they're going for long romantic walks, pony-trekking . . . I don't know, Jeanette.'

'No, it's just . . . this guy. Why did you go all funny when his name came up? What's the matter with him?'

'Nothing.'

'Don't give me that. You looked like you'd just smelled something really bad when his name came up.'

'It doesn't matter what I think, does it?'

Jeanette sucks margarita-ice through her straw and studies him carefully.

'Yeah, I think it does,' she says finally. 'Because you know what Kerry went through. You were there. We both were . . .'

Marco meets her eye. He and Jeanette went with Kerry when she had to identify Gary's body. It is not a day he ever wants to remember. After the identification, Kerry's legs had just collapsed under her and she dropped to the floor. The only thing that Marco had seen like it was a mother on the TV who was filmed receiving the news at an airport of her daughter's death in a plane bombing. Kerry had just sat there, her legs straight out in front of her, while an animal-like shrieking filled the air, a noise that seemed to have nothing to do with the small person beating her hands on the floor.

'So . . .' Jeanette continues ' . . . yes, it does matter what you think. You're close to her. You care about her. And nobody is going to fuck my sister up like that again.'

Marco ponders this. 'Robin won't. Not like that anyway. There's no danger of that.'

'What is the danger then?'

'All right, but you breathe one word of this conversation to Kerry . . .'

'Don't be stupid, Marco. Do you think I want her knowing

that I've come to you to ask about her? She'd go mental. You know what she's like.'

'OK, well what I think is . . . well, you remember Gary?'

'Of course I remember Gary!'

'No, but what he was like. A nutter, right? He lost it completely which was tragic because he was brilliant as well. But why did he lose it? Because he got self-obsessed. Totally obsessed with himself, with his life, with his problems. And in the end, he never noticed that there was Kerry having a terrible time, wasting herself completely just looking after him, keeping their heads above water. Right? So why was Gary self-obsessed, do you think? Because in the end he hated himself. He couldn't understand why it hadn't worked out for him, just couldn't work it out, so he began hating himself and it ate him away. The one good thing was that he never turned that hatred on Kerry. He loved her right up until the end, I know that. And he was a nutter. So if he had turned the hatred on Kerry it would have been, like, a serious business. But he didn't 'cause he loved her.'

'OK.' Jeanette is looking puzzled. 'But what's all this got to do with Robin? I mean, you've just said he's not like Gary.'

'Exactly. He's the opposite with just one thing in common – he's self-obsessed. The difference between Robin and Gary is that Robin must have been self-obsessed all his life and where Gary hated himself, Robin loves himself. He's got an ego *that* big . . .' Marco spreads his arms and knocks the drink of the girl standing behind him. She scowls at him until Jeanette meets her eye and she looks away.

'So, right, he loves himself. It's totally obvious. And what I don't know is how much he loves Kerry, which at least Gary had in his favour. You know how I think Robin sees her? As interesting. Like a specimen. I watch them sometimes when they're talking and he's got this smile on his face like a pleased parent. It makes me sick. I mean, who is he to look at her like that? Anyway, no, he won't do her damage in the same way that Gary did but I don't trust him. I've met boys like him before. All charming and nice and good-mannered – yeah, he's got all that. But he'll want Kerry to do what he wants, in the way he wants it. And he'll get nasty if she goes against him. Don't take my word for it, plenty of people probably think he's a diamond geezer. But I know he's bad news. Really bad news.'

Marco is surprised by the coherence and vehemence of this outburst. Clearly, Jeanette is as well. She is looking at him with a strange expression on her face as if something has just occurred to her.

'Yes,' she murmurs irrelevantly and then suddenly squeezes his hand sympathetically.

'But anyway,' Marco continues, embarrassed by this sudden unexplained gesture from Jeanette, 'the point is, will he fuck her up? And I don't think you should be too worried on that score. Because, after all, remember that Gary didn't. Not totally. Look at Kerry now. She's not a big mouth like you . . .' he grins at Jeanette ' . . . but she's hard as well.'

'Although, if he's like you say, how come Kerry likes him? I mean, she's not stupid, is she? He must have something.'

Marco ponders this. Why does Kerry like Robin? Maybe she does have a stupid side to her. Maybe most women are stupid when it comes to their choice of men. He decides not to test out either of these theories on Jeanette.

'I think she was quite unsure of him at first. But he is different and that's what she likes about him. Also, he's showing her a good time now, things Gary never could. She's doing things she hasn't done for ages . . . or has never done. I know she's happy. But I don't believe she'll let him just take her over completely.'

'Maybe not,' Jeanette says slowly. 'But, you see, when Kerry told me about him, I told her to go for it. I just meant have a laugh, play the field a bit. I don't want this to go all sour again. I know what you're saying about her but she's vulnerable as well. It's taken her this long to get her head sorted. She's doing well at college, she's enjoying it. I don't want any rich kid with his head up his arse messing about with that.'

Marco can't help feeling pleased that somebody at last appears to have accepted his analysis of Robin.

'Well, one thing's certain – there's nothing we can do about it. She'll go her own way.'

'That's what you think,' Jeanette replies darkly. 'What are you having?'

'Actually, sweetheart . . .' Marco affects the voice of the bar clientele ' . . . that margarita looks to die for.'

While Jeanette is up at the bar, he suddenly hears somebody call his name.

'Mar-co, what are you doing here?'

It is Nicole, the extra from the police series.

'I'm on a stake-out. We suspect illegal use of Class A drugs in this establishment.'

She trills with laughter.

'Tell me who's got them then and leave it to me to confiscate them. Can I join you?'

'Be my guest. Where's Papa?'

'What?'

'Oh nothing. Jeanette, this is Nicole.'

Jeanette cocks her head.

'Papa?'

Marco splutters with laughter and Nicole laughs as well as she catches on to what Marco had said previously.

'That advert,' she says, shaking her head.

They sit and gossip aimlessly and Nicole tells them that she may get a part in another police series as a prostitute.

'The thing is, guv,' Jeanette growls, 'we've only got that tom and I dunno if she'll even turn up in court on the day.'

'If only we could keep that pimp Leroy off the streets, but he's bound to get bail,' Marco adds.

'It's all very well for you, Sergeant Bacon,' Nicole mutters, 'but you don't know what 'e can be like. Any chance of somefink stronger than tea in this bleedin' nick? One of those looks nice.' She points at the margaritas.

'I suppose you've earned it.' Marco gets up and heads to the bar.

Don't Step on the Lines

Jeanette passes him on her way to the toilet. 'You're in there, Marco.' She grins. 'I'm off in a minute. You should stay. She likes you, mate.'

Marco glances back at Nicole who is twirling a peppermint-striped margarita straw round in her hand and she looks up and smiles at him. She has round cheeks and a cheeky gap-toothed smile. She is quite plump in a way that he likes. He tries to think who she hangs about with and whether she knows Danny.

When Jeanette comes back to the table, she tells him that she is going home.

'Thanks for the chat, Marco. We'll just have to see how things go.'

'Yeah, cheers, Jeanette, I'll give you a ring.'

Nicole watches her departing back.

'Bitch.'

'What?' Marco is startled.

'Look at that figure. It's just not fair.'

'Ah, well, looks aren't everything.'

'Yeah, sure,' Nicole replies. 'I nearly didn't get this part because I was too fat.'

'But you're not fat,' he replies.

'Yeah, I am. And it's not fair. I'm not meant to be fat, I'm meant to have a figure like hers.'

'You don't look fat to me,' he insists. 'You're sort of . . . curvy, voluptuous. Anyway skinny girls are boring. Look at that. She looks like a walking bog-brush. Men who go on about skinny girls are really just wishing they were boys.'

'I don't want to be skinny. I want to be normal.' But Nicole looks pleased.

'What are you doing here anyway?' asks Marco.

'I was meeting a friend but she had to go early 'cause she's working tomorrow. I was just leaving when I saw you.'

'This bar is horrible,' he observes.

'Do you want to go somewhere else?'

'Like where? We could go to Hanway Street maybe?'

'Well . . .' Nicole is blushing slightly ' . . . I would quite like

197

to get out of Soho. I haven't got much money left. But I've got a bottle of vodka and some wicked grass up at my house . . .'

'Where do you live?'

'Dalston.'

'Lovely . . .' Marco grins sarcastically.

'You don't have to come.'

'What, are you de-inviting me?'

'I don't remember inviting you in the first place.'

'I'll pay for a cab.'

'You're invited. Come on.'

Nicole lives in a house quite near to Danny. There is a pair of decks in an alcove in the living room.

'Whose are the decks?'

'Mine, it's how I relax. Just come home and mess about on them. I DJ sometimes as well. Let's go upstairs, I think the rest of the house might come crashing in soon. I'll just get some glasses.'

Nicole has a big room, filled with plants and cushions, a picture of Robert de Niro on the wall, and a skiing machine in the corner which clearly has not been used for some time as it is adorned with various items of clothing. The multicoloured sideways Y of a South African flag is also tacked on the wall above the bookshelf, something of which John Fisher would approve. In the corner of the room are big crepe-paper sunflowers which Nicole tells him her best friend makes for a living. There is a CD player by her bed and Marco is surprised to find operas by Verdi and Mozart among her CD collection.

'I wouldn't have had you down as an opera fan. I hate opera, it's really boring.'

Nicole looks at him scornfully. ''Cause you don't know anything about it,' she replies simply. 'That's as stupid as saying that books are boring.'

Marco does not reply to this. Apart from his shark book, he hasn't read anything for months. Why not? Maybe because when he is not out, he is usually nursing a hangover.

'I'm half-Italian,' he says irrelevantly.

'You should be ashamed of yourself then.' She begins expertly skinning up, humming what Marco assumes to be an operatic air as she tweaks and shakes the finished joint.

When they have smoked the joint, drunk some vodka and Coke, and have managed to get over their embarrassment and proceed to the obvious next stage, Nicole suddenly disengages herself from Marco to switch off the light.

'Why are you doing that?' he murmurs. 'Leave it on.'

'I don't want to. I find it . . . I don't want . . .'

Marco leans over and switches the light back on.

'Don't,' she says, putting her hands to her face.

He pulls her hands away and looks down at her body. 'You're lovely,' he says, 'I want to see you.'

'Please, Marco, please switch the light off.'

Marco can feel her rising anxiety and so he leans over and clicks the light off again. Her body is soft under his hands and he remembers an E-head called Tania that he slept with a couple of times over the summer. She was so thin that he sometimes didn't know whether he should be having sex with her or rushing her straight to the nearest anorexia clinic. He moves his hands down to Nicole's hips, grateful not to be feeling an angry jut of bone.

Chapter 15

Winter slides away, the spring term starts, the dark nights begin to retreat. Kerry continues to get good marks in college and her marks also continue to be better than Robin's. If this bothers him, he shows no sign of it, although it embarrasses Kerry a little, given that they often work together.

Robin is always doing things, suggesting things, reading about events and organising them into going. Kerry likes this about him, she has a tendency to contemplate doing something and then forget all about it, an inability to cope with booking processes. Robin has a directed energy that also motivates her. They travel again outside London, driving to Brighton at the weekend, going to Dublin for five days. Kerry buys magazines and duty-free at the airport, watches the ruby and sapphire runway lights as they take off, picks at her microwaved plane food, and feels as if she is suddenly part of another world.

Robin also pays for all of these trips and Kerry has given up worrying about it too much. As he says, he is doing it for his pleasure as much as hers; he wants Kerry with him and if she cannot afford it, then he can. She takes him to meet her own mum and dad one weekend, a visit which passes off with rather less drama than her visit to Yorkshire. Her dad is never particularly interested in what his daughters are up to and her mum just appears relieved at Robin's relative normality and politeness.

They spend more nights at Robin's house than they do at Kerry's. In part this is due to the comfort of the house, especially after Jill and Mac have gone to Thailand for six weeks. In part it is due to the fact that Marco's hostility to Robin shows no sign of abating. Robin continues to insist that it does not affect him personally and that he simply finds it incomprehensible.

But Kerry notices that he occasionally drops barbed comments about Marco and once, when they are drunk, they have an argument when Robin says that he cannot understand why Kerry continues to have anything to do with him. Marco is also spending less time in the flat now that he has begun a rather strange anarchic relationship with Nicole which appears to have no rules whatsoever. Sometimes they do not see each other for a week or so and sometimes she will suddenly turn up at two in the morning and not leave for several days. Kerry likes Nicole and wonders bitterly why Marco is unable to return the favour by even tolerating Robin. On the rare evenings when all four of them are together in the flat, there is always a very strange atmosphere with Marco surly, Robin studiously polite, Kerry on edge and Nicole cracking jokes in an attempt to lighten the atmosphere.

Kerry and Robin return to the flat one evening to get ready to go out. Sylvia Gordon has found out about Robin's existence and has invited them for dinner. Kerry is pleased, not only at the idea of Sylvia's meeting Robin, but at the opportunity to talk to her teacher about the Henry James assignment she is writing. This is one occasion when she cannot talk to Robin about it as he detests Henry James.

Robin is in a strange mood that evening, distant and aloof. Kerry has been telling him about Sylvia and she detects an odd reticence on Robin's part as if the subject irritates him. He grunts from time to time to prove that he is listening to her.

'Good,' he says as they enter the empty flat.

'What's good?' Kerry asks as she half listens to a message from Jeanette about a new job she has found. Jeanette moves in and out of jobs with some regularity, misbehaving as soon as she gets bored and then finding new ones when she gets sacked.

'Marco's not here,' Robin answers, flicking on the TV to the local news.

'Well, he does live here.' Kerry stands in the doorway, puzzled by this unusually forthright comment. 'So it wouldn't be too outrageous if he was.'

She doesn't want to be critical of Robin since Marco's rudeness would have tested the patience of most visitors.

'Yes, I can't understand that. Does he pay you rent? I mean, it's not as if you couldn't find somebody to have that room. Look at Susan, she would love to get out of Dollis Hill.'

The idea of swapping Marco for Susan does not greatly appeal to Kerry. Since she broke the news to her about Robin, they have continued to be friends and Susan invited them to Dollis Hill for a spaghetti Bolognese which Kerry was glad that Marco did not witness. There is still, however, a slight reserve between them.

'I wouldn't want to live with Susan. And I like living with Marco.'

Robin sighs as he flips channels.

'Well, I don't think he's a great flatmate, that's all. Somebody who has no other idea of recreation than shovelling drugs into his body . . .'

'But it would be OK if he was like one of your flatmates? If he smoked spliff until he was in a coma but spoke a bit nicer.'

Robin regards her with the sort of calm that he normally reserves for Marco. 'Don't knock it, Kerry. There's nothing intrinsically wrong with speaking nicely. Anyway, I don't want to have an argument with you about it. I'm just saying, you could get a better flatmate. Or come and live with me, if you want?'

'Come and live with you?'

'Yes, why not? We spend most of our time there anyway. You could have one of the rooms to work in . . .'

Kerry looks around the living room. Leave here? She has never even considered it. The flat had belonged to Jeanette before she moved in with Darren. Kerry had taken it on after Gary's death, clearing the arrears to keep the Housing Association happy with her name being added to the tenancy agreement.

'I'm not sure . . . I mean, I like this flat and everything. You know, having the option . . .'

'But you could leave Marco in it. He could get his friend

Danny in or something. I'm not saying you would have to give it up. We already practically live together anyway.'

'Marco and Danny! You think I'd let those two stay here together? Anyway, I don't think Marco would want to live with Danny.'

'It doesn't really have anything to do with what Marco wants. It's what *you* want that matters. And it would save you money because you wouldn't have to pay any rent. You could get rent from this place as well.'

'No,' Kerry says slowly. 'I can see what you're saying. But I just don't think that I'm ready to take that step now.'

'I hate that approach to life,' Robin exclaims impatiently. 'It's so cautious, so limited. You should just *do* things sometimes.'

'If you want to,' Kerry replies levelly. 'And as you said, it's what *I* want that matters. I don't want to move out. I'm quite happy with the way things are. Anyway, we can't talk about it now, we're going to be late. Can you call a cab please? We'll have to get it to stop for some wine.'

'I think spring is coming,' Sylvia announces as she opens the door. 'Isn't it lovely now the nights are getting lighter? You must be Robin. Come in, come in. Kerry darling, you know where to dump your jackets.'

John Gordon is sitting on the sofa as they enter the living room. He pushes back his little round glasses and grins as he sees Kerry.

While Sylvia is in the kitchen, they sit drinking wine while John tells Robin how he first met Kerry at a performance of *Julius Caesar*. They were both studying it for 'O' level and Sylvia was taking her class to see it, insisting that John accompany them too. Sylvia's class had giggled at the skinny boy, the teacher's son, in his Buzzcocks t-shirt, scowling with the embarrassment of having to sit with thirty girls. Kerry had ended up sitting next to him, as the audience of fifteen year olds had thrown bubble gum at the stage, laughed uproariously at Caesar's death and shouted 'Lend me your ears' in unison during Mark Antony's speech. Perhaps in rebellion against his mother, John had dropped English as soon as possible and ended up at Leeds University where he studied Chinese.

At the table, Sylvia places Robin next to her as if determined to get the measure of him. Kerry is startled when her chat to John about his baby is interrupted by Mrs Gordon's loud, arrogantly patrician voice ringing out: 'What an *extraordinarily* silly thing to say!'

John rolls his eyes at Kerry and they turn to find out the cause of this statement. Both of them are fairly used to it and Kerry does not feel unduly alarmed. Robin will just have to get accustomed to Sylvia.

It transpires that he has been explaining to her the basis of his dislike for Henry James and in particular *The Portrait of a Lady*.

'I was just saying . . .' Robin still has his fork halfway to his mouth ' . . . that I have no sympathy at all for Isabel Archer because she had no reason to marry Gilbert Osmond, let alone stay with him, and that removes any tragic element there might otherwise have been. Personally, I find her a completely unconvincing character.'

'Which is, of course, complete nonsense,' Sylvia adds.

'It's a viewpoint,' Robin says reasonably. 'I don't think you can just dismiss it as nonsense . . .'

John grins at him. 'You'll find that there's no such thing as an alternative viewpoint when it comes to my mum, Robin.'

'It *is* nonsense . . .' Sylvia persists. 'It shows that he hasn't understood the book at all.'

Robin puts down his fork slowly. Kerry would kick him under the table if she could. There has to be some way of communicating to him that this is Sylvia's idea of jocular debate, that her snobbery is mainly affectation, and that getting angry is not the correct response.

'So you think . . .' Robin begins icily ' . . . that the way that *you* understand the book is the only possible way of under-standing it?'

John is grinning broadly. He is clearly thoroughly enjoying

the sight of somebody else tangling with his mother for a change. Kerry can tell that Robin is genuinely irritated but that Sylvia has not realised this, mistaking his anger for the kind of spirited resistance that she enjoys so much.

'Oh, dear,' she blithely continues, 'I'm afraid that for me, saying that you don't like Henry James is like saying you don't like champagne or . . . or . . .'

'Cary Grant?' John adds helpfully.

'Or anything that *you* just happen to like,' Robin interjects aggressively.

There is a silence as Sylvia realises that he is not entering into this argument in quite the same spirit as she is.

They change the subject and Robin decides to turn on his full silent act. Kerry is inwardly fuming with him. Partly because she agrees with Sylvia about Henry James, and partly because for somebody who takes great pride in not caring what other people think of him, Robin is making a particularly inept job of demonstrating it tonight. Silence is not valued highly in the Gordon household and Kerry can feel Sylvia's coiled disapproval straining like a jack-in-the-box. She will start picking on him again soon, Kerry just knows it.

As if John can sense it as well, he begins a story about a couple he knows who are having problems because the girl has been offered a place at an American university and her partner does not want to leave his job to accompany her.

'It's a brilliant opportunity for her, but she's having all these traumas because she knows that it will basically mean the end of their relationship. Because he won't go.'

'Good for him.' Robin suddenly breaks his silence. 'I don't see what the problem is. He is doing what is necessary for him and she should do what is necessary for her. It just means that their relationship has run its course. They should just accept it.'

'Ah, yes,' Sylvia responds sarcastically. 'You don't recognise the concept of a dilemma, do you, Robin?'

Kerry's heart sinks.

'Not really,' he replies. 'People have to do what is right for them. You have to be prepared to take risks or you become just another unit.'

'My goodness,' Sylvia begins to collect the plates together, 'have you been reading *Nietzsche for Beginners*, Robin?'

She sweeps into the kitchen with the dishes and Kerry goes out to the garden to smoke, leaving John to cope with Robin. Sylvia is right, spring is coming. She can feel it in the soft breeze blowing against her face, the way that the sun is lingering reluctantly in the sky above the city. In Sylvia's garden there is an oval patch of tiny flowers shooting out of the earth – butter yellow, suffragette purple and swan white. John emerges beside her and she smiles at him.

'What are those flowers called?'

He peers through his glasses at the flowers.

'Crocuses.'

'It's a pretty disgusting word for such a nice flower.'

'Lots of flowers have ugly names. Crocus, Chrysanthemum, Geranium . . . they sound more like venereal infections than flowers.'

'Maybe it's better not to know their names after all. What's Robin doing?'

'He's in the toilet. He's a bit of an oddball, if you don't mind my saying so, Kerry?'

Kerry does mind but refrains from comment.

'I think he's in a bad mood tonight but I don't know why. He's not normally like this.'

'Uh-huh. Oh, well, my mum isn't the easiest person to deal with when you're in a bad mood.'

'It's a shame. I wanted them to get on.'

Kerry flicks her cigarette butt disconsolately and watches its arc as it falls to the ground.

'Let's go in,' she says.

Surprisingly, Robin is in the kitchen helping Sylvia to dry up when they go back. Kerry can hear them making polite conversation. Robin has realised that he has been graceless, a trait with which he would never want to be associated. Kerry sits down quietly, hoping that enforced contact will make them more agreeable to each other. When Sylvia comes out of the kitchen, she is wearing a bright, superficial smile.

'Robin has just been telling me that you spent the New Year in the Yorkshire Dales,' she says.

'That's right,' Kerry answers.

'Lovely,' Sylvia says.

'It was,' Kerry answers mechanically, 'really lovely.'

In the cab going home, Robin says, 'So that's another one of your closest friends who doesn't like me.'

'Oh, Sylvia's just like that . . .'

'I was expecting somebody completely different,' he muses as if to himself. 'Anyway listen, Kerry, I'm really tired and I want to get up early and do some work tomorrow. So is it OK if I just drop you and get the cab on? I'll call you tomorrow.'

'Sure, that's fine,' she answers, uncertain why she suddenly feels miserable and weak and inclined to degrade herself by saying that she wants to stay with him. 'No problem, I'll call you tomorrow.'

When they reach Kerry's flat, he leans over and kisses her. 'Sweet dreams.' He seems almost normal again.

'Are you sure . . .'

'Yeah, I'm sure.'

She gets out of the cab and walks towards the entrance of her flat. Behind her, she hears the cab start up again and rumble away into the night.

That night, Kerry forces herself to wake out of terrible dreams. Perhaps the worst aspect of her nightmares is the moment when she is fighting her way out of sleep back into consciousness and it is as if she is being pulled back by a gnarled long-fingered hand, like some cheap horror film, the dream refusing to let go of her easily, as if she is trying to run in water.

She is awake and sweating, her heart racing, stumbling through the darkness to switch on the light, blinking at its brightness, the sudden shapes around her. She makes her way into the kitchen to get some water, feeling the flat's emptiness. And she suddenly feels so alone, so bewilderingly isolated, that she has to take conscious breaths to calm herself, sing to herself a little as she fills the glass with water and drinks.

Gary will not get out of her dreams, he is a stubborn squatter there, asserting his right to occupy her sub-conscious. She doesn't want him there at all, especially when he is sneaky and hides behind other faces, even – confusingly – Marco's or Robin's. They can suddenly turn into Gary who must have been hiding there like an alien spirit the whole time. Tonight, however, he was explicitly Gary and he was saying that if Kerry wouldn't mind moving out of the flat, then he was going to move back in with Marco. That perhaps if they really worked at things, they could get back together and that Marco was making a film in which he was going to play the starring role. Then she dreamed – how familiar this part was – that they were on a plane together and that the plane was taking off as they held hands and sipped champagne but suddenly the plane began to stall, it began to drop out of the sky, it was crashing through trees, smashing and fragmenting, and Gary's face was contorted with fear at his approaching death and Kerry was straining against her seat-belt trying to reach out for him, and then she was struggling, fighting to be awake, taking those useless strides against the force of the water that pinned her back into the abysmal terror of her own weakness and lack of ability to prevent anything from happening.

The clock on the video says 4.07 in implacable luminous green letters. What a horrible time, what a terrible time, to be nervous and alone and awake in an empty flat. Kerry goes back into the bedroom, climbs into bed and shuts her eyes, leaving the light on, scared of the dark. Gary is dead. She identified his body, the sheet pulled back to reveal his bruised face, his eyes closed in the perpetual confusion between death and sleeping. *Eternal sleep, not dead only sleeping, fell asleep on . . .* All lies. Now he just exists in the dreams of those who survived him and whose dreams will they inhabit? Kerry had nodded that it was him. She went out into the corridor where Marco and Jeanette were waiting, through some rubber swing doors, following the Exit signs. Nobody was saying anything. Kerry

209

— exhausted from lack of sleep and worry and an abortion performed just a couple of days earlier – had felt a sudden rushing feeling, had felt her legs buckle under her and then a grief and loneliness so overwhelming had swept through her she found she was on the floor, looking up through her hair at two complete strangers whose faces were also etched with anxiety and pain, and who had no idea whatsoever what to do to comfort her.

Chapter 16

The approach of summer, for Marco, is not signalled by the arrival of swallows. Rather, it is the first time he sees people standing outside pubs in Soho, and it is a sight that fills him with pleasure and anticipation. After work he takes the Victoria line from Finsbury Park and goes to Oxford Circus so that he can tack through the streets – Wardour, Old Compton, Dean, Greek, Frith – saluting faces he recognises, approaching the crowd outside the pub from a distance and trying to distinguish Danny with his new mobile phone, or Nicole if he has agreed to meet her, standing with her inevitable pint of Guinness balanced on a car roof. He can feel the warm spring air, standing just behind Cambridge Circus, and other people can feel it as well; they are pouring into the warming streets, they are talking, laughing, drinking, flirting under the black and red of City of Westminster street signs, obeying the impulse of their animated blood, warmed by the sun. Marco loves how girls respond to the sun – their bare legs, the bright colours, the curve of their breasts under t-shirts – a kind of bright, proud, youthful arrogance that sometimes makes his throat catch. Nicole teases him for watching them, calls him a lech, but Marco knows that it is not just that; there is something awe-inspiring about the crowded streets, the response of humanity to the sun.

One evening, when he is finishing up and trying to decide whether to get the tube or the 19 bus, Gerald emerges from the back. 'Marco, telephone.' Gerald has given up phoning Gina since she accused him directly of being responsible for nuisance phone-calls, and has instead hired a private detective to track her movements. The appropriately slimy man sometimes appears to chat to him, and they disappear out to the back behind a firmly closed door. Marco knows that Gerald is getting

211

ripped off and that there is absolutely no evidence of Gina's infidelity, but Gerald is in the grip of an Othello-like jealousy and is easily manipulated by the detective whose malignity is far from motiveless.

When Marco picks up the phone, he is surprised to find that it is Anne.

'Marco love, would it be possible for you to drop by tonight? There's something I need to talk to you about. Your dad's got a branch meeting at 7.30 so could you come by around then? You can see him when he gets back, of course.'

'What's it all about?'

'I'll speak to you tonight, Marco. I don't want to talk about it over the phone.'

'Is there a problem?'

'I'll see you tonight.'

He puts down the phone, troubled. What's up with his dad? He knows that John has been going for tests at the hospital on a suspected cyst under his arm but didn't think that it was for anything more worrying than that. His dad is robust, has never had anything more alarming than gall-stones. Is he ill then? Marco feels a nasty fear like acid in his stomach.

He walks down Roman Road towards his parents' house. The evening is muggy, there is the smell of warm tar in the soupy air. It is as if somebody has placed a lid over the city and Marco can feel his head beginning to throb. Kids are playing out in the street, kicking a football about. The boy he saw on Christmas Day is whizzing about effortlessly on his roller-blades.

When Marco gets to the house, he is surprised to find that Angela's turquoise Peugeot is parked outside and that its owner is sitting in the living room holding a cup of coffee between her hands. They have not seen each other since Christmas.

'Do you want a drink, Marco? Tea, coffee?'

'Tea, please.' He perches on the end of the couch and tries to think of something to say to Angela while Anne makes tea.

When she brings Marco's tea, she comes straight to the point. John Fisher does not have a cyst. He has a – Anne pauses to get it right – non-Hodgkins lymphoma. His chances of surviving this are not good, although he has just started a course of chemotherapy. He has been told about it and wanted Anne to tell his children. There is silence for a couple of minutes and then Angela begins to cry.

'Did they say . . .'

'How long? No. It all depends on how he responds to the treatment. It could be months, it could be up to a year.'

Anne is dry-eyed and phlegmatic and Marco suspects that she has been alone with this knowledge for some time. He walks over to the mantelpiece and picks up Lenin, cradling him in his hand. John Fisher brought him back from one of his Progressive Tours to the USSR, along with a colourful lacquered spoon, a bag of badges for Marco, and Russian dolls for Angela. Marco remembers his dad telling the young Marco and Angela about the marble and chandeliers on the Russian Metro. 'Can you imagine that on the Central line? It will happen, though. One day.'

When pigs go flying over the Houses of Parliament, thinks Marco bitterly now, replacing John Fisher's little bald hero on the mantelpiece.

Angela sniffs. 'Mum, I don't know what to do now. I've got an announcement as well. I was going to tell you tonight – I'm pregnant.'

Marco decides that now is not the time to ask Angela who the father is, or whether there is some kind of foetal abnormality test that could ascertain whether Tony's genes are ascendant in their future offspring.

'That's wonderful news, Angela,' says her mum, tears now pricking at her eyes. 'Of course you should tell your dad. He'll be over the moon.'

'Congratulations, Angela,' Marco says insincerely, feeling only horror at this *Rosemary's Baby* scenario.

'And we're going to get married now,' she continues. 'In June, on the longest day of the year.'

It *will* be the longest day of the year, thinks Marco. It will be the longest day of my life.

'Presumably Tony will be asking me to be best man?' he can't resist saying, and even Angela has to laugh through her tears at the prospect.

'I think that place is booked,' she replies. 'It's going to be a friend from work.'

'I'll be a bridesmaid then.'

John Fisher returns from his branch meeting with a carrier bag full of newspapers and leaflets. Marco thinks that he looks tired and wan but this could be due to the fact that Marco is inspecting him closely with new eyes or, more probably, a result of the tedium of the branch meeting.

Anne is right about his reaction to Angela's news. His eyes also fill with tears and he hugs his daughter tightly. Tears are streaming down Angela's face and she is murmuring, 'Oh, Dad . . . Dad . . . oh, Dad,' until Marco cannot bear it any longer and gets up to go the toilet.

That night, he does not want to return to an empty flat. He phones Nicole to check that she is in and catches a bus up Mare Street to her house. He sits on the top deck, his mind empty, as if the news of his dad's illness has sucked out all ability to have a coherent thought. He sees buildings, hears fragments of conversation, feels as if he is somehow floating above it all. He is not there.

Nicole is banging out hard-house tunes on her decks when he arrives. She looks at him curiously.

'Are you OK?'

'I'm fine. Have you got a drink in the house?'

'There's some of those little beers in the fridge.'

'I'll have about five then.'

Later, in bed, Nicole puts on a CD. She has been trying to educate Marco into liking opera by playing it late at night, with a singular lack of success. Tonight, however, the tune is soft and melancholy, the voices rising and falling gently, complementing each other perfectly.

'This is OK,' Marco says. 'What's this then?'

'*Cosi fan Tutti*. Mozart. This is my favourite bit. It is called . . .' she peers at the CD cover ' . . . *Soave sia il vento*.'

'What does that mean?'

'You're meant to be the Italian. Something about the wind. The music in the background is supposed to be like a breeze.'

'Oh, right. Yeah, it's not bad actually.'

Nicole raises her eyebrows.

'Wonders will never cease.'

Marco rolls on to his back, staring at the ceiling. When his dad met his mum in Bulgaria, he was a young fit man. But now he is dying, he has something in his body, something he cannot control. His mum died as well; Marco is going to lose both parents, he will be an orphan. Or is it only children who can be orphans? Yes, because otherwise all old people would be orphans and that would be stupid. He will be alone, though. The music is rising and falling, voices softly intertwining. His dad is dying. The stubborn old Shelley-loving Stalinist is on his last legs. Nicole is lying next to him. His dad is going to die. His best friend ran headlong into a car. He is losing touch with Kerry. He works in a delicatessen. He is going to be an uncle. He has a stupid obsession with sharks. He has a stupid friend called Danny. He is a good cook. Where has all of this got him? What is to be done? His dad is going to die.

In the morning, Marco and Nicole rise early as Nicole has to get to a set where she is to play a road accident victim in a multiple motorway pile-up. It is a reconstruction for one of the TV programmes about the bravery and dedication of the emergency services. 'What a nightmare,' she mutters as she pulls on her jacket. Marco likes the fact that they never ask when they will see each other again on parting. Soon, he knows, it will get to the point when they will either start asking each other or they will just drift apart.

Marco spends the day mechanically spooning olives into tubs, slicing and wrapping cheese and ham and salami, his hands protected hygienically by plastic gloves like a surgeon. He is having to do most of the work now that Gerald keeps disappearing for long stretches of time, gripped by his need to prove Gina's infidelity. Marco has tried to calm him down but it is no good; jealousy has him by the throat.

In the afternoon, however, Marco is startled to see Gerald accompanied by Gina walking down the road arm in arm like a pair of newly-weds. They come into the shop giggling drunkenly. Marco raises his eyebrows at Gerald who throws his arms in the air.

'Marco! You were right! I am a complete idiot.' He grins stupidly at Gina and hugs her.

'Erm . . . what's going on?'

'I've been so stupid. Gina and I have talked things over, and everything's sorted out. Look!'

He produces two airline tickets from his pockets and slaps them down on the counter.

'Watch out, there's olive oil on the counter . . . what are these?'

'These, Marco, are two tickets for St Lucia. We are going away. Getting away from all the negativity that has been causing this hassle.'

Gina and Gerald hug each other again. Marco is beginning to feel queasy.

'That's really great, Gerald. But what about . . .' Marco gestures to the shop.

'Finished. I've had it with all of this. You've always got to change, Marco. It's not been making much money anyway. When we get back, we're thinking of moving out of London altogether.'

'So when . . .'

'Next week. Of course, I'll give you a month's wages in lieu of notice, not that you're entitled to any notice actually but we've worked well together, haven't we, Marco? Now let's shut up shop and have some champagne. Get some glasses from the back, would you, darling?'

Marco feels stunned but does not have it in him to harbour any resentment towards Gerald. The job has lasted longer than he had expected anyway. Unemployed. For somebody like his dad, the word is written in black, almost as bad as a wartime telegram arriving at the home of a family with a boy at the front. The great enemies of War, Poverty, Unemployment, Disease – capitalism's lieutenants which will nevertheless one day be vanquished by the iron will of the proletariat. Does John Fisher really believe that any more? Probably. Marco certainly doesn't. He is going to have to phone Lee to find out if there is any work going in his restaurant. Lee knows that Marco is a good cook. If the worst comes to the worst, he might see about doing a bit of washing up at the restaurant where most of Danny's Scottish mates work. No, fuck that, he'd rather starve.

The champagne cork pops and bounces off the ceiling. Gerald fills their glasses and raises his. Champagne foams out of the neck and down the side of the bottle.

'To new beginnings,' he says.

'To no more private detectives,' says Gina. 'To St Lucia.'

They turn to look at Marco. He can't think of anything particularly to toast. They are waiting expectantly.

'To young love,' he finally says. 'Except that obviously only applies in your case, Gina.'

Later, when they have drunk the champagne, Marco asks Gerald if he can have his month's wages. Gerald is almost tearful as he presses the money plus a fifty-pound bonus into Marco's hand.

'I'm sorry about the deli closing, Marco. But I've been thinking about it for a while. I need a new start.'

'What are you going to do when you get back?'

'Ah, well . . .' Gerald leans drunkenly towards him. 'We're thinking of getting out of London 'cause we're planning on having a baby.'

'Great,' Marco says, thinking about the number of people recently who have told him that they are getting married or having babies. Boring bastards. 'But who told you that you have to get out of London to have a baby?'

'Look out there, Marco.' Gerald gestures to the street. 'This city is finished. It's no place to bring up a child, you know.'

Marco ponders this. He looks out on to the street that Gerald has just motioned towards. It seems perfectly normal to him.

People going home from work, mothers with prams, couples with Sainsbury's bags. The majority of child abductions, or maniacs walking into schools and killing children, do not happen in London as far as he can tell, Fred and Rosemary West were not from London. It is far more dangerous outside London. Marco contemplates pointing this out to Gerald but decides not to spoil the upbeat mood that has been missing for so long.

'Where are you thinking of going then?'

'Warwickshire. My family have a place I can use. We're thinking of opening a clothes shop up there.'

'Great,' Marco replies insincerely.

He meets Danny after work in the Plasterer's Arms by Hoxton Square. It is an evening when almost everybody he knows appears to be in the same pub and in the mood for misbehaviour. The bar-staff keep glancing over at them. Somebody is dancing on the table, a beer-glass goes crashing to the floor, somebody is yelling about wanting a shamrock on their pint of Guinness. A German girl with pig-tails and a pink furry purse shaped like a heart starts telling Marco about clubs in Hamburg. He considers trying to get off with her, wonders whether this would represent some kind of disloyalty to Nicole but cannot be bothered thinking about it too much. He can feel boredom like an incoming tide lapping around his ankles. Everybody is too pissed, the night is getting too messy, nobody seems to have any drugs, and he cannot be bothered to hunt down Arnold. The German girl starts talking to somebody else and Marco drains his pint and rises to leave. Danny tries to persuade him to stay and go round the corner to the Blue Note with him, but Marco wants to walk home, so he stops Danny from nagging by lending him twenty quid.

The night is soft and warm as Marco makes his way down Rivington Street, thinking that he wouldn't mind living in one of the huge buildings around there that all the artists have taken over for studios. He is crossing a small road, and wondering whether he shouldn't have gone with Danny after all, when a

car comes screeching round the corner, forcing him to jump
back on to the kerb. It is a police car using neither siren nor
flashing blue light. He stares angrily at the policeman in the
passenger seat. The copper points to his face and shouts, 'Use
your fucking eyes when you cross the road, you stupid prat.'
Marco shakes his head disgustedly as the car pulls off again,
but after about twenty yards it suddenly stops and reverses at
speed up to him as if it, rather than the driver, has suddenly
changed its mind. Marco feels his heart begin to beat faster as
the copper gets out of the car.

'What did you say?'

The driver is also getting out of the car. He is grinning. The
first copper is looming above Marco. He has cropped blond
hair, the suggestion of a moustache on his upper lip.

'What did you say?'

'I never said nothing.' Marco looks around but there is
nobody about.

'Yeah, you did. You called me something. What did you call
me?'

'I never said nothing. I was shocked, that's all. You nearly
ran me over.'

The copper stares at Marco with contempt. 'We should have
run you over, you mouthy bastard. Now what did you call
me?'

'I never called you nothing.'

The driver is standing slightly behind them with his hand
on his belt.

'Let's just nick 'im. Teach him what happens to people who
start calling us names.'

'Come on,' Marco protests, 'I ain't done nothing. I've been
at work all day. I'm just on my way home.'

'Work?' The copper glares at Marco as if he has no right to
use the word at all. 'Work? You don't know the meaning of
the word. Put your arms against the wall. Now!'

Marco sighs as the copper starts to search him, relieved that
he was not able to find any drugs in the Plasterers' Arms. The
copper pulls out the money from his jeans pocket.

'What's this?'

'It's money.'

He feels a hand on his head, pulling him back by the hair.

'You getting lippy again? Don't get lippy with me, son, or I'll kick you into the middle of next week.'

'I ain't. It's my wages. I got paid today.'

Marco can suddenly feel his temper rising over his fear. His dad is dying, he has just lost his job, he is trying to go home. Fuck this shit, this bullying pig whose type he recognises from school: Carl Greene, a fat bully who couldn't run but could make your life misery. You had to let him get the ball off you during football games or he'd smash his studs into your knee. Now he's got a uniform and a car and some new stop-and-search powers and is demanding that Marco call him 'sir' and explain what the money he has worked for all week is doing in his pocket. Marco stares at him with hatred.

'What are you staring at, cunt?'

The driver is beginning to look a bit bored, as if he cannot really be bothered with all this. But his mate is watching Marco with his teeth bared. It appears that Marco has also stirred some distant memory in him – they are like two dogs who have circled and sniffed and are about to leap snarling at each other.

'I said, what are you staring at?'

Marco sighs and stares upwards. He is not going to answer any more of these stupid questions.

'You deaf as well as ugly?'

Marco looks him full in the face. Behind, the driver is leaning on the bonnet of the car.

'If you was in such a hurry that you nearly ran me over, how come you've got the time to be standing here hassling me when I'm just trying to get home from work?'

'Hassle? You don't know what hassle is. When I start hassling you, then you'll know about it.'

Marco meets his gaze. He wants to look away but can't. The copper's eyes are pale blue. What does he do in his spare time? Probably beats his wife. Probably the only thing this cunt shows any tenderness to is his dog. The driver is walking slowly towards them, feeling in his belt pocket. Marco knows he is about to be nicked and his eyes move to the copper's shoulder to check for his number but before he can register it, he feels an unbearable stinging burning pain, and a swelling in his throat as if he has just swallowed a whole grapefruit. He staggers and cries out; his eyes are on fire; they have blinded him. For a second, he is so tormented by the sensation that he has no idea what has happened, like the time when he was a kid and got stung by a wasp for the first time. He drops to the ground, his hands scrabbling at his face. Somebody kicks him but not that hard, just so that he topples over. There is the sound of laughter; he is choking, retching, swearing incoherently. More laughter, and then a voice in his ear, a hand on his shoulder.

'If I see you again, I'll give you a kicking you'll never forget. Then I'll nick you and charge you with assaulting a police officer. Understood?'

His money is forced into his hand, there is more laughter, then a car starting and pulling away.

Tear gas. It is far too benign a name for what it has just done to Marco. It makes it sound like itching powder, something you might find in a joke shop along with whoopee cushions and exploding cigarettes, something with the effect of a particularly strong onion. As Marco gets unsteadily to his feet in the now deserted street, he feels as if he has been poisoned. He is shaking violently. Nothing could ever have prepared him for the terrible sensation of having CS gas sprayed in his face. He is alone, does not even know the number of the car or which of the two coppers actually sprayed him. He looks down at the money in his hand. It is not all there – a fifty-pound note has been taken. He has just been mugged by two police officers. There is a man walking towards him.

'Did you see them?' Marco asks desperately. 'Did you see what they just done?' He knows the man could not have seen anything, but he has to ask somebody, establish contact with somebody. The man looks at Marco as if he were a Care in the Community case.

'They just sprayed me with CS gas – two coppers. I hadn't done nothing. They took my wages. CS gas.'

The man hurries past, shaking his head. What's the point? Marco thinks. Nobody will believe him. Even he can hardly believe it and he's had some pretty bad experiences with the police in the past. Nothing like this, though; a few slaps, a few threats. To be fair though, he had already been nicked when that happened. Not like this, where two coppers nearly run him over, pin the blame on him and then spray him with CS gas and nick fifty quid off him. And he never even got their number. Even if he had, he would have thought twice about complaining because he knows what can happen if you make a complaint. Like Moody Dave, who came out of a football game and the coppers tried to put him on a train to Newcastle even though he was living in New Cross. They were herding him with some other guys he had never met and when he got really scared that they were going to throw him on the train with five hundred Geordies, he tried to break through the line. An Alsatian took a big chunk out of his arm. For a while, Moody Dave was ecstatic as he thought he was going to get thousands in compensation. Like all of Moody Dave's projects, however, the result was somewhat different. He withdrew his complaint suddenly and refused to discuss it any further after some anonymous advice about what might await him if he didn't.

Marco is desperate for the light of their flat to be on as he turns the corner down the passage beside the abandoned church. It isn't. He sighs inwardly, he wanted to tell Kerry about it. The boys are sitting on the bench and nod at him as he passes; from the pub somebody is roaring out a karaoke version of 'House of the Rising Sun'. When Marco gets into the flat, he looks at his face in the bathroom mirror, but there is little evidence of his experience apart from red eyes. He sits in front of the TV while the shadow Home Secretary explains that he is sick of driving home from Westminster and seeing young children on the streets. Solution? A nine p.m. curfew. Marco puts his foot on the screen over the politician's face, pushing the TV back. He is going to let it topple over when he remembers that it is Kerry's TV and that she saved up for it while she was temping. When she moved here, he helped her carry it up in the lift. Marco lets the TV rock back into position. He wants to cry. He cannot. The TV is the only illumination in the room, bouncing its irregular flickering light-dark-light-dark off the walls. From the window of the darkened room, the other lights of the city glisten, unmoved and impervious.

Chapter 17

Kerry had thought that Robin's outburst against Marco was just a one off, the result of accumulated frustration at his rudeness and hostility. She was wrong. Robin continues to suggest that she leave the flat and live with him. When she refuses, he announces that he does not want to stay at her place any more. Kerry has learned that when Robin says that he will not do something, then he is as good as his word. She tries to force him to give in by not staying with him for a while, but this does not work. He just waits for her to come round to his house which, in the end, she always does.

Another thing that troubles her is that Robin seems to want to have sex less often. In the first months of their relationship, they would enter the house and almost immediately start taking off each other's clothes. Once, when nobody else had been in at Robin's house, she had arrived and he had slow-waltzed her across the kitchen, lifting her skirt around her hips and fucking her on the huge kitchen table. Sex between them is never predictable or boring, sometimes she is worried that other people in the house will hear them but at the time it always becomes irrelevant. They still make love now, and it is still as good, but sometimes when Kerry turns to him in bed and begins to touch him, he rolls over and says that he is tired, or he just does not respond at all until she stops, embarrassed. The problem for Kerry is that her desire is, if anything, greater than when they first met. And why should it not be? The nights are getting warmer, her body is singing, her blood is pulsing, she is still young, she wraps her arms and legs around another body – the miraculous lust, the vital exchange, the privilege bestowed, the movement of hands, the teasing exploration of tongues, the things he whispers to her, drops of semen like cloudy pearls.

The imbalance between them now makes Kerry feel slightly ashamed and then angry for being made to feel that way.

Robin also appears to be growing increasingly impatient with college and less inclined to talk to her about work. He has given up the habit of staying up all night to prepare assignments and once fails to hand one in at all. He says that he is finding the course boring, that it no longer challenges him and that the lecturers are even greater idiots than his fellow-students. Again, Kerry feels guilty because she cannot share this attitude; she is doing and enjoying a module on post-colonial fiction. Sometimes, in the mornings he tries to persuade Kerry not to go in and sometimes, reluctantly, she lets him persuade her.

One evening, she is sitting in the flat watching *Crimewatch* with Marco who is still unemployed. Nicole finds him odd days working as an extra which he describes as more boring than washing-up, but there is a possibility that Lee might find him something soon in the restaurant.

'It's my birthday on Friday week,' Kerry tells him.

'I know,' he replies, reluctant to tear himself away from the rogues gallery of credit card fraudsters, petrol station assailants, and mustard-coloured leather jacket thieves. Marco is always threatening to phone up anonymously and give Danny's name.

It seemed like just an ordinary morning for Scott Williams as he opened his scrap metal yard in Peckham. The headline in the paper that day: Britain Stands up to Europe over Beef Crisis . . .

'Do you want to do something?'

'Yeah, of course . . . look at that silly cunt. Is that a wig or what . . . what do you wanna do?'

'Oh, you know, nothing special. Go out for a drink or something.'

'All right. I'll cook first. Why don't you invite the babe-sister? I'll get Nicole to come up.'

'Yeah, that would be good.'

'What about Christopher Robin?'

'Come on, Marco, you can be nice to him on my birthday, can't you?'

'I can try.'

Don't Step on the Lines

We've had a flood of phone calls on the armed robbery in New Malden. Not as much information on the riot in Brixton. Our lines are open until midnight. Keep those phone calls coming and remember that your chances of being the victim of crime are very small. Goodnight and . . .

' " . . . don't have nightmares," ' Marco mocks. 'He's so smarmy. That woman copper they've got now is quite tasty, though.'

'Marco! She's not, she's horrible.'

'She's OK. I like her voice. I wonder if they'll have the two coppers who sprayed me with CS gas and robbed fifty quid off me on the programme next month?'

'I doubt it. How's your dad?'

Marco cracks open a pistachio nut and flicks the two half-shells into a saucer by his feet.

'The treatment he's having is making him sick. But his hair hasn't fallen out. Not that he had that much to fall out in the first place. But the doctors seem quite pleased with the way things are going.'

Kerry nods. Marco had been really down for a couple of weeks after hearing about his dad and then getting assaulted by the police the very next day. She had tried to persuade him to make a complaint anyway but he refused point-blank. Given that he didn't have either the assailants' or their car's number, she supposes that it is probably wiser not to. Who is going to believe Marco, who has three previous convictions for shoplifting, affray (the poll tax riot) and possession of drugs?

'So we'll do that then? What do you wanna eat?'

'That squid thing you do.' Kerry grins. 'It's delicious.'

Marco holds his head in his hands. 'That means I'll have to clean millions of them . . .'

'It's my birthday!'

'OK, OK. If you want squid . . .'

'I do.'

'I'll have to go up to Steve Hatt's then.'

'Thanks, Marco. I'm off to bed. Goodnight.'

'And don't have nightmares.'

And that night, for a change, Kerry doesn't.

'You shouldn't have arranged that.' Robin stands in the kitchen facing her across the table.

Kerry feels as if her face is swelling. Don't do this, she wants to say, just don't do this. She hates arguments, especially when she can see no option, can feel herself being coerced into confrontation, no exit apart from a humiliating climb-down that she is not prepared to make.

'Why not?'

'I was going to take you out.'

'We can still do that, though. Just some other time. It will be a laugh having people round.'

'With Marco there?' Robin knits his fingers together. 'I don't think so.'

'But it won't just be Marco. Jeanette will come. And Nicole – you know that he behaves better when she's there – and I might invite John – you remember him, and . . .'

She tails off. Robin is looking at her almost insolently, as if the people she is mentioning would not even make it on to his B-list. Kerry looks down at her hands and begins to twist her ring round and round on her finger. Her skin feels too tight for her body.

' . . . and Susan maybe.'

Robin nods slowly. Kerry can feel anger beginning to knot inside her. What right has he look down on her like this? Kerry has never reacted well to being patronised.

'Can't you change it?' he says at last. 'I would really like to see you on your birthday.'

'What do you mean? Of course you'll see me.'

Robin shakes his head. 'I'm sorry, Kerry. I'm not prepared to go through an evening with Marco. You've got to distance yourself from him.'

For a second, she is speechless at this imperative. He is really expecting her to agree with him, to back down, he thinks that he has clinched it with this threat.

'You mean, you won't come?'

'Sorry, Kerry. I put up with him for as long as possible. I really tried . . .'

'Tried? Rubbish! You just waited for a while, that's all. You didn't try at all. I'm not saying he wasn't rude to you. But don't say you tried because you didn't. You just let it go for a while.'

'There's no need to get angry . . .

'Too right I'm angry! You're so *selfish*. All you think about is yourself. Why can't you do what *I* want on *my* birthday? Why do you have to spoil everything?'

'Now *you're* being childish . . .'

'Don't be so fucking patronising!'

'Oh, well.' Robin throws his hands in the air. 'You're impossible to talk to sometimes, Kerry. There's nothing else to say. If you would rather spend time with Marco than with me . . .'

'You're just a bully sometimes. You want me to do exactly what you want. I'm not going to turn round to Marco and say, "Oh, sorry, we can't do what we planned any more because Robin doesn't like you." Especially not now. His dad's really ill as well. He's always stood by me when I've been in trouble. You want me to cut off from him just because you don't like him? Sorry, Robin. No way.'

'Maybe. I don't want to see you waste your time on worthless people, that's true.'

'Marco's not worthless. He's worth much more than some of your self-obsessed friends.'

Robin rolls his eyes. 'That's a matter of opinion.'

Kerry's rage is uncontrollable now. She is going to say things she will regret but she doesn't care. ' "*That's a matter of opinion . . .*"' she mimics him. 'That's absolutely typical of the kind of fucking platitude you come out with in the belief that you live on some kind of higher plane than everybody else. But, you know, it's not very convincing any more. I don't know what it is that makes you think you're so special, maybe it's because you're an only child . . .' Kerry regrets this one almost as soon as she has said it ' . . . but I can't be bothered with it. OK, if you can't just put up with Marco for one evening, then fine. Don't come. But I'm not going to change my friends for you and you had better just understand that . . .'

'But that's all I'm saying.' Robin smiles lop-sidedly with maddening calm. 'If you would prefer to spend the evening with Marco, then that's fine with me. Try not to get so hysterical over the fact that I don't want to have anything to do with it.'

Kerry shakes her head. 'Oh, right, yeah. Don't get hysterical, Kerry. Just like a girl, eh? You think you've found some profound way of living, Robin, but you're just a snob, a control-freak. You throw your money around but you're not a generous person . . .'

This last comment must have stung because there is a sharpness in Robin's tone when he answers.

'I haven't noticed you complaining about my lack of generosity before,' he remarks icily.

'Money isn't everything.'

'Any more little clichés? So, Kerry, can it buy you love?'

'Well, you've made it clear now that you *are* aware of it, and all of that stuff about how you're doing it for yourself and not for me is a load of crap. Well, don't worry about it. Send me an invoice, yeah?'

'Now who's being cheap?'

They stare at each other across the table. Curiously, Kerry is almost aroused. She is disgusted with him, but she still half wants the argument to be resolved. She knows, however, that the only way that the argument will be resolved is if she backs down and she will not do that. The argument is like a storm that has passed now and they are both at a loss because there is no way forward other than capitulation on somebody's part.

'Maybe I should go,' she says quietly.

He looks down at his hands.

'Do you want me to go?' Kerry insists, giving him a chance to break the dead-lock. If he says no, then the evening can still be retrieved.

Robin shrugs. 'It's up to you. You must do what you want.'

'Right then.' Kerry walks out of the kitchen down the hall. She half expects him to call out to her. She would have called

him back. But he doesn't. Should she go back? Then she sees
Jill. She is standing at the foot of the stairs, one hand on the
banister.

'Enjoy that, did you?' Kerry snaps.

Jill does not answer. She glances contemptuously at Kerry
and raises her eyebrows. Then she turns and climbs back up
the stairs. Kerry feels another hit of anger which is enough to
propel her out of the front door without paying any further
attention to the possibility of Robin's calling her back.

Out on the street, she suddenly realises that she has about
thirty pence in her pocket. Under no circumstances can she
return to ask Robin for money and she has used up the limit
on her cash-card. She could get a cab and ask the driver to
wait while she goes upstairs to borrow some off Marco. But
what if he's not there? And even if he is, what if he has no
money? She'll have to walk. What if she meets the boy with
his one copy of the *Big Issue* and *Cut Here* tattoo? Or somebody
like him? She hates Hackney. She's got to make her mind up.
Which way? Down Queensbridge Road and on to the Hackney
Road, right through to Old Street. There might be a quicker
way but she wants to stay on the main roads. Kerry sets off,
staring straight in front of her, hearing the sound of her feet
on the pavement. As she walks she begins to sing gently to
herself, taking careful steps to land in the squares of the paving
stones and not on the lines. She passes pubs and kebab shops,
the lumps of dripping meat slowly spinning past the blue flame
as if part of a torture process. She lights a cigarette and smokes
it right down to the filter. Some of the men passing her
studiously ignore her, and yet even in this it is as if they are
consciously acknowledging her deviancy. Two men together
by the entrance to a block of flats make muffled comments to
her departing back. Another says, 'Angel, that's a lovely colour
jacket.' She is suspect, asking for trouble, a curfew-breaker.
She just wants to get home.

Her feet are aching as she approaches the Old Street roundabout, the familiar white-curved structure holding up a block
of advertisements for credit cards, a white-toothed woman

smiling at hers as if it were the key to happiness. She tucks in behind a young couple who must be heading back to their converted warehouse off Rivington Street. When they turn off, she crosses the road. She can see the weather-vane at the top of the white point of the church above the trees now like a guiding lighthouse. Some kids are playing by the turning to her block. Is it over between her and Robin? Is she single again? She can hear footsteps and giggling behind her. They are getting nearer, louder, almost upon her. Then a woman's voice.

'Don't say hello yet, Marco, until we've finished these chips.'

Kerry turns round. Marco and Nicole are staggering drunkenly along behind her, fighting over a bag of chips, cans of lager clunking precariously in a thin blue-striped kebab-shop plastic bag by Marco's side.

'Where've you been?' Nicole asks, holding out the chip-bag to her.

'Robin's,' Kerry replies shortly, waving it away.

'Yeah?' Marco runs over to the side of the church and pretends to search for him. 'It's OK, Robin, you can come out now.'

'Where is he?' Nicole asks, licking a drip of tomato ketchup from her fingers.

'At home. We've had . . .' Kerry glances at Marco ' . . . a bit of a row.'

Marco's face breaks into a happy, drunken grin for a second, and then reshapes itself into an expression of fake concern.

'I can't tell you how sorry I am to hear that.'

They burst out laughing and a group of boys around the corner break into a high-pitched imitation. Nicole takes Kerry's arm.

'Never mind, you'll make up. That jacket's really nice, it's a beautiful colour . . .'

And Kerry laughs with relief as they reach the entrance to their block of flats.

Chapter 18

Marco is no longer woken by the sound of an alarm clock in the mornings. He rises when he gets bored of being in bed, enjoying the grey time of a weekday morning. Not having to be at work means that he can spend more time with his dad, although John Fisher worries that Marco is not out job-hunting. It is clear to Marco that not working is his natural condition; he begins to get used to it. It is not that he is lazy, because he is still very active. It is not even work that he particularly minds – it is the obligation of work, the timetable. He should have been born rich, he should have been born with a fat trust fund, or at least with a rare talent which would make him an instant millionaire after which he could settle down to do the things he liked. He would do the lottery but knows that it would only make him frustrated.

John Fisher is closely following elections in the Soviet Union. Communist electoral come-backs fill him with the kind of glee that most people reserve for their football teams beating superior opponents. It has been a pleasing season for John Fisher so far with Lech Walesa getting kicked out in Poland and the election of the Olive Tree coalition (a name for which he has nothing but contempt) in Italy, with a hard line faction of the party holding the balance of power. His F.A. cup final is, however, the Russian election. Nothing would give him greater pleasure than to see the evil vodka-sodden Yeltsin given his marching orders by the Russian people. He is in a win-win situation here because if Yeltsin does manage to stay in power, then it can all be blamed on a biased media, vote-rigging and the blatant interference of the IMF. Although he is meant to be resting, John Fisher still goes out on fund-raising missions to fill a container for Cuba.

'It will show just how shallow all their bleating about

democracy is,' he explains to Marco as they drink tea and watch a documentary about the Communist candidate's tour of Siberian factories where the workers have not been paid for six months and subsist by growing lettuces on their allotments. John Fisher shakes his head and tut-tuts.

Marco is not so sure about it all. He finds the images of peasant grannies with headscarves enthusiastically waving pictures of Lenin and Stalin somewhat disconcerting. Where are all the young people? After the collapse of the Soviet Union, John Fisher had engaged in a period of vigorous self-criticism about his blind acceptance of the Soviet system and the need to work differently in the future without having to follow any particular model. Now, however, he seems to have forgotten all about this in his nostalgic desire to see the red flag once again flying over the Kremlin and a proper Soviet team to cheer on at the Olympics.

'What about all this anti-Jewish stuff, Dad? What if the Communists enter into an alliance with the fascists?'

'Shhhh,' John Fisher is leaning forward to listen to a top-level nuclear physicist – now unemployed – explaining why he will not be supporting Yeltsin.

Russians are mad, Marco concludes. None of this has much to do with Communism so far as he can see. It is just mad Russians with their mad politics. They probably do need an Uncle Joe to keep them in order. Now, there are crazed yuppies exploring the outer limits of vulgarity, trigger-happy mafiosi, drug-pushing grannies, an alchoholic president, neo-Nazis, a disgruntled military, Islamic fundamentalists, every village demanding independence. Worse still are the young people coming over here with their appalling taste in music and their desire to make art statements. Marco remembers Dale the DJ promoter telling him that you can get Es in Portugal which have a hammer and sickle on one side and CCCP on the other. What would his dad make of that?

'Do you want anything, Dad? More tea?'

His dad shakes his head. 'You're all right, son. Sit down. Relax.'

Don't Step on the Lines

Marco watches his dad frowning at the TV set. The doctors are apparently pleased and surprised with his progress. They have described him as a fighter. He is popular with the hospital staff, especially the nurses with whom he flirts shamelessly, calling them all by their first names. It must be good to be a fighter if you have an illness. Marco can't really understand how you can fight illness. It just happens to you. You can't fight 'flu, diarrhoea, tooth-ache or herpes. They just happen and you have to wait until they go away. So how can you fight a non-Hodgkins lymphoma, and who was Hodgkins anyway? Marco knows that it's better to have a non-Hodgkins than a Hodgkins lymphoma but not why this is the case, nor how the two differ.

'Dad, why did you live here when you married Mum and not in Italy?'

John Fisher looks surprised by the question. 'My work, I suppose. Anyway, your mum wanted to come to England. It was terrible, though, when she arrived. One of the coldest winters for centuries, everything frozen, everybody with 'flu. She never got used to that cold. Used to walk about with this shivering expression on her face – it broke my heart. We've got neighbours now, just over from Colombia they are. The woman, when she walks down the road in winter, sometimes she's got that expression on her face. Like she's being bullied by the cold, can't get away from it. Some people just miss the sun.'

'Did she not want to go back?'

'Sometimes. But we did go back for holidays. Anyway, it wasn't always cold. She liked other things about England. It was fine in the summertime.'

John Fisher sighs and adjusts himself in the chair.

'Do you miss her sometimes?' Marco has never asked his dad this type of question before.

'You see, son, after your mum died I met Anne, didn't I? And we've been very happy together. She's a good woman . . .'

Marco nods.

' . . . but when I met your mum, I was a different person.

It's like I was somebody else then. She was . . . we were younger, you know? The first person like that, well, it's a bit special, isn't it? But it's so distant . . . sometimes I can't see it properly . . . it's been a long time. She had a good sense of humour, she would have laughed at you. When I knew her, I thought, She's perfect, she's the one for me. I knew I had to have her. She made me work though . . . yeah, she really made me work for it. With Anne it was different. But it's been good. I've been very happy with her. And she loves you, Marco. You know that, don't you? She loves you as much as she loves Angela. More sometimes, I think.'

'She's my mum,' Marco says simply. He has never understood adopted kids wanting to find their so-called real parents; there is something attention-seeking and self-indulgent in it so far as he is concerned. He feels slightly desolate. *When I knew her, I thought, She's perfect.* Will he ever feel like that about anyone or anything? He is always looking for the perfect hit. Gary used to laugh and say that Marco would stick his fingers in a plug socket if he thought he would get a buzz off it. John Fisher thought that he had found perfection in his young Italian wife, the perfect society in the Soviet Union. She died, and it fell apart. But at least he has had his moments. Marco has also had his moments, but he has never thought that he has been witnessing perfection. No matter how off his face he has been, there has always been that little dissenting voice inside him: *This is nothing, this means nothing.*

'She left me something, though.'

'Who, Anne?'

'No, Francesca. Your mum. I know you think I'm hard on you sometimes, Marco. I'm always nagging at you about your life. But it's only 'cause I care about you. I worry about you and Angela. You just drifting about, all those drugs you take . . .' he waves away Marco's disclaimer ' . . . and Angela about to get married to Herr Hammond. But you're still special to me, you're what I've got left of me and your mum. And you're so like her sometimes . . .'

Marco feels a terrible wrenching pain inside him. The moment of intimacy has come suddenly, he is not prepared for it, does not know how to sustain it meaningfully. He knows his dad does not either. It is enough. He has to change tack somehow.

'Herr Hammond? Yeah, that's going to be a laugh, that wedding. All the other von Hammonds too. Can't wait to meet them. There must be a nice little fascist state still left for their honeymoon . . .'

John Fisher laughs and then becomes more solemn.

'Having said that, Marco, I'm relying on you to behave yourself at the wedding. These jokes about Nazis are all right between you and me but I don't want Angela getting upset. It's her day, right? We've got to help make it special for her. That means you watching that mouth of yours . . .'

Marco is relieved that his dad has returned to normality. He looks at his watch.

'I've gotta be making a move soon. I said to Nicole I'd meet her in the pub.'

'She's a nice girl that one, Marco. I hope you ain't messing her about as usual.'

'I'm not!'

'Well, I hope not. She's a lovely girl. Too good for you, so don't start behaving with her like you do with all the others. Like you did with that Kerry . . .'

One of John Fisher's enormous misconceptions is that the only thing preventing a beautiful relationship between Kerry and Marco is callousness and irresponsibility on the part of the latter. He sincerely believes that Kerry is besotted with Marco and that Marco encourages her in this vain project as part of some egotistical power trip. Marco made the mistake of telling Kerry this once and, after laughing in a way that he found rather insulting – it's not such a ridiculous idea – she punished him the next time she met John Fisher by sitting and gazing at Marco with such a forlornly love-stricken expression on her face that Marco's dad had sulked with him for several weeks afterwards.

'I've told you, I haven't done nothing to Kerry. She's got her own life.'

John Fisher frowns and shakes his head. 'It's a shame, that's all. You shouldn't mess people about like that, Marco. Especially a lovely girl like Kerry.'

'Yeah, yeah, you don't know what you're on about, you old fool. Stick to your nurses. Anyway, Nicole's on telly tonight. She said to tell you to watch.'

'What is she this time?'

'She's a hunt saboteur. She reckons she's in the shot for about two seconds, jumping up and down and waving her arms about.'

'Hunt saboteurs! Care more about bloody calves and foxes than human beings that lot. Why isn't she jumping up and down and waving her arms about the state of the NHS, or three million unemployed?'

'It's a film, Dad. It's just a part.'

'That reminds me, Marco. I told Simon I would ask you. The local branch are organising a benefit for South Africa on Saturday. In the Cambridge Centre. I can't go obviously, but it would be good if you could. Take your girlfriend. They've got a band as well . . .'

Marco makes a rapid search of his Excuses home-page. He has been to quite a few of these events in the Cambridge Centre. Once he mistakenly took Danny. They got caught coming out of a cubicle together after Danny had produced some speed. Fortunately, the person who caught them assumed that this meant that they had been having an illicit homosexual en-counter. Among capitalist deviations this was ranked as slightly less offensive than snorting drugs and nothing was said to Marco's dad, although he must have been puzzled by the ensuing rumours about his son's sexual orientation.

'What's the band called?' Marco asks as a stalling tactic.

'Thatcher's Bastard Children,' John Fisher replies. 'Quite punky and alternative, I think. Some of the older comrades were pretty reluctant, but you've got to have something for the young people as well.'

'Yeah, I can make that . . . oh, wait a second. Is it this Saturday? Is it the seventeenth? The thing is, I've promised

Kerry I'll go out and celebrate her birthday. I'd feel bad letting
her down . . .'

'No problem . . .' John Fisher perks up, 'You could take her
to the benefit.'

The perfect birthday. An evening drinking warm cans of
Hoffmeister with a smattering of British Communists listening
to a punk band called Thatcher's Bastard Children.

'Yeah, that's true, but I think Kerry's already made arrange-
ments with her boyfriend. He's quite rich and he's taking
everybody out for some posh meal. I'll tell you what, though.
After the meal, I could see if everyone wants to go down there.'

John Fisher snorts with laughter. 'Marco, you're about as
good at lying as you are at getting up in the morning. I'm only
winding you up. I knew you wouldn't want to go.'

'No, straight up, Dad. Thatcher's Bastard Children. They
sound blinding . . .'

They both start to laugh. 'I'll tell you what I'll do,' Marco
says, 'I'll phone Tony and tell him about it. I'm sure he'd love
to go. Take a few of his mates down after work.'

His dad waves him away. 'Go on, clear off, Anne'll be back
soon. Remember what I said about that Nicole.'

'Are you OK? You don't need anything?'

'Never felt better. Now go on, go and see that girlfriend of
yours.'

Chapter 19

Kerry's argument with Robin lingers like the effects of a prolonged hangover. She does not see him for a couple of days; he appears to have given up coming to college altogether. Kerry remembers his mum's scepticism in Yorkshire about Robin's ability to stay the course and hopes that this is not coming to pass. She tries to go about as normal. She works in the library, hoping that he will come up behind her as he used to and put his hands on her shoulders, invite her for a coffee. She not only misses his company but also their activities together, the way that her life had suddenly been filled with things to do. Now she feels oddly hollow, at a loss, lacking in will-power. She reads mechanically, she writes an essay on Faulkner. Beneath her window, the green tree-tops move as if teased by sea-currents.

Kerry is frightened of splitting up with Robin because her life has changed with him. She does not want to go back to relying on herself again just now. She wants to be walking back along the river-bank with him after going to see *Wild Strawberries* at the NFT; she wants to be in his kitchen drinking wine; she wants to be in bed with him watching TV after making love, or sitting on the train and looking out at the green fields spattered with red poppies like spilled drops of paint. She does not even know whether they have split up. Robin has not appeared in college since their argument. Why doesn't he phone her? Doesn't he care? Has he grown bored of her like he has grown bored of college? Kerry grows impatient with these questions and resolves to settle the issue one way or the other.

One evening when Marco is out, she phones his house. Jill answers.

'He's not here, Kerry,' Jill tells her. Kerry did not announce her name when she called, even though she recognised Jill's voice. She does not like the fact that Jill uses her name like that, there is something scornful about it. *I know who you are.*

'Do you know where he is?'

There is a pause as if Jill is considering her response. 'I think that he might be at Susan's,' she says finally.

For some reason, Kerry finds this irritating. She puts down the phone and stares at it for a moment. She dials 141 and then Susan's number. Susan has a payphone outside her room. It bleeps as somebody Kerry does not recognise picks it up. She puts the phone down again, sighs and flicks on the TV, feeling miserable. She sits and watches a basketball game even though she has no idea about the rules. Strangely, she starts to enjoy watching the giant men loping around, the sudden injection of speed, the jealous way they shield the ball from the opponent, leaping at full stretch to slam it through a hoop. Human beings do some weird things. She smokes several cigarettes and hopes that Marco will come home, but he doesn't. She goes to bed and flicks through a book of women's sexual fantasies that Jeanette gave her for Christmas. It is crap, full of half-American phrases like 'my dripping pussy'. Kerry throws the book across the room.

The next day, she phones Robin again and this time he answers.

'It's me.'

'Oh, hi, Kerry.' Robin sounds absolutely normal, as if nothing has happened between them.

'What are you up to?'

'Just pottering about really.'

There is a silence. He is a bastard, he is making her do all the work.

'I would like to see you.' Kerry hates herself as she says it. She knows that she has been beaten.

'Great,' Robin says, 'why don't you come up? There's something important I want to talk to you about. I've had a brilliant idea.'

'What is it?'

242

'It's a bit complicated to talk about on the phone. Do you want to come up? Or meet in a pub?'

'I'll come up.'

When Kerry arrives at Robin's, he is waiting for her with a smile on his face. Without speaking he takes her in his arms, pulling her against him. Relief and desire spread through Kerry as he leads her to the bedroom. It was only a stupid row. She is just going to have to accept that he is not always going to behave in a normal way. What does it matter now as his tongue moves from circling her breasts, down over her stomach, and her hands are full of the soft curls of his hair?

'So what's your brilliant idea?' Kerry asks later as they lie in bed, her arm across his bare chest.

'I'm going to leave college.'

'What?'

'I'm going to leave. I'm bored of it, getting nothing out of it. I want you to leave as well.'

Kerry pulls away from him. 'Leave as well? What are you talking about?'

'I want us to travel together. I've been looking into it. I want to go away for a year. I've been thinking about doing a big trip. I know what you said about the money but I could pay for both of us. Wouldn't you like just to get out of London? I want to go to Africa first. Especially South Africa. It must be really exciting there now.'

Kerry imagines them travelling together: planes taking off at night, the glitter of unknown cities, warm evenings in strange places, ocean beaches, the sand between her toes. She feels a sudden rush of excitement at the thought of moving from one continent to another, at being in a place that has only existed for her as a shape on an atlas before. She imagines sleeping with her head on Robin's shoulder, sharing meals on buses. Things would happen to her. Things would be different. So many places that she had always assumed she would never see. Then Kerry thinks about the year left of her course.

'Couldn't we go when we finish college?' She turns on to her front and looks at his face.

'No,' Robin answers firmly. 'I've already phoned the department and told them that I won't be taking the summer exams. I've had enough of it. I just want to get away. And I want you to come with me. You've got to just do things when the moment is right. It would be terrible to hang about for a year waiting.'

'Couldn't you wait for me?'

Kerry knows that Robin's silence is a negative. She does not want to leave college, she wants to finish her course.

'I don't see why it should be difficult for you, Kerry. You could always go back to it later if you wanted. But can you honestly say that you would prefer to waste time churning out essays? When the moment is right, you've just got to do things.'

It is Kerry's turn to be silent. She is not going to leave college. The moment isn't right. She wonders if Robin has known all along that she wouldn't. She has told him about her need to study, the satisfaction that she gets from it, the way in which she feels that she has rediscovered something about herself; in the midst of all the confusion and uncertainty it has given her a point of reference, something tangible. Unlike Robin, she is not just going to throw it aside. He talks as if changing one's life were like changing a TV channel when a boring programme comes on. Her tutor has been talking to her about applying for grants for post-graduate work. She cannot help the thought that Robin is just toying with her, but she knows that if she said yes to his world trip, he would be pleased. This is an even more alarming thought – that either option is equally agreeable to Robin.

'I can't leave college,' Kerry says simply. 'I've got to finish.'

'Of course you can leave. It's simple.'

'No, you know I can't.'

Robin sighs. 'You know, Kerry, when I first met you what I really liked about you, what made you exciting as a person was the way you appeared to be totally in control of yourself. Not like most of the idiots at that college. Now, I have to admit, I've begun to see that you're quite weak. You want predictability, you want your old friends, your old flat, your old college course. You can't handle the idea of sudden change, of spontaneity, of just throwing things up in the air and seeing where they land. It's frustrating because you give the appearance of somebody who has a really clear idea about the world. But underneath it all, you're incredibly conventional. When will you be really happy? When you're standing at your graduation ceremony in a gown clutching a certificate? Mummy and Daddy taking a photo of you. Everybody clapping good old Kerry because she's come through some really hard times and got her head together. Your sister will be there, Marco will be there, you'll all go the pub afterwards and get drunk. It's so predictable. You can have that easily, it won't be the great triumph that you think. I'm saying that we can get away from all that. Take everything a step further.'

Kerry swallows. 'What you're saying is that I should hand everything over to you to decide. Even down to the money . . .'

'Oh, don't start on the money thing again! The money is irrelevant. You shouldn't even think about it. I've told you, I've got money, I choose to spend it on you. The money isn't the issue. Remember when I first invited you to Ireland and you said you couldn't because of the money? And I said . . .'

'And you said that what really mattered was whether I wanted to go or not. That you would pay so that you would remove all obstacles that weren't connected to what I wanted. I know your theory. And maybe money's not the most important thing, you're right. But it's linked. It would be your trip, I would be your travelling companion, that's all. You would have all the control. It's strange how every vision that you have of my fulfilment as a human being happens to correspond with what *you* want me to do.'

Kerry sits up in bed. She wants to put her clothes on. Naked, she feels ridiculously vulnerable now. Her skin feels very white. Robin is lying comfortably with his hands folded behind his head. Outside, a car radio crescendos and then disappears again. Kerry softens her tone.

'I would love to travel. What you're offering is a big temptation. But it's not that I *can't* give up my course, it's that I don't want to.'

'Well . . .' Robin turns to look at her ' . . . you know what that means then? Because I can't change. I can't just stay still. I want to go as soon as possible.'

Kerry nods. She gets out of the bed and begins to put on her clothes. Robin watches her as if it is a reverse striptease show being performed for him. Again, Kerry wants him to say something, she wants him to give in, to say that he will stay on at college, that he will wait for her. She knows, however, that Robin will say none of these things. He is selfish. She cannot hurl that accusation at him, however, because he is not ashamed of it. His selfishness was partly what made him attractive to her. He is a control-freak, but then losing control does not bother him particularly either, because he does not care enough about the objects or people under his control. She thinks of the power that his good looks gives him. People who say that looks don't matter are talking rubbish. If Robin were ugly, he would be ridiculous. He is confident in everything; in his money, in his looks, in his house, in his power. It did not hurt him that Marco and Sylvia did not like him, it does not hurt him now that he is bidding farewell to the body of a girl whom he told that he loved, whom he probably believed that he loved.

She is putting on her clothes in front of him for the last time. She will never undress for him again. He is going to travel around the world, he will meet other girls. Kerry can suddenly envisage it – some beach with night falling, waves on the shore, a honey-skinned girl with dark tumbling hair and charmingly faltering English. For some reason, in this vision, the girl is wearing a red vest.

Robin would have offered that to Kerry but, in the final analysis, it is not particularly important that it is not her. Once, his eyes appeared to burn right through her clothes, he was consumed with desire for her, he saw everything that was bright and new and unique about Kerry. But now he has drunk, he has tasted, he has experienced. Kerry had brushed other men away but she accepted him. What a triumph! What an ancient, time-worn triumph! Her friends did not like him, but Kerry did not care. Now he is judging her, telling her that she is weak, that she is predictable. And Kerry has no words to throw back at him, she has nothing to say that could possibly make any difference. She has foolishly offered herself, given herself away to somebody who thinks nothing of the gift, who has simply torn away the wrapping. She casts a last look at the man who reawakened her body, who has just casually offered her the world. Then she walks out of the room and closes the door behind her.

When Kerry gets home, Marco and Nicole are on the sofa. They are watching TV, waiting for Nicole's appearance as a raver in a crowd scene from a film described in the paper as a 'club-based thriller with an edge'.

'It's coming up now,' Nicole says as the undercover detective pushes his way through a pulsating warehouse party, on the tracks of a murderous cocaine trafficker.

'There you are!' Marco shouts, jumping up and pointing to the corner of the screen. 'Wa-hay! Hands in the air. Looks like you was really having it at that party.'

'It was quite a good laugh,' Nicole says as the camera pans away to the undercover detective's attractive black female colleague who does not realise that she has been spotted by some of the trafficker's thugs. 'We really did get off our faces. I was tripping. The director got really pissed off with us 'cause nobody was taking it seriously and they wouldn't stop when he shouted "cut". Also, we had to do it sometimes without sound and that was even more trippy.'

'Erm . . . I might as well tell you that I've split up with Robin,' Kerry interrupts. 'It's over.'

Neither Marco nor Nicole speaks for a second.

'What, tonight?' Nicole finally asks.

'Yeah. He wanted me to go away with him and leave college. I said no. But he's going anyway. So . . . I just thought I should tell you . . . that's all.'

Marco nods without saying anything.

Kerry walks into her bedroom and closes the door. From the living room she hears a series of loud bangs which are obviously caused by Marco leaping around in triumph. She can hear Nicole half giggling and telling him to stop it.

Kerry lies on her bed staring at the ceiling. She picks up the photo of Gary and looks at him. He would have hated Robin as much, if not more, than Marco. She feels depression like a cloud in water advancing through her blood cells. What a fuck-up. What a stupid ending. She has been left twice now. Once by a manic-depressive who drove to Essex and ran headlong into a car, and now by a handsome egotist who will soon be watching the green fields of England disappear through the small window of an inter-continental jet, while she will stay in this grey city, get on the Northern line in the morning and travel to college to attend seminars and sit in the cafeteria. She remembers Robin's cruel taunt about her degree ceremony and tears prick at her eyes. Not just for her, but for the people he mentioned so dismissively; for her mum and dad, for Marco and Jeanette, and even for the dead Gary. He thinks that they are losers and who can say that he is not right? Who does she think she has been kidding? Is this the best she can manage? She will study for another year to get a degree which – why not accept the general consensus? – will do her no good at all. The audience is unimpressed, their arms are firmly folded. In the living room, she can hear Marco and Nicole messing about, occasional shrieks of laughter from Nicole at something Marco has said. Their closeness depresses her. She is alone again. She switches off the light, closes her eyes and waits for her dreams.

Chapter 20

The fruit of the sea, Marco thinks happily as he looks at the squid lying with their delicate pink marbling on the draining board in front of him. He likes that expression. He was pleased really that Kerry had demanded squid for her birthday, because he finds going on a fish mission almost as exciting as his more usual night-time hunting sessions. And he particularly likes buying squid, especially when he is hungover; it makes him feel sane, purposeful. He has a hangover from last night but it is only an average measurement on the Richter Scale, and still has not really kicked in yet. It would have been worse if he had been able to persuade Nicole to go down to a party in the Charing Cross Road after they had got bored of the club they were in, but she had refused, saying that she would prefer to spend the next five hours hanging upside down from a meat-hook. So they went home, which on reflection was the right thing to do. In the morning he went to buy the squid in Berwick Street, with money borrowed from Nicole, and afterwards sat in the pub with Lee, drinking double Bloody Marys burning with Tabasco, and dropping gentle hints to remind him to hurry up with the restaurant job.

Marco is trying to decide whether to make squid *provençale*, which will be more filling but masks the flavour of the squid, or a more simple dish with coriander and lemon grass. Whatever, it has to be good because this is his offering to Kerry, his statement. The essential art of cooking squid is not to overcook them – the fundamental mistake of most of the stupid *tapas* bars where eating squid is more like chewing a condom.

Sharks are great fans of squid. Marco once saw a programme about a place in Brazil where the sea was fizzing with squid – there were squillions of them dancing on the night waves, glowing like tentacled extras under the lights of the film crew. They had all congregated there for some strange instinctive reason, some great squid party. It was an instinct, however, which signalled the end of the oceanic life for many of the participants, because the fishermen were unsentimentally hauling them from the waves. Other fishermen stood on the boat with rifles, taking pot-shots at the circling sharks which understandably did not want to miss out on this squid-feast. Every now and again, a great mouth would break the surface, teeth glistening, dripping salty water, inhaling the squid. Marco had watched the fishermen on their fragile bobbing boats with admiration. Supposing one of them toppled and fell into that bubbling cauldron of squid and shark? No chance that a shark in an ecstatic feeding-frenzy would be likely to make the obvious distinction between fisherman and squid. *C'est la vie.* An occupational hazard for the fisherman, just as a bullet between the eyes is one of the risks for a shark attempting to steal his catch. Of course, the big time losers were the poor wave-dancing squid who lacked both giant jaws and rifles, and consequently got picked on by both fish and fisherman.

The vengeance of the squid arrives, however, when it comes to cleaning them. Marco puts the radio on, ignoring the drum and bass stations to find a talk programme. Somebody from the Labour Party is explaining how they will magically create a New Britain without raising taxes. Marco stares down at his adversaries, rubbing his hands together, as if he is about to disembowel the politician. Then he detaches the head and tentacles away from the body and screws up his face as he inserts his fingers into it, feeling for the thin bone through the mush of its insides. When he has located it, he yanks out the whole horrible mess. *Unlike the Tories, we're not prepared to use the economy to make party political points.* Marco contemplates posting the head and innards to Robin, grinning at the thought as he drops them into the bin. He chops the tentacles away from the head and slices the body. *We will massively expand training programmes for young people currently on the dole . . .* Marco repeats the process with the rest of the squid until his hands are reeking of the grey ooze which is all over the chopping board. He puts the prepared squid neatly to one side and washes his hands, chopping board and knife. Then he sneaks into the bathroom and steals some of Kerry's Issey Miyake moisturising cream. He knows that she would not be best pleased by him doing this, but it is a price she will have to pay. Marco puts the prepared squid into the fridge, switches off the radio and does a back-flip on to the sofa, sniffing at his hands. A red balloon drifts up past the window through the grey sky, which carries also the warm purring of afternoon traffic, trailing the string released from some child's hand, wriggling from side to side, carried cloudwards by the currents.

Marco must have fallen asleep, because he is woken by somebody tickling his feet.

'You looked like a little angel there.' Jeanette grins at him.

'What are you doing here?'

'Charming! I've just brought Kerry home. We've been shopping. I understand you're meant to be preparing a feast for us?'

Marco rubs his eyes as Kerry comes into the room.

'What time is it?'

'Half-five.'

Marco glances at Kerry to check her mood. He has hated seeing her over the last few days, a kind of deflated, defeated air about her. He thinks of Robin as a sharp-toothed vampire who has been hanging on her neck slowly sucking the confidence out of her. It is because of this that he cannot really talk to her about it. There is nothing soothing that he can say. *You're better off without him* is obvious but not particularly helpful. He knows that Kerry thinks that she has failed again, that she holds herself somehow to blame. All that Marco thinks is that she was blind in the first place, believing that there was anything good about him when it should have been completely obvious that he was a Class A cunt. Still, that's women for you: not all there in the judgement department. Otherwise how come a moron like Danny is so successful? *Because he's better looking than you*, mutters a quisling voice at the back of his mind that Marco chooses to ignore.

The telephone rings and Kerry passes it to him.

'It's your mum.'

'Anne?'

'Hello, Marco love. Listen, I've got some news for you. I don't want you to get too excited but I thought you would want to know straight away.'

'What is it?' Marco can still smell squid strongly on his hands; the telephone is going to smell of it now.

'Well, your dad went in for a test today. And . . . erm . . . I know that it sounds a bit strange, but it's gone.'

'What's gone?'

'The thing, you know, the growth, the . . . cancer. It's just gone. They can't find it. They're saying not to get too hopeful, 'cause it might come back, but they're over the moon the doctors and everyone. Totally baffled.'

'That's brilliant. Is he there?'

'Yeah, but he's sleeping. I don't think he can take it in really. He's exhausted. Anyway, I want to ring Angela now and let her know.'

'Yeah. Thanks, Anne. I'll ring tomorrow.'

Marco replaces the receiver. Gone? Cancers don't just go away. His dad might be a fighter but this is ridiculous. Maybe it's just hiding, maybe the doctors didn't look hard enough, maybe it's moved. They said that he was doing well and now they're saying that it's gone. What does that mean, though? That he doesn't have cancer any more? It might come back.

'What's up?' Kerry asks.

'It's my dad. His growth . . . they're saying it's gone.'

'That's great, Marco!'

'Here.' Jeanette hands him a *Desperado* beer. 'Cheers.' And they clink glasses.

Marco remains for most of the rest of the evening in the kitchen, slicing and chopping and mixing. A few people arrive, including John, the son of Kerry's old English teacher, with his girlfriend Simone, and Susan. Nicole turns up with Danny in tow.

'Who invited you?' Marco grins, knowing that Danny has a

seventh sense when it comes to a free meal. His sixth sense is reserved for people holding back on drugs.

'I found him hanging about outside,' Nicole says, 'sniffing the air like the Bisto kid.'

'Nah, Kerry, if it's a problem I'll just go, right. Just say the word.'

'OK then, word,' Jeanette snaps. 'See you later. Aren't the Chemical Brothers playing tonight somewhere?'

'I was speaking to Kerry, not the Ugly Sister. Straight up, Kerry, I've got half a Pot Noodle saved up at home . . .'

'Shut up, Danny. Here, have a beer.'

'Top girl, do you want to marry me?'

'What, and make it three in a row . . .' Jeanette starts and then stops. There is an awkward silence. Marco looks at Kerry whose face has closed like a perched butterfly that suddenly clasps its wings vertically to hide their colours, becoming flat. He thinks of his conversation with Jeanette, the way in which he tried to show her that Gary and Robin were – although very different – two faces of the same coin. Perhaps now that Kerry has examined both of these faces, there will be new possiblities. Although not, of course, in the shape of Danny. Jeanette walks quickly into the kitchen, cocking an imaginary pistol at her head. Then she leans her hands on the sink and pulls a funny face at Marco in deprecation of her not untypical lack of tact. Danny starts recounting how he tried six times to get into the Slam album launch, finally getting in by climbing through a skylight, and then getting thrown out again.

'The worst thing is, I can remember getting thrown out 'cause they threw me like a basketball. But I can't remember why . . .'

Nicole laughs. 'I was there as well which you probably don't remember either. They threw you out, Danny, 'cause you got caught stealing other people's drinks, which was pretty stupid given that they were free, and then you asked the bouncer if he was Paul Gascoigne's fatter brother.'

'Did I? I do remember some fat Geordie shouting at me.'

'Yeah, well, that was the same fat Geordie who was throwing you out into the street two minutes later.'

Jeanette comes back in and puts her arm around Kerry, who smiles at her.

Marco notices that there is something wrong with Susan. She doesn't say very much at first, appearing almost to be sulking. Then as she makes her way steadily through the wine, she becomes flushed and aggressive. He can see that Kerry has noticed it as well. Susan appears to be reserving most of her contempt for the men present and rolls her eyes at the most harmless comments. 'Typical man,' she says, especially to Danny who regards her with a puzzled expression. She can't eat the squid either, because she is allergic to seafood.

Jeanette tells a story about Darren coming back so pissed from the football that he took his clothes off, went outside naked to look for his wallet which he had droppped, and got locked out. Jeanette had been asleep and had not heard him shouting so he had gone to a phone box, but they had the answerphone switched on. In the end, he had walked naked for about half a mile to the fire station where he had made the night of the bored firemen who had nearly died with laughter, before wrapping him up, driving him in the fire engine to his house, and breaking the door down. Jeanette slept through all of this and was woken up by Darren dressed in a fireman's jacket surrounded by half a dozen grinning members of Red Watch. Everybody laughs except Susan who rolls her eyes and says, 'What do you expect from a man?'

She snaps completely when Danny refers to a 'bird' he met in the Duke of Edinburgh.

'What do you mean, "bird"?' she snarls.

Jeanette rolls her eyes at Marco. Kerry is ignoring this interchange, talking to John and Simone.

'I mean, a bird,' Danny replies. 'You must have come across them. You know – they've got tits, can't drive, always shopping, moan about too much football on telly . . .'

'The opposite of a geezer,' Jeanette butts in. 'You know – big mouth, big ego, small penis, smaller brain . . .'

'It's not a joke!' Susan suddenly shouts, her cheeks aflame.

'Men are disgusting. They make me sick. They think they can just take all the time, they don't care about anybody's feelings. They just hurt people.'

'Yeah, well, of course you're right,' Jeanette says in an unusual attempt to placate. 'But you're not exactly telling us anything we didn't know before. Anyway, they do have their uses. Although not obviously in his case.' She gestures dismissively at Danny, who waggles his tongue at her.

'I'm going home,' Susan announces drunkenly.

'I'll get your coat,' Danny offers.

'Come on, Susan,' Kerry urges. 'Don't go. It's no big deal really. You can't get wound up by somebody like Danny.'

'No big deal! How can you say that? How can you of all people say that?'

Kerry looks at her puzzled. 'What do you mean?'

Susan shakes her head and begins to laugh manically, still shaking her head as if she has an insect in her ear. Marco is getting worried now. She is losing it big time. He kicks Danny under the table and scowls at him. Danny raises his palms in bewilderment. Jeanette is looking at Susan as if she were a bottle of curdled milk.

'You of all people, Kerry. God, if only you knew...'

'KNEW WHAT?' Jeanette is losing her patience.

'I've got to go.' Susan is beginning to cry now. She staggers towards the door, tears running down her face. 'I'm sorry, Kerry, I've messed everything up. I'm sorry. I'll phone you.'

She picks up her bag and Kerry makes as if to follow her but Susan waves her back.

'Please, just let me go home.'

Marco puts his hand on Kerry's arm.

'Let her go.'

The door slams behind her and there is silence.

Marco looks at Kerry who is sitting with the wrapping paper from her presents on the table in front of her.

'She's fucking mad,' Jeanette announces.

'At last we agree on something,' Danny adds.

'Shut up, you. You didn't make things any better.'

'It's not Danny's fault,' Kerry says wearily. 'She's obviously got problems.'

'Hey, Ms DJ,' Marco turns to Nicole, 'put some music on.'

Nicole begins flipping through the record collection, pulling out old albums and 45s.

Danny redeems himself by producing a small present for Kerry, wrapped in love-heart paper. When she unwraps it, she laughs. It is a gram of coke.

'I won it in a raffle,' he says. 'No, straight up. It was at this party. You should have seen the faces when it was me that won it.'

'Never more undeserved,' Jeanette says. 'Still, I'm not complaining.'

'Makes a change then.'

'Card, please, Marco. Who's got a note?'

Inevitably, they do not go to the pub, although Danny is despatched to the kebab shop to buy some more beers.

'And don't argue with him,' Marco instructs Danny. 'Just ask for the beers, pay for them, and leave. Can you manage that? We rely on that kebab shop.'

'Do you want to go then?'

'Who cooked the meal you've just eaten? Shut up and get a move on.'

In the end, they are all dancing and singing and everybody has forgotten about Susan's tearful exit. They drink the rest of the melon vodka that Kerry gave Marco for Christmas and finish Danny's raffle prize. Then Danny cunningly establishes that Jeanette has got an E in her purse, forcing her to get it out so that they can grind it up and snort it.

'This is disgusting,' Nicole says happily as she chops out lines on the mirror. 'It rips up your nose as well.'

They listen to old Dexy's and Specials albums. Marco loves watching Nicole dance. Once she starts dancing, she will go on for ages. She looks good, dances well, wearing a short stripy skirt with her bare, powerful legs. The coke has made him randy. Danny is lurching around singing noisily along to 'You're Wondering Now', holding the bottle of melon vodka. The telephone rings and Marco picks up the squid-smelling receiver, worried that it might be the neighbours. It is Robin.

'What do you want?' Marco asks rudely. His tone fills the room, changing the atmosphere instantly.

Kerry stops dancing with Danny who is pretending to be the character from *Dirty Dancing*.

'Who is it?' she says brushing her hair out of her eyes, still half laughing.

'Wait,' Marco instructs Robin. 'Kerry, do you want to speak to Robin?'

Everybody turns and looks at her expectantly. She walks to the phone, gesturing to Nicole to turn the music down. People begin a low murmured conversation, pretending that they are not straining to hear what Kerry is saying. In fact, she does not say very much, just a couple of *yeses* and *noes*, one *thank you* and an *I don't think so*. When she replaces the receiver, Jeanette cannot hold it in any longer.

'What did he want?' she demands.

'Nothing,' Kerry answers simply. 'I get to choose the next record, right?' And Nicole shrugs at Marco and turns the music back up again.

Chapter 21

Kerry wakes the next day with ice-cream and Coca-Cola pangs. Her nose is blocked and her throat is sore from so many cigarettes. She will have to send Marco out to the shop. What time did everybody leave? Did the neighbours complain? She remembers Danny trying to persuade everybody to go to a party in Pitfield Street and trying – unsuccessfully – to kiss Jeanette. She remembers Robin phoning at some point in the evening.

'I just phoned to wish you a happy birthday,' he had said.

'Thanks.'

'Have you got a lot of people round?'

'No.'

'Well, it sounds like you're having a good time, anyway.'

'Yes.'

'Kerry, I . . . look, I would really like to see you. I've been thinking about what we talked about the other day. I don't want us just to finish like this. I need to see you now. Come round. Come up to the house.'

'No, I don't think so.'

And she had replaced the receiver. Maybe she should have gone. No, she shouldn't. She feels a slight ache at the thought of not going. And Susan? What was she on? Kerry will have to ring her and find out if she's OK. What if she didn't make it home? It would be all Kerry's fault for not forcing her to stay. But she didn't really want her to stay, she was spoiling Kerry's birthday. But what was that 'you of all people, Kerry' stuff about?

Kerry makes her way tentatively into the living room. Records are lying all over the floor, ash-trays blooming with cigarette butts, her mirror on the table with an empty wrap and a cashpoint card on it, glasses and cans and bottles spilled over the floor. Marco and Danny had used some of the older, unwanted records to pretend they were clay-pigeon shooting, Marco shouting 'PULL!' and Danny sending them spinning out of the window. They had all voted on what could go. After they had all sung along to 'Wonderwall', they had decided they didn't like it any more and sent it spinning out as well. Kerry regrets this now. She looks out and sees to her horror that a couple of the records are still stuck in the branches of the trees. The neighbours are definitely going to complain. They had ended up sitting on the balcony, watching the sun rise over London, the red-orange glow beaming back from the plate-glass windows of the office blocks, early morning planes making their final descent into Heathrow. Kerry had thought how strange it was that the passengers would be having their breakfast trays cleared away, stretching their weary limbs, getting their stuff together – totally oblivious to the wrecked people watching their plane from the balcony of a tower-block thousands of feet below.

Nicole staggers into the room, shaking her head at the detritus from the night before. 'I'm totally . . .' She yawns instead of finishing her sentence.

'Yeah,' Kerry agrees. 'It all got a bit messy. Snorting that E was the final straw.'

'Seemed like a good idea at the time, though.'

'Do you want tea or coffee?'

'Tea. Then we'll send Marco to the shops.'

Kerry grins at her. She likes Nicole, hopes that Marco doesn't start messing her about as he has done with other girls in the past. Then she thinks that it is more likely to be the other way round.

'So was it really nothing that Robin wanted last night?' Nicole asks.

'He wanted to see me.'

'Typical,' Nicole snorts. 'Men are always doing that. Throwing you away, reeling you back in again. Goes on for ages with some of them.'

Don't Step on the Lines

'You sound like Susan.'

Nicole laughs. 'Now that . . .' she clicks on the kettle ' . . . is a girl with problems.'

'The thing is, Nicole, not that many people liked Robin. Which means that they think I'm well shot of him. But I did, you know? It's not that easy . . .'

'Oh, I didn't dislike him as such. And let's face it, he's a good-looking boy. But I did have to agree with Marco that he wasn't really for you. There was something about him, something a bit creepy, that feeling that he would give himself a blow job if he could . . . Milk and sugar?'

'Milk, no sugar. But who *is* for me then? I don't think what I want is that complicated.'

'That's the million-dollar question, Kerry. Anyway, don't fool yourself about the uncomplicated bit . . .'

Marco comes into the living room. 'Urrrr,' he grunts in greeting.

'Tea or coffee, babe?'

'Brandy,' he mumbles, collapsing onto the sofa. 'No. Er . . . tea, no, wait . . . coffee, black, three sugars. What happened to Danny?'

'Well, after you both got on the phone to abuse people . . .'

'Oh, no! Who did we phone?'

'You phoned somebody called Moody Dave, shouting something about him being a boring bastard and having no hair and to get himself a wig. You also – and I tried to stop you from doing this, Marco – phoned Tony pretending to be the international operator and asked if he would accept a reverse charge call from Germany from Herr Heinrich Himmler.'

'Oh, no . . .'

'Yeah, it doesn't seem as funny now, does it? Although, he said he would accept the call. He must have thought Himmler was just somebody from the Frankfurt Stock Exchange. Until Danny shouted "*Sieg Heil*" down the phone at him. Here's your coffee.'

'Moody Dave will understand but my dad's gonna kill me

for that one. The wedding's coming up soon as well. So what happened to Danny?'

'Jeanette threw him out. I think he went off to try and find some party in Hoxton.'

'And where's Jeanette.'

'She phoned Darren at 7.30 this morning and made him drive round and pick her up.'

Marco puts his hands over his eyes.

'Come on, Kerry,' Nicole says, 'I'll give you a hand to clear up. Marco, here's a fiver. Go to the shops and get some eggs, some Coke, and a newspaper.'

'Why don't you go?'

''Cause it's not my job to go to the shop. It's your job to go to the shop.'

'Why won't women ever go to the shop? Just nip out and buy some Coke or some fags. If there's a bloke around, he always has to go.'

'If you come up with the answer on the way, you can tell us when you get back. Hurry up, 'cause I really need a big glass of Coke with lots of ice.'

Marco groans and hunts around for his trainers.

They spend the rest of the day in front of the TV watching black and white films, and several editions of the national and local news. There is a hunt for a girl who went missing outside a nightclub in Nottingham. Kerry thinks that girls are always going missing from outside nightclubs in provinicial towns and cities, and nobody seems to find this unusual or disturbing. She tries to phone Susan, but there is no answer. There is a knock on the door but they don't answer it because they know it is the neighbour. Eventually, a note is slid under the door saying that she is going to complain to the Housing Association. Kerry doesn't feel too bad because she knows that they are normally reasonable and that the noise wasn't too excessive anyway. Some of the parties on the estate where she used to live with Gary had made them feel as if the whole of their walkway was bouncing up and down. She'll go and talk to the neighbour tomorrow.

Don't Step on the Lines

Kerry hopes that Nicole and Marco won't want to go out but they don't. In the end, they buy a takeaway and some beers and watch more TV until they can't be bothered any more and go to bed. Kerry tries to read but her eyes can't focus properly on the print. She can't get rid of the image of Susan crying and shaking her head. *You of all people, Kerry.* What was she on about? Comedown paranoia begins to whirr inside her mind like the tiny, beating wings of a trapped bird.

Over the next couple of weeks, Kerry goes out a lot so that she won't sit in the house moping. She tries to vary her patterns; going to the cinema with John Gordon, to bars with Jeanette, to a party where Nicole is DJing. She begins to revise for the summer exams, although she doesn't have to do many because most of her courses are continuous assessment. Kerry doesn't really mind exams anyway, she finds them quite exciting.

Kerry tries to phone Susan a couple of times but she is never there. She leaves messages but Susan does not return her calls. She doesn't see her in college either, although when she checks, Jenny says that she has seen her on a few occasions. 'Looking rough,' she adds darkly. In the end, Kerry is worried enough about the number of times that Susan is absent from college to risk a trip to Dollis Hill. If Susan's not there, she'll leave a note. At least she will have tried.

Susan lives in a shared house owned by the college, about ten minutes from the tube station. Kerry takes the tube to Baker Street and changes on to the Jubilee line. She is unfamiliar with the line and its stations and has to keep looking up from her book to check where they are. She remembers that it is pretty near where she had come to have her abortion, only that time she was in a taxi. The train emerges from the tunnel into a grey afternoon light – she is getting near. The station is just over the boundary in Zone 3 but there is nobody in the booth collecting tickets so Kerry flashes her 1 and 2 travel card at an empty space and tries to remember which exit she has to go out of.

She walks down an endless street of semi-detached houses,

all around the air still and hot, punctuated by the sound of birds in their suburban chorus. At least, she thinks, these houses have gardens. You could sit out in the summer, or have a barbecue. Not like her flat, squeezed in behind Old Street, with its constant racket of sirens or helicopters or karaoke or five-a-side footballers. She arrives at the door of number 117 but there is no answer to her knock. She sighs at the wasted journey, but then notices that the window upstairs, which she is sure belongs to Susan's room, is wide open. She shouts her name, slightly muted at first but then more loudly. There is a tiny flicker at the window as the curtain moves faintly. Susan is in there.

'Susan,' Kerry shouts, 'I know you're up there. I'm just going to sit here until you open the door.'

Kerry is not sure but she thinks that she hears a muffled 'Go away'. She knocks on the door repeatedly, then sits on the step, lifting her skirt and letting her ankles warm in the sun. Finally, she hears somebody coming down the stairs, there is a pause, and the door is opened.

'What do you want?'

'Can I come in?'

'Why?'

Kerry begins to grow impatient.

'Stop being such a drama-queen. I want to talk to you. Now, are you going to let me in?'

Susan immediately looks alarmed at Kerry's sharp tone and holds the door open for her. Kerry remembers that the last time she came here, she was with Robin. They had shared an easy unstated feeling of – she has to be honest – superiority. It must have been obvious to Susan. They had taken a taxi home afterwards, Marco had been out, they had had the flat to themselves . . . Kerry feels a quick stab of pain which she fights down.

They walk up the stairs to Susan's room. Kerry would hate to live in a house like this; the smell of damp, the hall with its woodchip wallpaper, bikes by the door, the round timed light switch that you have to push in, the other rooms with their

Don't Step on the Lines

Garfield pictures on the door, the communal kitchen with the notice from an outraged vegetarian about washing the grill-pan after cooking bacon. It is nineteen-year-old territory.

Susan's room is a mess. She has a photo of her family on her bedside table, there is a plate with a half-eaten piece of toast and marmalade on it, a plugged-in hairdryer hanging off the end of the desk. The bed is unmade, crumpled tissues lie beside it like fallen clouds. There are also empty bottles of wine and one of whisky.

'Sorry about the mess,' Susan says.

'Susan, what is going on?'

'I can't tell you.' She hunches her shoulders defensively. She is struggling against tears.

'Why? Why can't you tell me?'

'I can't tell *you*.' Once again, the emphasis on Kerry.

'Look, Susan, this is starting to get right on my nerves. If it's got something to do with me, if it's something I've done then you should tell me, stop all these insinuations.'

'It's not you, it's me. I've done something terrible . . .'

'What? What have you done?'

Susan starts to cry. Kerry hands her a tissue impatiently. Finally, Susan turns a swollen face towards her.

'You know how Robin used to come up here sometimes?'

'Come up here?'

'Yeah, you know, like when you weren't seeing him, he used to come up here. We just used to go to the pub, talk about things, you know.'

Kerry is baffled. 'No. He never mentioned it.'

Susan sniffs. 'Well, he did. We used to talk about everything. I loved it. I . . .' she looks down at her hands ' . . . I loved him. Now you know. I was so jealous of you, Kerry. I thought I was going to die of jealousy. I imagined being you, we used to talk about you and . . .'

'Talk about me?'

'Yeah, but not in a horrible way, just about things, you know? I used to feel like I was you, imagine the things you had done together, only with me in your place. The only thing that made my life worth living was seeing him. Sometimes I've thought about killing myself. Really. It sounds stupid. I lie in bed and think about all the different ways – pills, hanging, slitting my wrists. But I can't 'cause I'm such a coward. So I would just drink instead. I even thought about going home, but that would be a nightmare. What would I do? Anyway... one night Robin came up. We went to the pub and he told me that you had had an argument, something about Marco. I don't know why he hates Marco so much, I've always really liked him, he makes me laugh. Anyway, I'm sorry, Kerry, but I was pleased. Not just because you had had a fight but because he was talking to me, telling me about it, making me feel important.'

'I bet he did,' says Kerry, feeling a sense of dread at what she is about to hear.

'So, we got really drunk and we came back here. I was telling him everything as well, about home, about everything really, and I told him . . . I told him that I had never had a boyfriend and . . . I'm really sorry, Kerry . . . he suggested . . . he said . . . I just couldn't say no. I wanted him so much. I wasn't trying to hurt you, I wasn't even thinking of you. He said that if that was what I really wanted then we should just . . . you know . . . so we did.'

'You slept together,' Kerry says harshly. It all makes sense. Robin in one of his acts of warped generosity.

'Yes. I'm really sorry, Kerry . . .'

'Stop saying that. Just the once?'

'Oh, yes.' Susan laughs bitterly. 'Yes, because he told me afterwards that he still thought there was a chance that you and he would stay together and that he was sorry but he cared more about you than about me, which was obvious really. But then, after that, he wouldn't speak to me. I never saw him in college, he wouldn't answer the phone to me, I kept getting the answerphone or that horrible girl. There's nothing worse than the sound of an answerphone when you're trying to get through to somebody. That click, the beeps . . . you feel such an idiot. One night I got so desperate I went to his house. Luckily you weren't there. Anyway, that girl answered the door and she was really rude to me, told me to go away and couldn't I take a hint and all that sort of stuff.'

'Yeah, she's a bitch. So you haven't spoken to him again since?' Kerry takes a cigarette packet from the top pocket of her Levis jacket.

'Once . . . you see . . . the reason I've just been going mad. The reason I don't know what to do is that . . .' She stops and looks at Kerry.

'Oh, no! You're not . . . you're pregnant, aren't you? Didn't you use . . .'

'No. That's not his fault, though. I told him I was on the pill.'

'Yeah, but didn't he think it was a bit strange that this person he was about to initiate into womanhood was on the pill? Anyway . . . what did you tell him that for?'

'I thought . . . I didn't want him to change his mind.'

'Oh, for God's sake! So have you told him about it?'

Susan nods. 'I finally managed to get hold of him by phoning at seven in the morning. I told him and he was, like, really calm about it. He said that I had to realise that it was entirely my decision. That it was my responsibility as well 'cause I had lied to him about the pill and everything. If I wanted a baby then I should have it, but he was not prepared to have anything to do with it. If I wanted an . . . you know . . . to have that operation . . .'

'An abortion,' Kerry says.

'Yeah, then I should go ahead and have it done and he would give me the money. But that he couldn't see me any more. He was going to go away with you, travelling. Are you going to go?'

'I'm not going anywhere. I'm not seeing him any more. Look, Susan, what are you going to do about this?'

'I don't know, I don't know. I mean, I have to tell you this, Kerry, I don't really approve of it. For me, it is taking an unborn life, but it's still a life, do you know what I mean?'

'No. But I'm not going to get into a big debate about where life starts. You need to go and see someone who will be able to talk to you properly about this, discuss the options. I can't tell you what to do but . . . do you want a baby?'

'Oh, no. Oh God, no.' Susan looks utterly horrified and bewildered by the thought. 'I couldn't . . . I mean, I can't even look after myself, let alone a baby. No way.'

Something stirs in Kerry's memory at these words. She can't feel particularly angry with Susan any more. What a mess. What a stupid, sordid mess.

'I still really miss him,' Susan says. 'I can't help it, it was like an illness. It still is. When we . . . you know . . . when we did it, I was so happy. I thought . . . and this is really horrible, Kerry . . . but I thought that he would finish with you and we could be together. But he's been so nasty, so cold. I never thought that he would be like that. I knew he didn't like me in the way he did you, but I thought he did . . . you know . . . care about me . . . even as a friend. People shouldn't behave like that. Maybe it's to do with his dad and everything. Maybe some of that rubbed off on him, being an only child and all.'

'His dad? What are you talking about?'

'You know, what he did and everything. How he died.'

'He was a civil servant. What's so special about that? He worked for the government.'

'As a spy! He worked for the Secret Service for years. Didn't you know that? He was a strange guy, I'm not really sure exactly what he did but he was around a lot in the early-eighties. Robin told me when we were talking about Ireland once. His dad had been there, some kind of secret negotiations. He was killed in a plane crash. You must remember it? An army general and some civil servants were killed when an RAF plane crashed on take-off. His dad was one of the so-called civil servants.'

'How come he told you all of this?'

'I dunno.' Susan looks almost pleased. 'He just did. We used to talk about everything.'

'Ah yes. So you did,' Kerry says sarcastically, and Susan drops her eyes.

'Have you told anybody else about this?' Kerry asks finally.

'No. Who could I tell? I've been going mad. You were my

only friend and how could I tell you? I feel terrible about it all. If I wasn't such a coward I would . . .'

'Cut it out, Susan. You've got to get your act together. Don't you know anyone who could go with you to get some counselling, see about maybe having an abortion?'

Susan gazes so mournfully at Kerry that she almost laughs.

'OK, I'll go with you. I want to go home now, but give me a ring tomorrow and I'll come with you. I've got a number.'

'Did you love him?' Susan asks suddenly.

The question takes Kerry by surprise. Did she? She had certainly cared about him, she had wanted to stay with him, she had loved being with him. But did she love him? She thinks of Gary and their final months together. She had been so unhappy but there was no doubt that she had loved him.

'I don't know,' Kerry replies truthfully. 'If I did, I don't any more.'

'You see, I think he knew that. He really wanted you to love him. You were always a challenge to him.'

'Do you think so? He wanted me to do what he wanted. When I wouldn't, that was it. He's a very selfish person. He likes power-games. I don't. Like what he did with you . . .'

'That's pretty sad, isn't it? That somebody would only sleep with you as a power-game and to get back at someone they had just had an argument with. Do you want some whisky by the way? I'm going to have some.'

'There's none left.' Kerry gestures at the empty bottle.

Susan opens a drawer and produces a new full bottle from among her knickers and socks. Kerry can't help laughing.

'My name is Susan McGuire. I'm an alcoholic . . . do you want some?'

'Go on then.'

Susan passes her the bottle and they sit on the floor swigging from it.

'What you're saying, Susan, that somebody would only want to sleep with you for bad motives . . . that's not true. But you've got to do something about it. I'm not saying it's easy but you've got to get out of that self-pitying mode. Because if there's anything unattractive about you, it's that. All that crying when you're drunk and going on about being ugly and stuff. It might sound like a bit of a cliché but you've got to get a grip. There's nothing worse than somebody who thinks that the biggest loser in the world is themselves. It's not true in your case. But people will start believing it if you tell them enough. And you lay yourself open to people like Robin . . .'

'Unlike you, you mean?' Susan says sharply and Kerry laughs and touches her finger from her lip to an imaginary iron and hisses.

Before Kerry leaves, she dials 141 and phones Robin's number. When he answers she puts the phone down.

'Who were you phoning?' Susan asks.

'Just a friend. They weren't in.'

Susan sees her to the door.

'Kerry, I know you don't want to hear this any more, but I really am sorry. I never wanted to hurt you. You're a brilliant person.'

'It's OK. You haven't hurt me. I'll phone you tomorrow about that thing.'

Kerry takes a different tube journey on her return. She changes on to the Central line and travels to Bethnal Green, thinking about Marco's dad and his mysteriously disappearing growth. She walks quickly across London Fields towards Robin's house. Jill answers the door.

'Kerry! I'm not sure if . . .'

'Get out of my face, you stupid slag.'

Kerry jostles past her.

Robin comes out of the kitchen, wiping his hands on a tea-towel. He is wearing a green Ben Sherman shirt unbuttoned, flapping loosely around him, and is bare-footed.

'Kerry, there's no need to talk to Jill like that . . .'

'Isn't there? I don't know what the arrangement is between the two of you any more. Anyway, I don't want to talk to her at all. I want to talk to you. *You*,' Kerry points at Jill, 'beat it. And don't hang around, trying to earwig. I know what you're like.'

'You can't talk to me like that in my house . . .'

'Can't I? Let me tell you something, sweetheart. You are that . . .' she puts finger and thumb together ' . . . fucking close to getting what you should have had some time ago. So I strongly suggest that you disappear up those stairs . . .'

Jill glances at Robin and he nods. She sighs and makes her way up the stairs.

'Come into the kitchen, Kerry. But don't try that tone of voice on me, because it might suit your sister but it doesn't suit you and I'm certainly not impressed.'

'I don't really care whether you're impressed or not. I've come for something quite straightforward. I want a cheque for three hundred pounds.'

Robin folds his arms. Kerry is relieved to feel none of her usual ambiguous responses to him. He is ugly.

'Oh yes. And what do you want that for?'

'I've just been to see Susan in Dollis Hill. You remember her? The girl you generously had a one-night stand with when you were in a bad mood with me. The one that you've left totally fucked up and with the minor problem of an unwanted pregnancy. Unfortunately, she hasn't passed the Robin Thomas test of strong and self-defined individuality. She's a mess. I'm taking her tomorrow to see somebody about her . . . no, *your* little problem. She may decide to have an abortion. In which case she will need three hundred pounds or so. If it's more, I'll get it later from you. If it's less, I'll send you the change. Come on, Robin. All you have to do is write a cheque. You're good at that. See it as removing an obstacle.'

'I've already told her that if she wants the money for an abortion, then I'll give it to her. There's no need for you to start acting like some demented fairy godmother. And there's no need for that sarky tone about money again. *You're* hardly in a position to make snide comments about me writing cheques . . .'

Kerry ignores the last part of this statement.

'How was she meant to get it off you? Especially with that social worker bitch acting as your gatekeeper. I don't know why you ever split up with her, you were made for each other. But then, of course, I don't know whether you have really split up, do I? Maybe her boyfriend doesn't mind 'cause you're just so right-on about things in this house. Anyway, I've seen now what your philosophy is really about. I don't want to see any more of it. Just give me the money and I'll go.'

Robin sighs and takes out his cheque-book.

'Who would you like me to make it out to?'

'Me. I'll cash it and get the money.'

Kerry watches Robin's familiar handwriting, his spiky signature.

'You know something, Kerry,' he says as he gives her the cheque, 'you may disapprove of me, you may not like me any more, but I want you to know something. When I told you I loved you, up in Yorkshire, I meant it. I really did love you. Maybe I'm selfish, maybe there's something wrong with me like you say. I can't change. But you should have stayed with me. We were brilliant together. And you know that.'

As he gives her the cheque, he touches her hand. He steps closer to her, he is putting his hands on her shoulders. He is going to slide them down her arms. Kerry can feel an awful trembling. The terrible deviancy after all this, after everything that has happened, after all her anger and contempt, of letting her desire for him overtake her. She knows that she should not let it happen, but she feels the tug of an appalling temptation. She *could* let it happen. She could let his hands slide down from her shoulders.

'People like Jill, like Susan, like Marco . . . they're irrelevant,' he murmurs in her ear.

Kerry snaps back and shrugs his hands from her shoulders.

'No. You're wrong.' She snatches the cheque. 'They're not irrelevant. You can't just decree somebody irrelevant. And let me tell you something . . .' she takes the arrow, dips it in poison and draws back the bow ' . . . you say you loved me? Maybe you did. But I don't think I ever loved you. And I don't want to see you ever again.'

'You bitch!' Robin's face is twisting now. He is clenching

and unclenching his fists. 'Go back to your insignificant little life then. You're nothing, you know that? You could be something but you don't want to be. You're just a spineless little coward. And that's the worst sort of loser.'

And he slaps her. It is not a hard slap, it just glances off her cheek. It doesn't hurt at all. Kerry can hardly believe it. She stares at him for a second. He has just slapped her! He stands there looking both ashamed and thrilled by what he has just done, by his transgression. He would probably like her to slap him back. She starts to laugh, shaking her head.

'Oh, no . . .' she starts.

'There!' Robin shrieks. 'Now you can run home and tell that idiot Marco that I hit you and he can come round and beat me up with some of his mates. That's what you want, isn't it?'

Kerry folds up the cheque and puts it in the top pocket of her jacket. 'Stop it, Robin,' she says. 'You're making a total fool of yourself.'

And she turns and walks down the hall, out of the front door for the last time, shutting it carefully behind her.

Chapter 22

'Please stop now and put down your pens. Make sure your student number is on all the booklets and that they are fastened together with the string provided.'

Kerry puts her pen into her jacket pocket and wipes her hands. The exams have gone to plan. She is confident that she has performed as well as she could. If she gets good marks in these papers then she only has to avoid poor marks in her final year to get a first. The summer stretches in front of her, the temp agency has promised her some work for the following week, but now she has a few days off to savour. She walks down the heat-baked steps of the college and crosses the road to the pub where most of her course are already assembled.

Susan is sitting at one of the tables, working her way through a double whisky and Coke. She is no longer pregnant. Kerry thought hard about her promise to help. She no longer had any real feelings of friendship towards Susan and knows that she will not have much to do with her any longer. But somehow she did feel as if she had a slight debt towards her, as if what had happened was in some way her fault as well. Perhaps because she knows now that Susan had needed a real friend and Kerry had not provided this, not even support.

They went together to an office in Oxford Street, and Kerry waited for Susan in a room where a radio was playing irritating background jazz and a kettle and little jars of tea and coffee were set out thoughtfully on a table for those waiting. Kerry had made herself a coffee while she waited. Behind a screen, one of the receptionists was arranging to meet her sister after work in the Coach and Horses. 'I'll tell you all about it when I see you. He's such an idiot.' Kerry wondered who they were talking about. It was strange, she thought, how accustomed they must be to the constant flow of women passing through this place. Desperate women, frightened women, calm women, determined women, women on their own, women with boyfriends holding their hands, women from Catholic countries like Spain and Ireland, women with suitcases. All of these women with a different story – some amazing, some banal – but all with one thing in common. Kerry looked at the women waiting: some dressed like secretaries, some wearing light summer clothes, some with wedding rings. All of these women were there because of a moment, an instant – perhaps sad like Susan's, perhaps ecstatic. Behind the screen, the receptionist was laughing lazily and telling her sister that she would have to go because there was somebody waiting to be seen.

Susan spent a long time with the counsellor, which Kerry did not find particularly surprising. She hoped that Susan wasn't going to start coming out with all her Catholic hang-ups and end up talking herself out of it. The world did not need a new inhabitant with a mixture of Robin's and Susan's genes. Kerry felt sorry for the counsellor. She had seen her as Susan went into the room – a middle-aged woman in a Laura Ashley dress who would probably need intensive counselling herself after an hour with Susan. Kerry picked up a magazine and began to read an article about Siamese twins. What if she and Jeanette were joined together? They would kill each other after half an hour.

When Susan came out, however, she seemed quite cheerful. They paid forty-five pounds for the consultation, and Susan was booked into the clinic for a week's time where she would have to pay a further two hundred and seventy-five.

'That's really near my house,' she exclaimed when the receptionist handed her the address of the clinic. 'You'll still come with me, won't you, Kerry?'

'OK,' Kerry had sighed, remembering her vow never to go back there.

Susan cried after the abortion and started talking about what the baby might have looked like, what it might have done in life, what her parents would do if they found out, whether she was going to go to hell – until she was really stretching Kerry's patience. Kerry wondered whether Susan was just suffering withdrawal symptoms from not having had a drink for twenty-four hours before the operation.

Now, however, Susan is making up for any lost time. Kerry carefully steers herself into a seat so that she is not next to her. She checks her watch because she is meeting Jeanette in an hour. Then tomorrow Marco is taking her out to celebrate the end of college and the start of summer. He has lined up a string of parties, including one at which Nicole is DJing.

Poor Marco has spent the last week recovering from the mental trauma of his sister's wedding. He was already in the dog-house for the Himmler phone-call on Kerry's birthday. Kerry couldn't get much information from him other than that it had been easily the worst experience of his life, that Tony's best man had made Tony look like a liberal dove, that the music was terrible, and that there hadn't even been any nice women because they were all blonde with fake tans and such moody expressions that it looked as if they had put their lip-stick on upside down. There had been a row when Tony kept making snidey comments to remind John Fisher that he had paid for most of the wedding, a row intensified when Tony's best man had caught Marco loading bottles of Bollinger into a rucksack.

Kerry has not seen or heard from Robin since the afternoon round at his house. He did not turn up for the exams and she wonders whether he has already left the country. She feels strangely calm about it all now, she has also, oddly, stopped having nightmares. She did have one dream where Gary announced that he had been nominated for an Oscar and that he wanted Kerry to come to the awards ceremony. They had travelled by plane which had inevitably begun to lose height but Kerry had escaped by opening the emergency door and sliding down the chute. Robin does not appear in her dreams at all, not even disguised.

Marco is glad that Kerry has come out with them. They are sitting by the pin-ball machines outside the main dance area, both pissed. He has spent the afternoon round at his dad's, laughing at some of the specimens at Tony and Angela's wedding. John Fisher has to go back to the hospital for more tests, but the doctors are hopeful that the growth will have disappeared for good. Marco's dad was more concerned that morning about the unsurprising victory of Yeltsin in the Russian elections and how best to fight the Helms-Burton law against Cuba.

Kerry wriggles through to the bar to buy some drinks. Marco watches her squeezing through the crowd, flapping her note at the barman. He feels a lump in his throat as he sees her smile flash out as she drops some of her change and exchanges a joke with the barman. There is something so right about her, so composed, even her clothes – black skirt, trainers, faded Levis jacket, hair pulled back with a red hair clasp. What an idiot that Robin was. How could he not realise what he had in Kerry? Marco even feels a surge of anger towards Gary. Why couldn't he hold it together? He might not have been able to get any acting jobs but he had Kerry. What is in store for her now? She comes towards him carrying two bottles of Budwar in her hands and Marco realises that, whatever happens, he will always know Kerry, that she will always be his friend. Maybe she will find someone else, maybe Marco will dislike him as much as Robin – no, that's not possible – but Marco will always be there, watching her with the mixture of pride and envy and love that almost sends a shudder running through him.

After Nicole's party, they walk to Columbia Road for a drink. A mad orange sun is rising above London. Marco loves walking like this, half-wasted, not caring about anything, paying attention to no authority, thinking about the first sip of a cold pint. The stall-holders are setting up as they arrive just in time for the opening of the pub, eating sausage sandwiches, drinking tea from plastic cups, calling and laughing to each other. Marco recognises a few people in the pub, most of them still buzzing from whatever they were on last night, fending off their come-down, some trying to make it right the way through until night comes again. He can see that Kerry is tired but when he asks her if she is OK, she smiles and nods.

They sit in the comfort of the pub as the sun grows warmer and warmer, flooding them with heat. Giant green plants go walking past the window as somebody struggles home with their early-morning purchase, their nose in the leaves. They are not saying much any more but it doesn't matter. They are sitting in a pub in a flower market with the sun warming them, sometimes smiling at each other, occasionally making the trip to the bar.

Finally, they get hungry and Marco suggests that they go to the fish stall to buy king prawns. They make their way out on to the street, shielding their eyes from the sun. Women trailing kids hold great bunches of flowers in their arms. Couples sit outside the pub reading the Sunday papers, raising pints lazily to their lips. The stall-holders who were just setting up when they arrived have been busy; the stalls are awash with colour, or stacked with plants greedily photosynthesising from the rays of the sun.

'Oh my god, look at the state of that,' Nicole suddenly exclaims.

It is Danny, weaving his way unsteadily towards the pub, eyes as red as two traffic lights, dragging a girl along behind him, whose hand he drops when he sees Marco. He stops in the middle of the road to celebrate this chance meeting, legs apart, arms raised, shirt half-unbuttoned, exposing his midriff, starfish-shaped in the middle of the road, all around him the gluttony of colour from the bright flowers in boxes, while people push impatiently past him. Then Marco notices one of the blind walking plants heading straight for his back.

'Danny, mind out . . .' Kerry shouts.

'Kerry! Wa-haay. Give us a kiss, darlin'.'

'Danny! Watch . . .'

But it is too late. Danny goes crashing to the ground together with plant and plant-owner. Nicole picks him up and dusts him down, while the man who had bought the plant retrieves the new addition to his house and glares at Danny.

Marco turns to Kerry and laughs. 'Summer's here,' he says, and she smiles and takes his hand in the narrow street, surrounded on all sides by the startling, show-off colours of the sun-warmed flower market.

'Let's buy some flowers,' Kerry says suddenly. 'For the house.'

'What sort of flowers?'

And Kerry, who does not know the names of flowers, points to a bunch with long green arching stems and creamy-white pitcher-shaped heads. 'Those,' she answers.

'Let's see how many pints of beer they cost first,' Marco warns but Kerry steps forward and signals which flowers she wants to the stall-holder. When the transaction has been made, she turns back to him, smiling, delicately cradling the flowers to her and breathing in deeply the rich, sweet scent rising from the paper cone in which they have been wrapped.